C000001808

FUN & PROFIT
FROM
COLLECTABLES

Acknowledgements:

James Baker
Claire Benson, Gary Davis

Published by Collecticus
PO Box 100, Devizes, Wiltshire, SN10 4TE

No part of this publication may be reproduced without written permission from the publisher

First edition

© 2017

ISBN 978-1-873313-23-7

Typeset and make-up by
Wentrow Media, 49 Lancaster Road, Bowerhill Trading Estate, Melksham, Wiltshire, SN12 6SS

Printed by
Henry Ling Limited, 23 High East Street, Dorchester, Dorset, DT1 1HD

CONTENTS

INTRODUCTION

Welcome to **FUN AND PROFIT FROM COLLECTABLES**.

The charm of the collectables industry is obvious. Pieces of social history are being traded and collected. This is tangible nostalgia.

You can buy lots of books on the subject of collectables, but many of them concentrate on fancy, expensive china and hard-to-find antiques. In this book you will find a whole range of items including, beer mats, vehicle tax discs, bubble gum wrappers and theatre programmes. The book is full of affordable collectables and the majority are perfect for trading.

This book is the result of over four years of hard work from the Collecticus team, sourcing and photographing the items and compiling the text.

Collecticus is the name we gave to our monthly collectables auction when we launched it over twelve years ago. Each auction has its own monthly magazine, which carries the same name.

We believe the concept of this book to be totally unique. Every item in this book is either currently being offered for sale via our auction mechanism or has already been sold by us. This means that items that interest you can either be bid on or just tracked to establish the prices achieved. The book is linked to a website (www.collecticus.co.uk/auctions)

Today's collectors have our ancestors to thank for collecting various items over the centuries. Many such items are now today's antiques, but this book isn't really about the pure subject of antiques. Instead, we are concentrating on the branch of 'collectables' classed as original (generally old) interesting and fascinating items that have value to collectors. We are less interested in items that have been manufactured new, specifically for the 'collectables' market.

A common definition of an antique is 'a collectable object that is over 100 years old'. It therefore follows that there is some crossover between collectables and antiques. However, many items over 100 years old (for example a postcard) is not traditionally defined as an antique. Crafted objects are usually reserved for the tag of 'antique'.

Other terms, such as 'vintage' and 'retro' have crept into the collectables glossary.

'Vintage' often refers to items that are over 50 years old.

Throughout the book, you will find 'crossover' subjects where similar items fall into different categories. It's a good tip to look out for 'crossover items' when buying collectables for resale or for their potential investment value.

If you are thinking about buying and selling collectables as a full or part-time business, then this book will improve your knowledge, particularly in relation to values. We have a dedicated section on how you can turn a small investment into a stock worth £50,000 or thereabouts.

Couple this new found knowledge with the right mindset and you could make some serious money. Have confidence in yourself and remember that 'money is a tool' use it wisely and you could reap big rewards.

If you are a collector who collects for the love of it, then the contents of this book should make you squeal with joy. Step back into the past and let memories flood back, or, if the item was around before your time, let your imagination run riot.

When you buy collectable items, you are purchasing a piece of social history. It could, for example, be a concert ticket for an iconic sixties band. This ticket permitted the holder to enjoy a performance, it's a tangible receipt of payment for a moment in time. Whatever items you choose to collect, enjoy them to the fullest. Share your enthusiasm and good fortune with others.

ITEM DESCRIPTIONS

It can be quite difficult to establish the actual date of production/issue of many old collectable items, hence, throughout this book all specified dates are those believed to be correct by our experts. Where the date cannot be specified with a degree of authority, the date will be specified in brackets.

The description of the condition of an item is often far easier to establish than the date, but some collectors may have varying views. The condition description of each item in this book tries to err on the side of caution.

Letters in brackets indicate the condition of the item:

Poor   (p)
Fair   (f)
Good   (g)
Very Good   (vg)
Excellent   (ex)
Mint   (mnt)

Conditions may be combined to give a more accurate description. For example, an item in poor to fair condition would be listed as (p-f).

The estimated value of a collectable item will very often vary between experts. The prices specified throughout this book all have a lower value and a higher estimated value specified. The prices are based on normal trading conditions. Some collectors will often pay a premium to obtain an item they have been seeking out for years.

Example

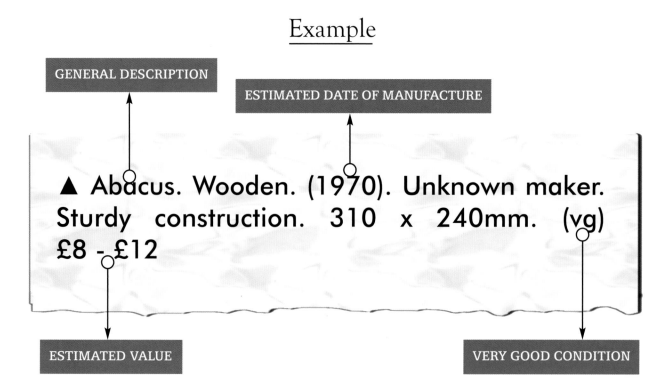

GENERAL DESCRIPTION

ESTIMATED DATE OF MANUFACTURE

▲ Abacus. Wooden. (1970). Unknown maker. Sturdy construction. 310 x 240mm. (vg) £8 - £12

ESTIMATED VALUE

VERY GOOD CONDITION

ABACUS

The abacus dates back hundreds of years, long before the modern written numeral system.

From approximately 1900 onwards, they were widely manufactured as toys and used by children as counting aids.

In some African countries, the abacus (plural = abacuses or abaci) is still used by merchants as calculating tools.

▲ Abacus. Wooden. (1970). Unknown maker. Sturdy construction. 310 x 240mm. (vg) £8 - £12

ACTION MAN

First introduced by Palitoy in 1966. This concept of poseable action figures was an instant hit.

Accessories include weapons, uniforms, equipment and vehicles. These are in demand particularly if 'mint in pack'.

To celebrate the 40th anniversary of Action Man, in 2006 Palitoy released new versions of the original models. These retailed at around £35 each and are still collectable but not as much as the original versions.

▲ Action Man. Action Soldier. Original but basic model with no accessories. 1970. Original box but with no top flap but otherwise in good condition. £40 - £50

▲ Emergency Fire Tender with original box. 1978. Size 600 x 370 x 290mm. (vg) £30 - £35

▲ Action Man Is Here. 45rpm record. (1968). Side 1 Official Action Man March. Side 2 Authentic Battle Sounds. Vinyl (vg), sleeve (g) £12 - £14

ADVERTISING

This is a huge collecting area with plenty of variations to the theme. There are crossovers with many collecting categories.

Advertising through the decades reflects progression of our social history. It's a truly fascinating subject. It also feeds the insatiable appetite of many collectors who are on a permanent nostalgia trip.

Old magazines and newspapers contain many advertisements and can be cut out, although purists may frown at defacing the publications. At least it's a cheap way of starting an interest or collection.

Enamel signs are top end of the advertising collectables market.

A hundred years or so ago, manufacturers of some products advertised their products on postcards. These have since been the subject of many modern reproductions, which can be acquired for next to nothing. The most sought-after originals start at around £15 each in good condition+.

▲ Secret Magic Sticks. Sip-Ade soft drink powder packets. (1965). Sales point trade card. 315 x 210mm. (g) £6 - £8

▲ Fry's postcard. (1915). Postally unused. (vg) £15 - £18

▲ Angus Watson & Co. Skippers. Marketing reply card. (1925). Unused. (vg) £10 - £12

▲ St. Ivel postcard. 1923. Postally unused. Message in pencil. (g) £12 - £15

──── ADVERTISEMENT ────

LOOKING BACK - 50s ADVERTS

Contained in the pages of this book is a small sample of those eye-catching advertisements that had us all dipping into our wallets during the '50s.

Find a suitably comfortable chair, make yourself a cup of cocoa, relax, and enjoy Looking Back...

Price £4.95

Order from: Collecticus
Tel: 01380 811750
Internet: www.collecticus.co.uk

By post: Collecticus, P.O.Box 100, Devizes, Wiltshire, SN10 4TE
(Cheques/Postal Order's payable to 'Hartley Publications Ltd')

ADVERTISING - Enamel signs

Although prone to the enamel chipping, these were designed to withstand all weathers, often hung on the outside walls of shops and other business premises. There's a huge market in these signs. So much so, that a trade has emerged in the manufacture of reproduction signs. Fortunately, the repros are very easy to distinguish because they are often made of a lighter tin and not enamelled. Furthermore, the weathering of a seriously old sign helps to establish age.

Collectors are often more than happy to purchase an old advertising sign with chips to the enamel, on the grounds that this gives the sign more of an authentic 'old feel'.

A good selection of enamel signs can be found at the larger Collectors' Fairs, auction houses, autojumbles and, to a lesser degree, at large car boot sales.

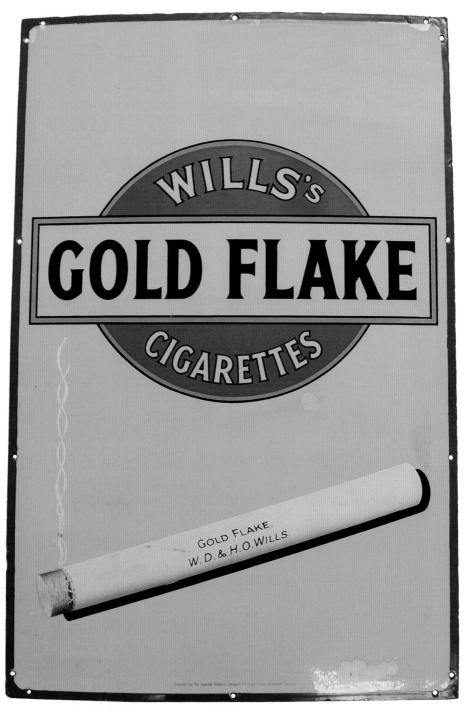

▲ Gold Flake enamel sign. (1950). 910 x 610mm. (g) £100 - £120

ADVERTISING - Showcards

Advertisement signs made of heavy duty card are often designed to stand on shop counters, or hang on walls. Also known as 'standees'. They are normally not on the large side.

▲ Levis Jeans showcard. (1960). 300 x 275mm. (vg) £14 - £18

▲ Cape Apples mobile showcard. (1980). 290 x 240mm. (vg) £3 - £4

▲ John Bull publication showcard. (1956). 375 x 250mm. (vg) £8 - £12

ADVERTISING - Postcards

The era that purist collectors are looking for is approximately 1904 - 1925. The period approximately 1926 - 1970 still feature some interesting advertising postcards but, with some exceptions (car manufacturers for example), can generally be purchased at more reasonable sums.

Condition and rarity are the usual obvious price indicators. British products are generally the most sought after and it's often the more obscure product (particularly with interesting artwork) that will command a higher price.

Surprisingly, the iconic Pears Soap advertising postcard (circa 1905) 'Bubbles' is not rare and can therefore be purchased for far less than say, a Fry's Five Boys card.

▲ Champion's Vinegar. (1925). Postally unused. (vg) £15 - £18

▲ Quaker Oats. (1920). Postally unused. (f-g) £4 - £6

▲ Hornflowa Buttons. (1925). Postally unused. (vg) £8 - £10

▲ Epps's Cocoa. (1915). Postally unused. (vg) £15 - £18

▲ Wood-Milne. (1915). Postally unused. (f) £6 - £8

▲ Eastmans (Butchers). (1920). Postally unused. (vg) £15 - £18

▲ Tit-Bits. (1920). Postally unused. (g-vg) £6 - £8

ADVERTISING - Postcards

▲ Selfridge & Co. Postmarked 1909. Message in ink. (g) £8 - £10

▲ The Morris Oxford. (1955). Postally unused. (vg) £8 - £12

▲ Pulbis. (1925). Postally unused. (g-vg) £10 - £12

▲ Pearks' Butter. Postmarked Hammersmith 1907. Message in Ink. (g-vg) £6 - £8

▲ Camp Coffee. (1910). Postally unused. (f) £6 - £8

▲ TWA. (1960). Postally unused. (g-vg) £4 - £6

▲ Fletchers tomato sauce. (1920). Postally unused. (vg) £12 - £14

▲ Hartley's marmalade. (1910). Postally unused. Message in pencil. (g-vg) £15 - £18

▲ Armitages. (1925). Postally unused. (vg) £8 - £10

▲ Lipton Tea. Postmarked Stockwell 1907. Message in pencil. (g-vg) £4 - £6

▲ Co-Op Tea. (1910). Postally unused. (vg) £12 - £14

▲ Epps's milk chocolate. Postmarked Norwich 1910. Message in ink. (g-vg) £12 - £14

▲ Chivers' Golden Plums. (1915). Postally unused. (g-vg) £3 - £5

▲ Bullier. (1910). Postally unused. (vg) £10 - £12

▲ Chivers' Greengages. (1910). Postally unused. (g-vg) £3 - £5

ADVERTISING - Periodicals

Advertisements in magazines, newspapers, comics etc... tell a wonderful story. They are easy to date and offer an insight to our way of life over the past 150 years or so.

The cutting-out of advertisements from lovely old magazines has become a common trait of the modern collecting era. If framed, the advertisements can look quite attractive and can complement specialist collections. For example, a collector of old razor blade packets may derive much pleasure from an old Gillette advertisement and would readily hang such a 'work of art' on the wall.

A variety of different (old) advertisements, all in identical frames, can make a great theme for a room in a house or a pub, restaurant, café etc...

▲ Nescafe. 1975. A4 page from a magazine. (g) 60p - 80p

▲ Rollei. 1977. A4 page from a magazine. (g) 20p - 40p

▲ Tonka. 1975. A4 page from a magazine. (g) 50p - 70p

▲ Adidas. 1977. A4 page from a magazine. (g) 40p - 70p

▲ Weetabix. 1970. A4 page from a magazine. (g) 40p - 60p

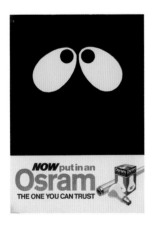

▲ Osram. 1965. A4 page from a magazine. (g) 40p - 60p

▲ Saudia. 1975. A4 page from a magazine. (g) 40p - 60p

▲ Pentax. 1977. A4 page from a magazine. (g) 40p - 60p

AERONAUTICA

The study of, and collecting of, items relating to civil and military aircraft.

This collecting theme is wide and has many variations that can be classed individually as specialist subjects in their own right, for example, those relating to 'Concorde'.

An area to become interested in is civil aircraft markings. An airline emblem/logo/livery/ensign can be both colourful and fascinating. Some airlines have changed them over the years, whilst others have gone out of business. It's quite a field all of its own. Postcards of aircraft with the emblems clearly visible can be neatly displayed in an album, in alphabetical order. You will be amazed at how many there are.

▲ BOAC 747 sales brochure. 1969. Centre pages loose. (vg) £6 - £8

Air France

Air France was created in 1933 from a merger of several airline companies, including Air Union and Air Orient.

In 1945 all air transport in France was nationalised. Their first Air France jet airliner began service in 1953 (de Haviland Comet).

▲ Boeing 747 Air France model. (1988). ERTL Jet Tran. (g) £2 - £4

▲ Air France to Nice leaflet. Riviera Express. (1957). (g-vg) £3 - £4

▲ Air France to Paris leaflet. (1957). (g) £3 - £4

► Air France baggage label. (1956). (f) £3 - £5

► Wings Across the World tea card. No.11. 1962. Lyons Tea. From a set of 24. (ex) 10p - 20p

AERONAUTICA - BEA

BEA (British European Airways) began in 1946 and operated until 1974 when it merged with BOAC to form BA (British Airways).

BEA took delivery of its first jet aircraft in 1960 and in 1964 a BEA Trident 1C aircraft became the first scheduled commercial air service in the world to perform an automatic landing.

▲ BEA Elizabethan Class aeroplane postcard. (1960). Postally unused. (vg) £3 - £4

▲ Fly BEA postcard. (1955). Postally unused. (vg) £4 - £5

▲ BEA Passenger Ticket. 1959. (vg) £4 - £5

▲ BEA Trident Fleet leaflet. 1970. (vg) £2 - £4

▲ BEA International Timetable. 1960. (vg) £6 - £8

▲ BEA Magazine. No.127 October 1959. (g-vg) £4 - £6

▲ BEA cap badge. (1955). (vg) £22 - £24

▲ BEA cabin crew flight badge. (1950). (vg) £8 - £12

▲ BEA Vickers Viscount postcard. (1960). Postally unused. (vg) £2 - £3

◄ BEA matchbook. (1965). Empty. (g-vg) £3 - £4

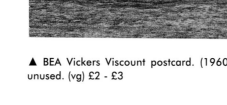

▲ BEA cabin baggage tag. 1968. (vg) £3 - £4

AERONAUTICA - Laker Airways

Laker Airways was a British independent airline founded by Sir Freddie Laker in 1966. Details were first unveiled to the press in February of that year, and the airline commenced commercial operation on 29 July 1966 from its base at London Gatwick Airport.

◀ Laker pinbadge. (1978). (g) £10 - £14

In 1977, Laker Airways became the first long-haul, "no frills" airline, operating low-cost flights between London Gatwick and John F Kennedy Airport in New York. This service was known as Skytrain, and was a revolutionary step in the advancement of air travel. The inaugural flight of Skytrain was on 26 September 1977.

▲ Laker unopened tube of sweets. (1978). 50mm long. (vg) £3 - £5

Unfortunately, when the recession hit the UK in 1980, Laker Airways did not have the financial stability to survive. The airline finally collapsed on 5 February 1982 with debts of £270m, making it the biggest corporate failure in British history. While Laker Airways failed, it did pave the way for future low-cost airlines such as EasyJet, and as such has had a lasting legacy.

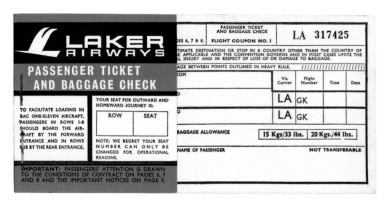

▲ Laker ticket. (1978). (vg) £4 - £6

Sir Frederick Laker
(1922-2006)

Sir Frederick Alfred Laker was born 6 August 1922, in Canterbury.

He formed Laker Airways in 1966, having previously worked as managing director of British United Airways. He was knighted in 1978 for his services to the airline industry (namely, the introduction of Skytrain).

Sadly, Freddie passed away 9 February 2006, aged 83, due to complications following surgery to fit a pacemaker. He is survived by his wife Jacqueline Harvey (a former air hostess), and his two children.

▲ Commemorative postal cover. 1979. (vg) £3 - £4

AERONAUTICA

South African Airways

South African Airways (SAA), which was known by its Afrikaans name of Suid-Afrikaanse Lugdiens (SAL) during apartheid, is the largest airline of the Republic of South Africa, with a fleet of 60 aircraft plus another 25 on order.

The airway was founded in 1934 after the South African government acquired Union Airways.

▲ SAA Flying Springbok deer symbol. Metal badge. (1975). 32mm. (vg) £10 - £12

Pan Am

Pan American World Airways (Pan Am) was the United State's principal international airline until 1991 (when it collapsed). The airline was started in 1927, as an air mail and passenger service operating between Florida and Havana, and quickly flourished.

Pan Am was a trend-setting company, introducing many innovations to aviation services such as computerised reservation systems; and the brand was particularly iconic through the 1960s. For example, it is a Pan Am Boeing 707-321 from which the Beatles are emerging in the famous photograph of their arrival at John F Kennedy Airport in 1964. Pan Am even started a waiting list for future flights to the moon, and a (fictional) Pan Am "Space Clipper" appeared in Stanley Kubrick's 1968 science fiction masterpiece, 2001: A Space Odyssey.

▲ Pan America Super-6 Clipper postcard. (1965). Postally unused. (f-g) £3 - £5

KLM

KLM Royal Dutch Airline was founded in 1919. Its first flight was on May 17th 1920, London to Amsterdam. Today, as the world's oldest and longest continually running airline, it has 115 aircraft in its fleet, and employs more than 32,000 people.

◄ KLM enamel badge. (1980). 15mm. (vg) £6 - £8

▲ Junior KLM Skipper metal badge. (1965) 60mm. (g) £10 - £12

AERONAUTICA - Airports

Going back to the earliest days of aviation, aircraft took off and landed on grass strips. As the air industry developed, aerodromes were built and many eventually became airports.

Aero-enthusiasts are particularly interested in the history of commercial airport development. There are plenty of interesting collectables, particularly from the 50's, 60's and 70's, to satisfy the demand.

▲ Heathrow Terminal 1 Certificate. A certificate issued by the British Airports Authority to a passenger who passed through Terminal 1 on the opening day, 6 Nov 1968. (vg) £12 - £16

◀ Brighton Airport. Information leaflet. (1965). (vg) £2 - £3

▲ London Airport Guide. Pitkin Pictorials. 1962. 32 pages. (vg) £4 - £6

▲ Esso Guide to London Airport. 1965. (g-vg) £3 - £4

▲ British Airports. Ian Allan ABC publication. 1959. (vg) £5 - £7

▲ Air Traffic Control. Nelson Doubleday publication. 1966. USA 64 pages 210 x 140mm booklet with full set of stickers affixed. (g-vg) £4 - £6

Airport opening dates

(Note: many were in existence as aerodromes prior to the dates shown).

Belfast (Aldergrove) - 1963

Birmingham (Elmdon) - 1939

Bournemouth (Hurn) - 1940

Bristol (Lulsgate) - 1939

Cardiff (Rhoose) - 1952

Edinburgh (Turnhouse) - 1947

Glasgow (Renfrew) - 1954

Jersey - 1937

Leeds/Bradford (Yeadon) - 1931

Liverpool (Speke) - 1930

London (Gatwick) - 1958

London (Heathrow) - 1929

Luton - 1938

Manchester (Ringway) - 1938

Southampton (Eastleigh) - 1932

Stansted - 1952

AERONAUTICA - Airport postcards

▲ Gatwick Airport. (1980). Postmark illegible. Message in ink. (g) £1 - £2

▲ Bristol Airport. (1975). Postally unused. (f-g) £2 - £3

▲ Manchester Airport. (1995). Postally unused. (vg) £1 - £2

▲ John F Kennedy, New York. (1975). Postally unused. (vg) £1 - £2

▲ Penzance helipad. (1965). Postally unused. (g) £2 - £3

▲ Oslo Airport, Fornebu. (1960). Postally unused. (vg) £3 - £4

▲ London Airport. (1960). Postally unused. (vg) £3 - £5

▲ Jersey Airport. Postmarked Jersey 1971. Message in ink. (g) £2 - £3

▲ Luton Airport. (1970). Postally unused. (vg) £2 - £4

▲ Manchester Airport, Concourse. Postmarked Manchester 1967. Message in ink. (f) £3 - £4

▲ Eppley Field, Nebraska. (1965). Postally unused. (g) £1 - £2

▲ Manchester Airport from the air. (1980). Postally unused. (g) £1 - £2

▲ Nice Airport. Postmarked Nice 1966. Message in ink. (vg) £2 - £3

▲ Zurich, Kloten Airport. (1965). Postally unused. (g-vg) £2 - £3

▲ Heathrow Airport. (1970). Postally unused. (vg) £2 - £3

AERONAUTICA - Concorde

Concorde was a joint development between Aerospatiale (Toulouse) and British Aircraft Corporation (Filton, Bristol) under an Anglo-French treaty. It was a turbojet powered supersonic aircraft.

There was initially some dispute between France and Britain over the spelling of the name of the aircraft with Britain changing the name to 'Concord' for a short period. A later agreement settled for 'Concorde'.

The first test flight was on 2 March 1969 (Andre Turcat). Almost a month later, the British version had its first test flight taking off from Filton, under the command of test pilot Brian Trubshaw.

The event made Trubshaw a well-known name in Britain. He was born in Liverpool in 1924 and educated at Winchester College. In 1944 he was flying Lancasters and Stirlings for Bomber Command. He died peacefully in his sleep at his home in Tetbury, Gloucestershire in 2001.

The first scheduled flight of Concorde was on 21 January 1976.

Concorde was finally retired from service, following the Air France crash on 25 July 2000.

▲ Brian Trubshaw signed (BAC) photograph of Concorde. Clear, blue ink, 250 x 205mm. No dedication £50 - £70

BAC/SUD-AVIATION CONCORDE.

The maiden flight of Concorde prototype 002. The Concorde supersonic airliner is expected to enter service in 1973 and will carry up to 144 passengers at speeds of around 1400 mph.

▲ Maiden Flight postcard. Colourmaster. Concorde 002 (the first UK built and flew from Filton to RAF Fairford on 9 April 1969). Postally unused. (vg) £4 - £6

▲ Matchbox label. No.18 of a set of 18. Finlays Newsagents. (g) 30p - 40p

▲ Corgi diecast model. Produced from 1973 to 1980. Red, white and blue tail. G-BBDG. Unboxed, with display stand. 190mm long. (vg) £15 - £20

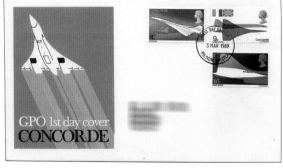

▲ Concorde first day cover. Postmarked Filton 3 March 1969. (vg) £3 - £4

▲ Concorde Machmeter postcard. This instrument was located at the front of the cabin and showed passengers when they reached the speed of sound (Mach 1) and twice the speed of sound (Mach 2). (1975). (vg) £1 - £2

AERONAUTICA - Air Displays

Programmes are the most important collecting area for Air Displays. These are generally full of aviation images and information.

The Farnborough airshow is now one of the most important events of its kind in the world. It evolved from the SBAC - a national trade association for companies manufacturing civil air transport - the Society of British Aerospace Companies. The Association was formed in 1915 as the Society of British Aircraft Constructors. Their first air show was held at Hendon Airfield in 1932. The venue was moved to Farnborough in 1948. This was the first time the SBAC event was open to the public. Prior to 1948, the air displays had been restricted to invited guests. The 1948 Farnborough programme is particularly hard to find and a 'must' for any collector of air display memorabilia.

▲ Farnborough programme. 1948. 24 pages. 210 x 135mm. (f-g) £24 - £28

▲ Farnborough programme. 1950. 32 pages. 210 x 135mm. (g) £12 - £14

▲ Farnborough programme. 1951. 32 pages. 210 x 135mm. (g) £8 - £10

▲ Farnborough programme. 1953. 32 pages. 210 x 132mm. (g) £8 - £10

▲ Farnborough programme. 1959. 22 pages. 225 x 225mm. (g-vg) £8 - £10

▲ Air Pageant programme. Gatwick Airport. 1949. 32 pages. 245 x 185mm. (g) £8 - £10

▲ Air Display programme. Lee-On-Solent. 1956. 32 pages. 250 x 185mm. (g-vg) £8 - £10

▲ National Air Races programme. Birmingham Airport. 1949. 44 pages. 250 x 200mm. (g) £10 - £12

AERONAUTICA - Air sickness bags

The collecting of air sickness bags has taken a blow as more and more airlines are now using plain bags. It's the bags with the airline insignia printed on them that are sought after by collectors. Niek Vermeulen has a collection of over 5000 different bags.

▲ Air India. (vg) £1 - £2

◄   Cathay Pacific. (vg) £1 - £2

▲ Malaysia Airlines. (vg) £1 - £2

Contributory factors to air sickness includes the consumption of alcohol and drugs. A good tip to help avoid air sickness is to face forward, stay as still as possible and focus on objects at the furthest point of the cabin. Various medications are available to help avoid it.

▲ Korean Air. (g-vg) £1 - £2

▲ Biman Airlines. (vg) £2 - £3

▲ KLM. (vg) £1 - £2

▲ Helios Airways. (g-vg) £1 - £2

▲ Easy Jet. (g-vg) 50p - £1

▲ Jet Airways. (vg) £1 - £3

▲ Aeroflot. (vg) £1 - £3

▲ Lufthansa. (vg) £1 - £2

▲ Airfix OO City of Truro. Complete kit. (vg) £4 - £6

Now part of the Hornby empire, Airfix was started in 1939 by Nicholas Kove. However, the manufacture of model kits didn't happen until ten years later. The first aircraft kit was not produced until 1955 (Supermarine Spitfire).

As well as aircraft models, Airfix products include ships and model railway accessories. A good source for Airfix products is internet auctions.

The Airfix Modellers Club was a joint venture between Airfix and Fleetway Publications and ran from 1974 to 1981. Promotions in Fleetway comics helped business thrive. Enthusiasts have now formed the Airfix Collectors Club and at the time of writing, the email contact is brookjeremy@hotmail.com

▲ Airfix 72 Dog Fight Doubles. Mirage & Mig 15. Complete kit. (1975). (vg) £6 - £8

◀ Airfix Modellers Club badge. Made by Fattorini. (1975). (vg) £3 - £5

▲ Esso Airfix OO Tank Wagon. Complete kit. (1965). (vg) £6 - £8

▲ Airfix magazine. Vol.1, No.2. 1960. (g-vg) £6 - £8

▲ Airfix magazine. Vol.2, No.3. August 1961. (g) £4 - £6

▲ Airfix magazine. Vol.3, No.4. September 1962. (vg) £4 - £6

▲ Airfix construction kits booklet. Autumn 1962. (g) £3 - £4

▲ Airfix magazine. Vol.3, No.9. February 1963. (vg) £4 - £5

▲ Airfix magazine. Vol.3, No.11. April 1963. (vg) £4 - £5

▲ Airfix magazine. Vol.3, No.12. May 1963. (vg) £4 - £5

AKAN GOLDWEIGHTS

These were originally small geometric alloy shapes, which later (mid 18th century onwards) were produced in large quantities in artistic forms.

These little objects were a measuring system for weighing gold dust. They were made by the Akan people of West Africa and represent their culture (animals, people and symbols).

Not only do these objects make interesting collections, they are an opportunity to acquire a piece of history and they have every chance of increasing in value.

▲ Akan figurine goldweight. Man holding torso. Brass. (1850). 55mm high. (g) £35 - £40

▲ Akan geometric goldweight. Brass. (1750). 15 x 15mm. (g) £10 - £15

▲ Akan geometric goldweight. Brass. (1750). 25 x 10mm. (g) £10 - £15

▲ Akan geometric goldweight. Brass. (1750). 20 x 15mm. (g) £10 - £15

ALARM CLOCKS

This is a fantastic collecting subject with lots of scope to build a valuable collection that could prove to be a good investment (if bought correctly in the first place).

A degree of patience will be needed to find the right examples as the best ones are generally snapped up on e-based auctions.

You would be lucky to find a bargain at a car boot but it's well worth remembering to keep a look out. A good chance of acquiring good examples (at fair prices) is at a large collector's fair.

▲ Smiths. Noddy & Big Ears pictorial alarm clock. (1965). Working order. (vg) £20 - £25

Wind-up alarm clocks became popular at the turn of the twentieth century with Westclox being one of the manufacturers, producing the Big Ben and Baby Ben.

Children's pictorial alarm clocks from the 1950's are particularly desirable and can change hands for around £30+ depending on desirability, condition and whether or not in working order.

There's a brilliant website to reference Westclox alarm clocks (including details of reproductions) at www.clockhistory.com

▲ Westclox. Baby Ben. (1925). Made in Canada. Not tested. (g) £10 - £12

▲ Bradley. Mickey Mouse pictorial alarm clock. 1977. Working order. (g-vg) £10 - £12

AMERICAN LICENCE PLATES

▲ Iowa licence plate. (vg) £5 - £7

Each of the American States has its own motor vehicle registration system. Some issue more colourful number plates than others.

Collectors look for attractive plates and/or rare old issues.

If you are just looking for the attractive issues then expect to pay between £5 and £8 for a standard plate.

▲ Georgia licence plate. (g-vg) £4 - £6

The plates can look good if mounted on a wall and are indeed popular with teenagers. They are deemed to be 'cool'. However, the supply (particularly via auction websites) is plentiful and the market may not be one that investors would be too interested in.

▲ Alabama licence plate. (g-vg) £4 - £6

▲ Florida licence plate. (g) £3 - £4

▲ Tennessee licence plate. Special 'dealer' issue. (f) £4 - £6

ANDY CAPP

Andy Capp is a comic strip character created by Reg Smythe (1917 - 1998). The Daily Mirror and Sunday Mirror introduced Andy Capp to their readers in 1957.

The Andy Capp character is a working class chap who married Florrie. His hobbies include darts and pigeon racing.

▲ Andy Capp. Wade teapot. 1997. (ex) £10 - £12

▲ Andy Capp. Valentine postcard. Postmarked South Devon 1974. (vg) £1 - £2

Reginald Smyth (without the 'e') became a professional cartoonist. He adopted the professional name Reg Smythe. He was born in Hartlepool in 1917, the son of a shipyard worker. Reg died in 1998. A bronze statue commemorating Andy Capp now stands in Hartlepool.

ANNUALS

A fascinating collecting area but with the drawback that it can become addictive and before you know it, your collection could consist of 1000 books and the floorboards start bending under the strain.

The tip is to specialise within a particular category. For example, rather than collect every TV Show annual, you could concentrate on a few shows.

There's a strong 'crossover' into other collecting areas. For example, collectors of Coronation Street memorabilia would be interested in the related Annuals but not in those of other shows.

Values depend on rarity and condition. Annuals were, in the majority, given to children as presents. Consequently, some have suffered from 'scribbling crayon syndrome' and thereby devalued. Others have suffered from irresponsible handling, thereby causing damage to the spines.

Many annuals had the price printed, bottom right, of an early page. When given as gifts, the prices were often cut out (known as 'price clipping'). A price clipped annual is worth fractionally less than one with the price intact.

The printing and finishing process of Annuals was not always to the highest of standards and, in quite a few cases, the pages become loose with use, because the binding of the book was the cheaper 'glued to spine' option as opposed to 'sewn'.

A 'hard to find' annual with excellent spine and in excellent condition, not price clipped and with no markings, can command a relatively high price at auction.

Popular categories of annuals are 'TV Show', 'Pop', 'Comic' and 'Sci-Fi'.

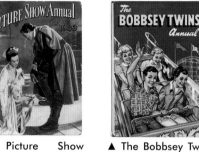

▲ Picture Show Annual. 1939. (g) £4 - £6

▲ The Bobbsey Twins Annual. 1960. (g) £4 - £6

▲ Mrs Hippos Annual. 1935. (f-g) £4 - £6

▲ Film Fun Annual. 1951. (f) £4 - £6

▲ Bugs Bunny Annual. 1963. (f-g) £4 - £5

▲ BJ And The Bear Annual. 1980. (g) £5 - £7

▲ The Schoolgirls' Own Annual. 1923. (g-vg) £10 - £12

▲ Jason Annual. 1990. (g-vg) £1 - £2

▲ The Osmonds Annual. 1975. (g-vg) £3 - £5

▲ TV Tornado Annual. 1970. (vg) £4 - £6

▲ Tiger Tim's Annual. 1930. (f-g) £5 - £7

▲ The Beano Book. 1989. (g) £1 - £3

▲ Picture Show Annual. 1958. (f-g) £3 - £5

▲ Twinkle Annual. 1978. (g-vg) £1 - £2

▲ Okay Adventure Annual. 1956. (g) £3 - £5

▲ Chicks' Own Annual. 1953. (f-g) £5 - £7

ANNUALS - TV Show related

▲ Clangers Annual. 1971. (f) £4 - £6

▲ Danger Mouse Annual. 1983. (g) £1 - £2

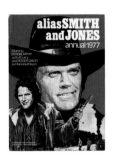

▲ Alias Smith And Jones Annual. 1977. (g) £10 - £12

▲ Back To The Future Annual. 1990. (vg) £1 - £2

▲ Baretta Annual. 1977. (vg-ex) £6 - £8

▲ The Double Deckers Annual. 1972. (vg) £4 - £6

▲ Pixie, Dixie And Mr Jinks Annual. 1975. (g-vg) £4 - £5

▲ Centurions PowerXtreme Annual. 1987. (vg-ex) £1 - £2

▲ The A-Team Annual. 1984. (vg) £3 - £4

▲ Just William Annual. 1978. (ex) £3 - £4

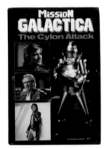

▲ Mission Galactica The Cyclon Attack. 1980. (g) £1 - £2

▲ Black Beauty Annual. 1975. (g-vg) £3 - £5

▲ Magpie Annual. 1972. (f). £2 - £3

▲ Playschool Annual. 1979. (vg) £3 - £4

▲ The Six Million Dollar Man Annual. 1977. (vg) £4 - £5

▲ Bugs Bunny Annual. 1974. (f) £1 - £2

▲ Roland Rat Superstar And Friends Annual. 1984. (g) £1 - £2

▲ Lancer Annual. 1970. (g) £5 - £7

▲ Space 1999 Annual. 1976. (g-vg) £2 - £4

▲ The Sweeney Annual. 1978. (g-vg) £2 - £4

▲ Laramie Annual. 1961. (f) £8 - £10

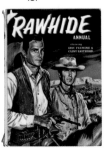

▲ Rawhide Annual. 1962. (f-g) £8 - £10

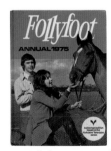

▲ Follyfoot Annual. 1975. (vg) £3 - £4

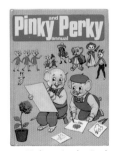

▲ Pinky And Perky Annual. 1975. (g) £3 - £4

▲ Scooby-Doo Annual. 1983. (g) £2 - £3

ANNUALS - TV Show related

▲ The Beverly Hillbillies Annual. 1965. (g) £5 - £7

▲ The Grange Hill Annual. 1982. (g-vg) £3 - £4

▲ Hazell Annual. 1979. (g) £4 - £5

▲ Crackerjack Annual. 1969. (ex) £5 - £7

▲ Dallas Annual. 1981. (g-vg) £4 - £6

▲ Starsky And Hutch Annual. 1978. (vg) £3 - £4

▲ Knight Rider Annual. 1982. (vg) £3 - £4

▲ It Ain't Half Hot, Mum Annual. 1977. (g) £3 - £4

▲ The Banana Splits Annual. 1970. (f-g)   £2 - £4

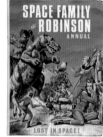

▲ Space Family Robinson Annual. 1967. Some loose pages. (f) £2 - £3

▲ Tarzan Annual. 1974. (g) £2 - £4

▲ Minder Annual. 1986. (vg) £2 - £3

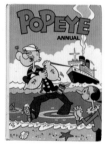

▲ Popeye Annual. 1976. (g) £2 - £4

▲ The Muppet Show Annual. 1977. (g) £2 - £3

▲ Redcap Annual. 1965. (vg) £5 - £7

▲ Tiswas Annual. 1981. (g-vg) £5 - £6

▲ Behind The Bike Sheds Annual. 1985. (g-vg) £2 - £4

▲ The Paul Daniels Magic Annual. 1982. (vg-ex) £3 - £4

▲ Fantastic Four Annual. 1979. (g) £2 - £3

▲ Logan's Run Annual. 1978. (vg-ex) £4 - £6

▲ "Chips" Annual. 1981. (g-vg) £4 - £6

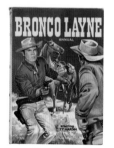

▲ Bronco Layne Annual. 1969. (g) £8 - £12

▲ Burke's Law Annual. 1965. (f-g) £8 - £12

▲ Magnum PI Annual. 1982. (g) £3 - £5

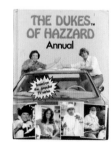

▲ The Dukes Of Hazzard Annual. 1983. One loose page. (g) £3 - £5

ANNUALS - TV Show related

▲ Daktari Annual. 1968. (g) £3 - £4

▲ Angels Annual. 1978. (vg) £5 - £7

▲ Dad's Army Annual. 1978. (g-vg) £3 - £4

▲ Blakes7 Annual. 1979. (g) £3 - £4

▲ Huckleberry Hound Annual. 1968. (g) £3 - £4

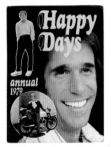
▲ Happy Days Annual. 1979. (g) £4 - £6

▲ Neighbours Annual. 1991. (ex) £1 - £2

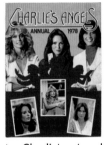
▲ Charlie's Angels Annual. 1978. (g) £4 - £6

▲ Dempsey And Makepeace Annual. 1986. (f-g) £3 - £4

▲ Buck Rogers In The 25th Century Annual. 1981. (g-vg) £3 - £4

▲ Look-in How Annual. 1975. (vg) £3 - £4

▲ The Professionals Annual. 1983. (vg) £3 - £4

▲ Ollie And Fred's Fun Book. 1966. (g) £5 - £7

▲ The Flintstones Annual. 1968. (f) £2 - £3

▲ Captain Scarlet Annual. 1968. (f) £2 - £3

▲ Supersonic Annual. 1978. (vg) £3 - £5

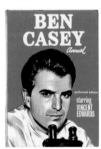
▲ Ben Casey Annual. 1963. (vg) £10 - £12

▲ Kung Fu Annual. 1975. (g) £2 - £3

▲ Worzel Gummidge Annual. 1980. (vg) £3 - £4

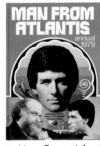
▲ Man From Atlantis Annual. 1979. (vg) £4 - £6

▲ The Lone Ranger Annual. 1957. (f-g) £8 - £10

▲ The Kenny Everett Video Show Annual. 1980. (vg) £10 - £12

▲ Basil Brush Annual. 1970. (f) £2 - £3

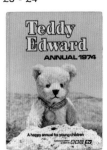
▲ Teddy Edward Annual. 1974. (g-vg) £1 - £2

▲ Kojak Annual. 1977. (g) £2 - £4

ARTISTIC DRAWINGS

▲ 'snice on Ice. Drawn and painted by J.June Anderson. 1948. 184 x 117mm £6 - £8

Whilst classic works of art are truly collectable, this book doesn't pander to the purists of the art world.

There's an alternative source of old original works of art that will not break the bank. They were drawn in pencil, ink, crayon and water colours.

60 years ago and beyond, popular pastimes included drawing. Works were often crafted in autograph books or similar, specifically for a family member or friend. It wasn't a case of rushing the drawing but putting time and effort into something that the artist knew would be kept and treasured.

It also involved a degree of trust as the autograph books would, on occasions, have to be loaned to the artists to give them time to produce as fine a work as possible.

▲ I Say Policeman. Drawn by A.E.S., 1920. 135 x 108mm £8 - £10

Little did these artists know that in many years to come, their works would be sought by collectors. Values are determined by age but mainly 'quality of work'.

Some of these pictures are worthy of framing and you never know, there could be a work of a famous person to be found in this rather obscure sector of the art world.

▲Butterflies. Drawn and painted by Emma Frazer. 1917. 134 x 108mm £4 - £6

▲Britain & France. Drawn by Tom Carmichael. 1940. 134 x 108mm £3 - £4

▲Two Horses. Drawn and painted by R.Burrows. 1949. 150 x 99mm £1 - £2

◄ House. Painted by M.D., 1933. 183 x 120mm £1 - £2

► So Polite. Drawn and painted by Nellie Underhill. 1914. 167 x 136mm £3 - £4

ARTISTIC DRAWINGS

▲ Robin Readbreast. Painting. Elsie Hawkesford. 1915. 160 x 130mm £6 - £8

▲ Lucy Hollaway. Ink drawing. 1915. 165 x 130mm £8 - £10

▲ The War Baby. Pencil drawing. R. Coleman. 1918. 175 x 125mm £15 - £20

▲ Jig. Crayon drawing. E.S.W. 1913. 155 x 135mm. £4 - £6

▲ Spaniard. Ink drawing. A. Brown. 1915. 165 x 130mm £1 - £2

▲ Aw! You Make Me Tired! Pencil drawing. R. Coleman. 1918. 175 x 125mm £10 - £12

▲ Cat. Painting. Doris Middleton. 1913. 160 x 135mm £4 - £6

▲ Portrait. Pencil drawing. A.E.S. 1920. 130 x 105mm £2 - £4

▲ It's That Man Again. Drawing and painting. M.Little. 1948. 180 x 115mm £2 - £3

AUTOGRAPHS

The collecting of autographs is known as philography.

The first rule of philography is to ensure that the autograph is genuine. There have been numerous cases of autograph forgery and internet auctions are a common target for forgers.

When buying rare and valuable autographs it is best to use established and reputable traders. Alternatively, you can become an expert yourself with the help of the websites of reputable traders. Use their sites for comparison purposes.

▲ Eartha Kitt. Clear, black ink, 180 x 130mm. No dedication. £10 - £12

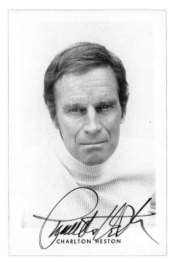

◄   Albert Semprini. Clear, black ink, 120 x 105mm. No dedication. £15 - £18

▲ Richard Todd. Clear, blue ink, 125 x 85mm. Dedicated. £8 - £12

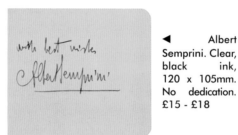

◄   Jeremy Beadle. Clear, blue ink , 80 x 60mm. No dedication. £6 - £8

▲ Una Stubbs. Signed first name on reverse. Clear, black ink, 135 x 85mm. Dedicated facsimile signature on front. £1 - £2

▲ Charlton Heston. Clear, black ink, 185 x 125mm. No dedication. £40 - £50

──── ADVERTISEMENT ────

George Baker

THE FAME COLLECTION - GEORGE BAKER

The Fame Collection offers an opportunity to purchase authentic autographs at realistic prices. Its a great opportunity to make a   potential long-term investment. The autograph is on the front page of a full-colour A5 4-page publication, which includes a biography of the star. The back page is numbered and embossed for proof of authenticity. George Baker was best known for his portrayal of Inspector Wexford.

Price **£8.20 (£6 plus VAT plus £1.00 P&P)**

Order from: Collecticus

Tel: 01380 811750

Internet: www.collecticus.co.uk

By post: Collecticus, P.O.Box 100, Devizes, Wiltshire, SN10 4TE (Cheques/Postal Order's payable to 'Hartley Publications Ltd')

The Fame Collection

AUTOGRAPHS

▲ Horatio Nelson. 1758 - 1805. Famed for the Battle of Trafalgar, in which he was shot and killed. Clear, brown ink, 115 x 25mm. No dedication. £400 - £450

▲ Fred Astaire (1899 - 1987) and Ginger Rogers (1911 - 1995) were dance partners extraordinaire. They made ten films together between 1933 and 1949. Clear, black & blue ink, 350 x 280mm. Ginger Rogers dedicated. £450 - £550

▲ Gerald (Gerry) Ford. 1913 - 2006. The 38th President of the United States of America, served from 1974 to 1977. He was born Leslie Lynch King and was adopted after his mother divorced and re-married. He legally changed his name in 1935.

In 1948 Gerald Ford married divorcee Betty Warren, a former fashion model and dancer. Betty Ford was born in 1918 and died in 2011. Clear, black & blue ink, 250 x 200mm. No dedication. £150 - £200

▶ Dwight D. Eisenhower. 1890 - 1969. The 34th President of the United States of America. Slightly faded, blue ink, 250 x 200mm. No dedication. £300 - £350

AUTOGRAPHS

▲ Chico Marx. 1887 - 1961. The elder of the Marx Brothers. He was born 'Leonard Marx' in New York. The Marx Brothers act began in Vaudeville and progressed to the big screen, becoming world famous. Their films included, 'A Night At The Opera', 'A Day At The Races' and 'A Night In Casablanca'. Chico was an accomplished pianist. He died in Hollywood in 1961. Slightly smudged, black ink, 125 x 87mm. No dedication. £300 - £350

▲ Buster Keaton. 1895 - 1966. Born Joseph Frank Keaton in Kansas, USA. He was one of the earliest film stars with legendary roles in silent movies. He made a fortune from the film industry. He spent over $300,000 on a luxury home in Beverley Hills in 1926. As the silent movies made way for the talkies, Keaton's career declined. He suffered from alcoholism but later recovered. He died of lung cancer, aged 70. He is buried at Forest Lawn Memorial Park, Hollywood Hills. Slightly smudged, blue ink, 252 x 202mm. Dedicated. £600 - £700

▲ Gene Kelly. 1912 - 1996. Born Eugene Curran Kelly in Pittsburgh, USA. He was one of the world's biggest film stars in the 1940's and 1950's. He will always be remembered for his role in the blockbuster film 'Singin' In The Rain'. Clear, black ink, 250 x 200mm. No dedication. £200 - £250

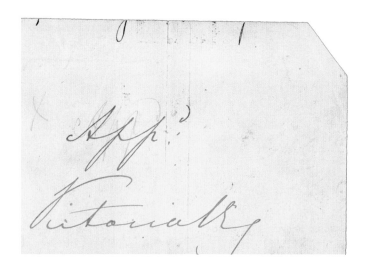

▲ Queen Victoria. 1819 - 1901. Victoria reigned from 1837 to 1901. She was born in Kensington Palace, London and died at Osborne House, Isle of Wight. Clear, brown ink, 130 x 90mm. No dedication. £250 - £300

AUTOGRAPHS

▲General Italo Gariboldi. 1879 - 1970. Italian Royal Army senior officer. Awarded the Knight's Cross of the Iron Cross by Hitler in recognition of his leadership in the Battle of Stalingrad. He was later condemned to death as a traitor but was released by the Allied Forces in 1944. Clear black ink signature. 290 x 205mm. Dedicated. £50 - £60

▲Marshal Tito. 1892 - 1980. President of Yugoslavia (1953 - 1980). Josip Broz Tito was considered to be a benevolent dictator. A Yugoslav statesman and revolutionary. His policies helped bond the nations of the Yugoslav federation. Clear blue ink signature. 235 x 180mm. No dedication. £200 - £250

▲Henry Irving. 1839 - 1905. Henry Irving was a renowned actor of the Victorian era. He was born in Somerset in February 1838. He became manager of the famous Lyceum Theatre in London, transforming it from near closure to huge success. He was the first actor to be awarded a knighthood. He died suddenly in October 1905 of a stroke and is buried in Westminster Abbey. Signed postcard. Postmarked Torquay 24 March 1905. Clear black ink. £25 - £30

▲Ada Reeve. 1874 - 1966. British actress, film and stage. Her father was the actor Charles Reeves. She began her career in pantomimes as a child actress. Black ink signature on postcard postmarked Edinburgh 1905. No dedication. £20 - £25

▲ Robert Watkin-Mills. 1849 - 1930. Prominent Victorian bass-baritone. In his later years he moved to Canada where he appeared with the Montreal Philharmonic Society. Black ink signature and dated March 1905 on postcard postmarked Fulham 1905. No dedication. £10 - £15

▲ Lucy Kemp-Welch. 1869 - 1958. Renowned British artist whose specialist subject was 'working horses'. She produced the illustrations for the 1915 edition of Anna Sewell's classic book, Black Beauty. Black ink signature on white card, slotted into a postcard. No dedication. £20 - £30

▲Ben Davies. 1858 - 1943. Celebrated Welsh tenor. He made his Covent Garden debut in 1892. In later years he toured Australia. Clear black ink signature on a postcard (no postmark). No dedication. £10 - £15

AUTOGRAPHS

▲► Queen Mary. Clear, blue ink, on postcard. No dedication. £60 - £80

▲ Norman Wisdom. Clear, black ink, 152 x 103mm. Dedicated. £8 - £10

▲ Victor Spinetti. Clear, black ink, 140 x 90mm. Dedicated. £8 - £10

◄ Cary Grant. Clear, black ink, 90 x 60mm. Dedicated. £50 - £60

▲ Basil Cameron. Autograph on front cover of 1948 programme. Clear, blue ink, 205 x 135mm. No dedication £3 - £6

▲ Bobby Robson. Clear, blue ink, 215 x 90mm. No dedication. £14 - £18

▲ Colin Cowdrey signed letter. Clear, blue ink, 180 x 135. No dedication. £5 - £7

▲ Edward G. Robinson. Clear, black ink, 175 x 125mm. Dedicated. £80 - £100

▲ Laurence Olivier. Clear, black ink, 140 x 82mm. No dedication. £8 - £10

▲ Edward Fox. Clear, black ink, 140 x 90mm. No dedication. £4 - £6

▲ Peter Sellers. Clear, blue ink. Also comedian Mario Fabrizi who worked frequently with Peter Sellers, including in the 1960 British Lions film 'Two-Way Stretch'. 115 x 70mm. No dedication. £60 - £80

▲ Wendy Craig. Clear, blue ink, 140 x 90mm. No dedication. £4 - £6

▲ Ian Botham. Clear, black ink, 150 x 100mm. No dedication. £3 - £5

AUTOGRAPHS

▲ Reita Faria. Miss World 1966. Clear, blue ink, 140 x 90mm. No dedication. £8 - £10

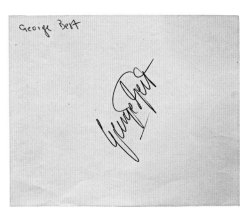

▲ George Best. Clear, black ink, 130 x 105mm. No dedication. £50 - £70

▲ Earl Roberts. Clear, black ink, 140 x 85mm. No dedication. £40 - £60

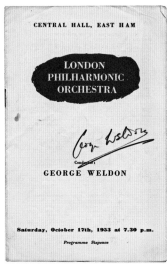

▲ George Weldon. Autograph on orchestra programme. Clear, pencil, 205 x 135mm. No dedication. £4 - £6

▲ Laurel & Hardy. Stan Laurel clear, black ink, Oliver Hardy, very faded, blue ink. 250 x 205mm. Dedicated. £120 - £160

▲ Ted Heath & his Orchestra. Clear, blue ink, 135 x 85mm. No dedication. £16 - £18

▲ John Junkin. Clear, black ink, 140 x 90mm. No dedication. £10 - £14

▲ James Bolan. Clear, blue ink, 140 x 90mm. No dedication. £4 - £6

▲ Esther Rantzen. Clear, blue ink, 163 x 100mm. No dedication. £4 - £6

▲ Richard Branson. Clear, black ink, 180 x 125mm. No dedication. £4 - £6

AUTOGRAPHS

▲ Burt Lancaster. Autograph book page. Clear, black ink, 150 x 100mm. No dedication. £40 - £50

▲ Frank Sinatra. Autographed programme. Palace Theatre, Manchester. 20th July 1953. Clear, blue ink. No dedication. £180 - £220

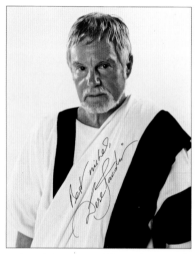

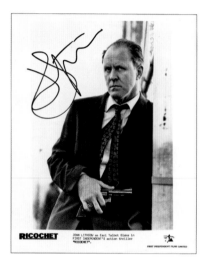

▲ Derek Jacobi. Publicity photograph. Clear, black ink, 255 x 203mm. No dedication. £6 - £8

▲ John Lithgow. Publicity photograph. Clear, black ink, 255 x 203mm. No dedication. £8 - £10

▲ Count Basie and his orchestra. Autographed programme. Tour programme 1959. Clear, blue ink, 265 x 210mm. £70 - £90

▲ John Hurt. Publicity photograph. Clear, black ink, 255 x 203mm. No dedication. £6 - £8

▲ Matthew Modine. Publicity photograph. Clear, black ink, 255 x 203mm. Dedicated. £14 - £16

AUTOGRAPHS

▲ Kathy Staff. Clear, black ink, 152 x 102mm. No dedication. £10 - £12

▲ Richard O'Sullivan. Clear, blue ink, 140 x 90mm. No dedication. £6 - £8

▲ Anna Ford. Clear, black ink, 150 x 100mm. No dedication. £8 - £10

▲ Margi Clarke. Clear, black ink, 75 x 65mm. No dedication. £2 - £3

▲ Joan Sims. Clear, black ink, 147 x 100mm. No dedication. £8 - £10

▲ Anita Dobson. Clear, blue ink, 125 x 70mm. No dedication. £3 - £4

▲ Carmen Silvera. Clear, blue ink, 140 x 100mm. No dedication. £6 - £8

▲ Mollie Sugden. Clear, black ink, 140 x 10mm. No dedication. £10 - £12

▲ Glenda Jackson. Clear, black ink, 140 x 90mm. No dedication. £6 - £8

▲ Nigel Havers. Clear, black ink, 140 x 90mm. No dedication. £3 - £5

▲ Gaby Roslin. Clear, black ink, 147 x 100mm. No dedication. £2 - £4

▲ Keith Floyd. Clear, black ink, 147 x 100mm. No dedication. £16 - £18

▲ Nick Ross. Clear, black ink, 150 x 100mm. No dedication. £3 - £4

▲ Les Dennis. Clear, black ink, 147 x 100mm. No dedication. £3 - £4

▲ Brian Walden. Clear, black ink, 147 x 105mm. No dedication. £6 - £8

AUTOMOBILE ASSOCIATION (The AA)

The AA has been part of our motoring history for over 100 years and therefore deserves a high ranking in the field of collectables. There are plenty of different items to collect. These include badges, old membership certificates and the early keys for the AA roadside telephone boxes.

▲ 1950 Morris Z van. (1995). Days Gone Model. 80mm long. Model (m), box (ex) £3 - £4

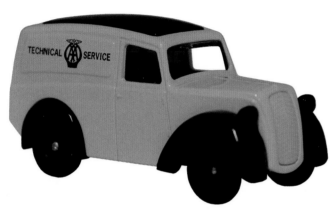

▲ Oban No.4. AA road map. (1948). (g) £4 - £6

▲ York No.11. AA road map. (1950). (g) £3 - £4

AA Membership cards

▲ 1933. (g) £8 - £12

▲ 1940. (vg) £8 - £12

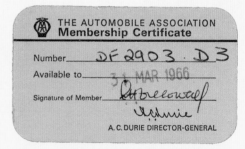

▲ 1966. (g-vg) £6 - £8

▲ 1992. (vg) £2 - £3

AUTOMOBILE ASSOCIATION

AA badges

The first AA badges were issued in 1906 and each one was numbered. The very first (number 1) was issued to the AA's first chairman, Colonel Bosworth.

The badges had fixing bolts for car grilles or attachments for badge bars.

Smaller badges were allocated for motorcycles.

Badge numbers reached 999,999 in October 1930.

▲Badge number 861126. (1928). Car. Nickel plated. (g-vg) £40 - £50

In October 1930 the numbers began again but had the prefix letter O. After that, each 100,000 then had a suffix letter. These numbers began with the suffix A and continued until 1952 (suffix letter T). The war years (suffix letters M, N and P) saw far fewer membership registrations.

◄ Badge number 61404J (1934) with badge bar fixing clamp. Car. Chrome plated. (g) £20 - £24

Motorcycle badges were flat (as opposed to the later domed shape) until 1956 and carried the suffix letters R - T. The domed motorcycle badges (W,X,Y,Z,A) were issued 1956 - 1967.

▲Badge number 54645T (motorcycle - flat). (1956) with handlebar fixing clamp. (vg) £15 - £20

▲ Badge number 59479X (motorcycle - domed). (1959). (g) £10 - £12

The design of the badge changed slightly in 1945, when it became domed and always with a yellow backing plate. The AA letters merged into the surround. These badge numbers started at 010000 (no prefix or suffix letters) and ended at 0999999. After that, there were prefix letters 'O' and then 'OA' to 'OZ' lasting from 1945 - 1957.

The domed badges continued until 1967 when they were replaced with the square badge (no numbers).

▲Badge number 0965640 (1945). Car - domed. (g-vg) £12 - £14

The final (prefix) number sequences were:-
1A - 9A = 1957 - 1959
1B - 9B = 1960 - 1961
1C - 9C = 1962 - 1963
1D - 9D = 1964 - 1965
1E - 9E = 1966 - 1967

▲Badge number 2C83658 (1962). Car. (vg- ex) £7 - £9

▲ Badge number 4B15834 (1960). Car. (g-vg) £6 - £8

AUTOMOBILE ASSOCIATION

Roadside
phone box keys

In 1911, the AA started to install telephone boxes on certain roads, and cabinets containing towels and brushes at hotels; by 1919 members were being issued keys to these boxes. The keys are incredibly easy to buy, sell, and trade thanks to their small size and light weight, but they are not worth huge sums. Any key issued prior to 1947 had a round head, and these offer the best investment potential. Anything dated from 1947 onwards (made by Yale) is likely to sell for a small sum.

(A) The first key (1912 – 1919) is now hard to find and has a minimum value of £35 (in good condition). It has a fretted crossed 'AA' in the head.

(B) The next key was a size larger than its predecessor. It was made by H & T Vaughan of Willenhall and was only issued in 1920. It is not readily available, so it is one to watch out for. Expect a minimum value of £15 (in good condition).

(C) This is another key that was only produced for one year (1921). It is smaller than previous examples. Like the 1920 key, this one carried the date, but it was also stamped with the words "The Key to the Open Road." It is interesting to note that the year was never included again on any of the keys. Expect to pay £20 for an example in good condition.

(D) From 1922 – 1946 the rounded head shape continued (minus the year). The "Open Road" line was replaced with the message "Property of the Automobile Association." This key is still fairly hard to find but cannot be classed as rare, so the value of this one drops dramatically to £8 in good condition and a little more for examples in better condition.

(E) In 1947 the design was changed and stamped by the maker Yale (who had taken over the business of H & T Vaughan). This lasted until 1966. Many were produced so they are reasonably easy to find and, in good condition or better, can sell for £3.

(F) The final key was issued in 1967, coinciding with the change of logo. Supply was plentiful so the value is half its predecessor, although this type will quite often fetch more if the condition is very good or better.

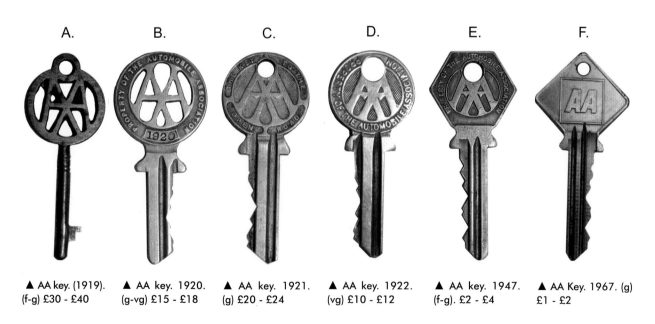

A.	B.	C.	D.	E.	F.
▲ AA key. (1919).	▲ AA key. 1920.	▲ AA key. 1921.	▲ AA key. 1922.	▲ AA key. 1947.	▲ AA Key. 1967. (g)
(f-g) £30 - £40	(g-vg) £15 - £18	(g) £20 - £24	(vg) £10 - £12	(f-g). £2 - £4	£1 - £2

AUTOMOBILE ASSOCIATION

Annual
Handbooks

▲1925. (g) £30 - £35

▲1927. (g) £25 - £30

▲1931. (f-g) £10 - £12

▲1937. (f) £6 - £8

▲(1948). Post war edition. (f) £5 - £7

▲1951. (f-g) £5 - £7

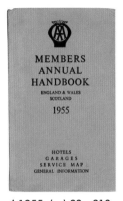

▲1955. (vg) £8 - £10

▲1957. (g) £5 - £6

▲1963. (vg) £8 - £12

▲1966. (g-vg) £6 - £8

▲1970. (g) £3 - £4

▲1974. (g-vg) £3 - £4

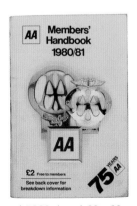

▲1980. (g-vg) £2 - £3

▲1982. (g-vg) £2 - £3

▲1990. (g-vg) £2 - £3

▲1995. (vg) £2 - £3

AUTOMOBILIA

The study and collecting of items relating to motor vehicles.

There's a massive range of collectables in this category. Look out for 'Autojumbles' (dates and locations can be found via Google) to find some obscure and wonderful collectables).

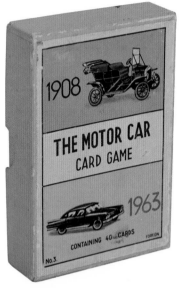

◄ The Motor Car Card Game. 1963. Complete set of 40 cards. No instructions. Original box. (vg) £3 - £5

▲ Nenette car polisher. (1960). Dust absorbing polisher with wooden handle in its original tinplate holder. (355mm high). The marketing claim for this product was; "a few minutes a day with Nenette and your car will never lose its shiny new look". (vg) £6 - £8

▲ Don't drink and drive beermat. (1980). (g) £1 - £2

◄ Vauxhall Cresta key fob. (1970). (g) £3 - £4

► Rolls Royce pin badge. (1985). (vg) £4 - £6

Owners Handbooks

This is a classic example of using commonsense when buying collectable items. Ask yourself, how big and where is the potential market? The answer in this case is that the biggest market rests with the owners of the cars to which the 'owner's handbooks' relate. Given that there are thousands of models of motor cars, the potential market for each specific model becomes limited. However, particularly thanks to internet auctions and autojumbles, when you do find the right buyer, you have a desirable collectable for that person. However, it's not necessarily a case of naming whatever price you like. The potential buyer is likely to know the value and be aware that if your asking price is too high, another is likely to come onto the market. Also, the potential buyer may possibly become annoyed over a greedy asking price and, as a matter of principle, choose not to deal with you.

▲ Ford Anglia Owner's Handbook. 1964. (g) £6 - £8

AUTOMOBILIA - Magazines

Old motoring magazines are a printed record of how the motor industry has evolved over the decades. Advertisements not only help to tell the story, cut out, they become collectable individual items. This creates a bit of a dilemma as it means damaging and devaluing the magazine. However, if it's a case of profiteering, then (carefully) extracting (and perhaps, mounting) old advertisements can be quite profitable.

▲ The Light Car. 12 May 1939. (f-g) £4 - £6

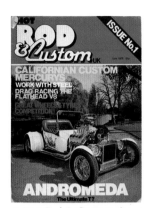

▲ Hot Rod & Cutsom. Issue No.1 June 1978. (g) £8 - £10

▲ The Autocar. 28 October 1949. (f) £2 - £4

▲ Autosport. 13 October 1955. (vg) £3 - £4

▲ Modern Motoring and Travel. December 1964. (f) £1 - £2

▲ The Motor. 7 September 1955. (g) £3 - £4

▲ The Motor. 20 January 1960. (g) £2 - £3

▲ The Autocar. 27 November 1953. (f-g) £2 - £3

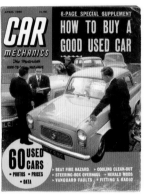

▲ Car Mechanics. April 1962. (g) £2 - £3

▲ The Autocar. 20 August 1948. (g) £3 - £4

▲ The Autocar. 14 March 1947. (g) £3 - £4

▲ The Autocar. 27 August 1948. (g) £3 - £4

▲ The Autocar. 17 August 1951. (g) £2 - £4

▲ The Autocar. 22 June 1951. (f-g) £2 - £3

AUTOMOBILIA

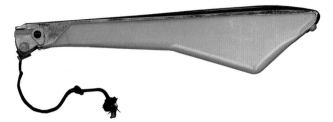

▲ Trafficator arm. (1960). Made by Lucas. Unused (vg). Original box in fair to good condition. A great piece of motoring history. £15 - £20

Trafficators

Before the introduction of flashing amber lights to indicate whether a motor vehicle intends to turn left or right, cars were fitted with 'trafficators' to serve the same purpose.

A 'trafficator' is a signal arm unit that was affixed to the door pillars of a car, which when activated would automatically be raised and lowered, thereby telling motorists and pedestrians which way the car intends to turn. Each one had a small bulb inside to aid its visibility, particularly at night.

Motoring related invoices tell a story. They are a little piece of our motoring history. How much did a particular vehicle cost on a certain date?

Whilst not particularly valuable collectable items, they complement collections relating to particular makes of vehicles.

Ornately designed invoices are also of interest to billhead collectors.

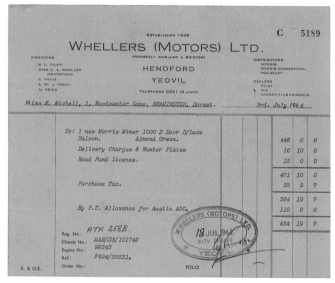

▲ Wheelers, Yeovil. 1964 invoice for a new Morris Minor. (vg) £2 - £3

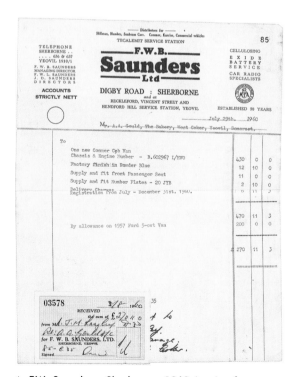

▲ F.W. Saunders, Sherborne. 1960 invoice for a new Commer Cob van. (g-vg) £1 - £2

▲ Nursteed Motor & Engineering, Devizes. 1962 invoice for a used Austin 10cwt van. (g-vg) £2 - £4

AUTOMOBILIA - Postcards

▲ Morris Oxford (Series V). 1959. Postally unused. (g-vg) £12 - £14

▲ Morris Oxford Traveller. 1957. Postally unused. (vg) £10 - £14

▲ Wolseley 15/60. 1958. Postally unused. (vg) £10 - £14

▲ Morris Cowley 1200. 1954 Postally unused. (vg) £10 - £14

▲ MG Magnette (Mark III). 1959. Postally unused. (vg) £12 - £16

▲ Wolseley Fifteen-Fifty. 1956. Postally unused. (vg) £10 - £14

Motorways

▲ M6 Motoway, Keele, Staffs. Postmarked Stoke on Trent 1973. Message in ink. (vg) £4 - £6

▲ M6 Motoway, Knutsford. (1975). Postally unused. (vg) £5 - £7

▲ M5 Motoway, Strensham. (1970). Postally unused. (vg) £4 - £6

▲ M4 Services, Severn Bridge. (1975). Postally unused. (vg) £2 - £4

Volkswagen Factory

The Volkswagen factory in Wolfsburg is responsible for producing one of the most iconic motor cars in the world - The Beetle.

In 1955, the Wolfsburg factory produced its one-millionth Beetle.

▲ Bild 2. (1960). Postally unused. (ex) £4 - £6

▲ Bild 6. (1960). Postally unused. (ex) £4 - £6

▲ Bild 7. (1960). Postally unused. (ex) £4 - £6

▲ Bild 8. (1960). Postally unused. (ex) £4 - £6

AVON

Avon Cosmetics began in the USA in 1886 and was known as The California Perfume Company. It was the brainchild of David Hall McConnell. After he died in 1937 the business was taken over by his son, David McConnell Junior. He renamed it 'Avon'.

Britain was introduced to the Avon product in the mid-1950's. The door-to-door 'Avon Ladies' became very well known, particularly thanks to television campaigns and the famous "ding-dong Avon calling".

Avon Cosmetics have produced many collectable items over the years. A popular line with collectors today is the novelty glass bottle (mainly produced in the 70's and 80's). They originally contained perfumes and after shave lotions. A good source is car boot sales, charity shops and internet auctions. They can be bought for reasonable sums and the best chance of making an investment is to find items in very good condition with no chips and with their stoppers, and preferably with their original boxes.

▲   Magnifying   Glass. Imperator aftershave. (1975). 255mm long. (vg) £5 - £7

▲ Racing Car. (1970). 190mm long. (vg) £5 - £7

► Elusive. Skin So Soft. Plain bottle with original box. (1975). 75mm high. (vg) £2 - £3

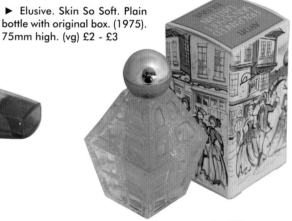

▲ Lion. (1973). 140mm high. (vg) £5 - £7

▲ Teddy Bear. (1975). 80mm high. (f-g) £3 - £4

▲ Knight chess piece. Smart   Move.   (1975). 150mm high. (vg) £4 - £6

BABYCHAM

Babycham was created by Francis Edwin Showering in 1953. Much of the success can be attributed to a powerful marketing campaign "I'd love a Babycham". It was the first alcoholic drink to be advertised on ITV (1957).

The famous leaping baby chamois (a cross between an antelope and a goat) has featured on items such as drinking glasses, beer mats, bottles, trays and models. The Babycham chamois is also referred to as a 'deer' and 'bambi'. The earlier items are now sought after by collectors.

▲ Babycham chamois model. (1965). Plastic. (vg) £12 - £14

◄ Babycham original bottles, converted to salt and pepper shakers. (1980). (vg) £7 - £9

▲ Babycham ashtray. (1980). Ceracord Ltd backstamp. (vg) £12 - £14

◄ Babycham drinking glass. (1980). (vg) £2 - £4

▲ Babycham large beermat. (1985). 190 x 190mm. (g) £2 - £4

BABYCHAM - Beer mats

▲ Got sparkle got life. (1970).
(g) £1 - £2

▲ I'd love a Babycham.
(1975). (vg) £1 - £2

▲ Pub of the year 1982. (g)
£1 - £3

▲ I'd love a Babycham.
(1958). (g) £4 - £6

▲ Celebrate today with
Babycham. (1975). (g) £1 - £2

▲ Babycham plain. (1975).
(vg) £1 - £2

▲ Disco and after. 1980. (g)
£1 - £3

▲ I'd love a Babycham.
(1960). (g) £3 - £4

▲ Pub of the year 1983. (g-vg)
£2 - £4

▲ Party planner. (1980). (g)
£2 - £3

▲ The genuine champagne
perry. (1960). (g) £3 - £5

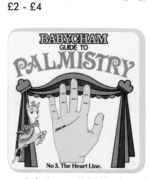

▲ The Babycham girl Aquarius.
(1975). (g-vg) £1 - £2

▲ Palmistry. (1975). (g-vg)
£1 - £2

▲ The Babycham girl Leo.
(1975). (g-vg) £1 - £2

▲ A passion for fashion.
(1975). (g-vg) £1 - £2

▲ Babycham plain. (1960).
(f-g) £2 - £3

▲ Magic in a glass. (g) £2 - £4

▲ Experience the sparkle.
(1985). (vg) £1 - £2

▲ One good thing. (1970).
(vg) £2 - £3

BADGES
(All shown - actual size)

Some collectables traders just specialise in badges. There's plenty of money to be made, once you understand the market.

The larger car boot sales are brilliant for finding old and collectable badges.

Because they are such small items, storage is no problem and if trading via the internet, postage and packing is cheap and easy.

Pre-1960 enamel badges are most sought after. A particularly popular theme is militaria.

▲ NUTG. National Union of Townswomen's Guild Chairman. Enamel. (1965). (vg) £6 - £8

▲ British Legion. Enamel. (1950). (vg) £6 - £8

▲ Emergency Food Officer. (1945). (vg) save for very small enamel damage. £15 - £20

▲ Women's League of Health & Beauty. Enamel. (1950). (g-vg) £6 - £8

▲ Peterbilt. USA truck comp. Enamel. (1975). (vg) £4 - £6

▲ Federation of Women's Institute. Norfolk. (1945). (f) Slight damage to enamel and missing pin. £2 - £5

▲ Dunscore Ladies Curling Club. Enamel. (1980). (vg) £1 - £3

▲ Swimming. Enamel. (1970). (g) £2 - £3

▲ Inst of The Horse & Pony Club. Enamel. (1975). (vg) £3 - £4

▲ British Transport Travel Club. Enamel. (1960). (g-vg) £5 - £7

▲ Women's Land Army. Enamel. (1940). (g) £8 - £10

▲ RNLI Ladies Lifeboat Guild. Enamel. (1950). (vg) £10 - £14

▲ On War Service. Brass. 1915. (vg) £14 - £16

▲ On War Service. Enamel. 1914. (g) £8 - £12

▲ WVS. Civil Defence. Enamel. (1965). (vg) £3 - £4

▲ Crawfords Biscuits. Brass. (1950). (g-vg) £10 - £14

▲ Red Cross & St.John War Organisation. Enamel. (1940). (vg) £14 - £16

▲ Greenpeace. Enamel. (2000). (vg) £1 - £2

▲ British Red Cross Society Associate. (1950). (vg) £4 - £6

▲ Liverpool Football Club. Enamel. (1990). (vg) £1 - £2

BADGES - Button

Button badges are generally plastic coated on metal. They are affixed to garments using a built-in angled wire with a sharp point or by a safety pin that is attached to the back of the badge.

► Bazooka bubblegum. (1965). (g) £8 - £10

▲   Go   Electric. (1975). (vg) £5 - £7

▲ Trico wiper blades. (1960). (vg) £7 - £9

▲ Green Cross Code. (1980). (vg) £2 - £4

▲ Red Star Band Aid. (1984). (vg) £2 - £4

▲ Chix Space gum. (1965). (vg) £7 - £9

▲ Crest toothpaste. (1980). (vg) £3 - £5

▲ Britvic. (1960). (vg) £7 - £9

▲ Free Nelson Mandela. (1985). (vg) £3 - £4

▲   Ocean   Sound. (1990). (vg) £1 - £2

▲ Clarks Commandos. (1980). (g) £3 - £5

▲   Philadelphia. (1980). (vg) £3 - £4

▲   Police.   (1985). (vg) £2 - £4

▲ Jaffa Fun Club. (1965). (f-g) £4 - £6

▲   Mickey   Mouse. (1935). (g-vg) £22 - £26

▲   Kingpin   Flour. (1970). (g-vg) £3 - £5

▲ Kia-Ora. (1980). (vg) £3 - £6

▲ Australian butter. (1935). (f) £8 - £12

▲   World   Cup   82 Rediffusion. (f-g) £2 - £4

▲   Union   Jack. (1985). (g) 20p - 30p

▲ Boomtown Rats. (1980). (vg) £2 - £3

▲ John Bull Tyres. (1965). (vg) £6 - £8

▲ Lyonzade. (1960). (g-vg) £7 - £9

▲ Wall's Sky Ray. (1970). (g) £6 - £8

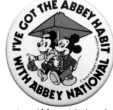

▲   Abby   National. (1975). (vg) £3 - £5

▲ Lyons Maid Space Age Britain. (1970). (vg) £7 - £9

▲ Bowyers Bumpers. (1975). (f) £2 - £3

▲   My   Grandad's   A Smasher. (1975). (f) £6 - £8

▲ My Mum's A Smasher. (1975). (g) £7 - £9

▲ Coco Lyons Tea. (1975). (vg) £6 - £8

▲ Queen's Silver Jubilee (1977). (g) £1 - £2

BADGES - Button

▲ Heinz Invaders. (1980). (g-vg)
£1 - £2

▲ Gas. (1975). (f-g) 20p - 30p

▲ Roger Rabbit. 1988. 75mm diam. (vg) £1 - £2

▲ Anchor Butter. (1985). (g)
30p - 50p

▲ Pepsi. (1985). (vg)
50p - 70p

▲ Lloyds. (1980). (vg)
20p - 30p

▲ Pernod. (1975). (g-vg)
40p - 60p

▲ Windsor. (1990). (vg)
10p - 20p

▲ Channel 4.
(1985). (vg)
40p - 60p

▲ Red Arrows. (1980).
(vg) £1 - £2

▲ Irn-Bru. (1980).
(vg) £1 - £2

▲ Schweppes.
(1980). (g) 40p - 60p

▲ Beefeater. (1990).
(vg) 10p - 20p

▲ Torbay Aircraft Museum.
(1980). (vg) 10p - 20p

▲ Quavers. (1985).
(vg) £1 - £2

▲ Greenpeace.
(1990). (vg) 20p - 30p

▲ Paultons Park.
(1980). (g) 10p - 20p

▲ Mr Whimpy England World
Cup. 1982. (g) £1 - £2

▲ Lambs Powerboat Racing
Team. (1990). (vg) 70p - 90p

▲ Dulux. (1980). (g)
60p - 80p

▲ Brooks. (1980). (vg)
60p - 80p

BALLET

The art of ballet dancing can be traced back to the fifteenth century.

The first professional ballet company was the Academie Royale de Musique, which was formed in 1672.

Ballet went into decline until its revival in France in the 1830's.

The ballet in Britain has remained popular since Victorian times.

There's plenty of memorabilia to be collected and because ballet is not a mainstream interest, prices of desirable items are not overly expensive.

Look out for old programmes, tickets, photographs, postcards, posters and autographs.

▲ The Bolshoi Ballet Film programme. The Rank Organisation. 1957. (g-vg) £8 - £12

BALLROOM

The TV programme 'Strictly Come Dancing' is partially responsible for the revival of the interest in ballroom dancing. Whilst not the most popular collectable area, there's plenty of scope to build a collection.

Plenty of LP records were released in the 60's and 70's to cater for ballroom music fans. The covers of these records depict ballroom scenes and popular bands of the day. The covers are becoming collectable but cannot be described as valuable.

▲ Cinderella Ballroom Polish. A very rare Boots product (most of contents remain) from the 1920's. The powder polish simply had to be sprinkled over the ballroom floor to produce "a fine dancing surface". (f) £8 - £12.

BANDALASTA

Produced in England by Brookes and Adams, Bandalasta is a plastic ware made from a synthetic resin. The items were light and resilient.

The products lent themselves to picnic ware and hence there were full picnic sets made of Bandalasta. Brookes and Adams produced cases for the picnic sets and these are now very collectable.

Although not sold as 'unbreakable', advertisements claimed that the product would not fracture as easily as china or glass.

▲ Bandalasta beaker. (1930). No.165. Marble horn colour. (vg) £7 - £9

BANKING

Whilst banking can be traced back to the fifteenth century, the modern banking system has its roots in the seventeenth century.

The statutory definition of banking includes; receipt of public money; collecting and paying cheques drawn by customers. However, in recent years banking has been revolutionised by the internet and cheques are becoming less popular.

Collectables over two hundred years old, relating to the banking industry would obviously be sought after, however, it is probably fair to say that the subject of 'banking' isn't overly captivating and therefore a themed collection shouldn't be too expensive.

Banking is a significant element of our social history and, whilst rather highbrow, it offers plenty of scope for research.

▲ Somerset & Wilts Trustee Savings Bank savings book. (1950). (g) £1 - £3

▲ Wilts & Dorset Banking Company cheque. 1854. (vg) £8 - £10

▲ Bury Corporation bus ticket. Bury Savings Bank advertisement on the reverse. (1925). (g) £1 - £2

▲ Barclays cheque. 1949. (vg) 50p - £1

▲ Barclays cheque. 1956. (g-vg) 40p - 60p

◄ Champion Hurdle programme. 15 March 1972. (g) £3 - £4

Lloyds Bank sponsored raceday programme. The Champion Hurdle, Cheltenham National Hunt Festival 1972. The race was won for the second year running by the mighty Bula.

▲ Barclays cheque. 1909. Very good condition but hole punched. £2 - £4

▲ Canadian Bank cheque. 1933. (vg) £1 - £2

▲ Clydesdale cheque. 1956. (g) 50p - £1

▲ Lloyds Bank sixpenny pieces bag. (1965). (f) 30p - 40p

▲ Lloyds Bank paper money bag. Threepenny pieces. (1960). (g-vg) £1 - £2

▲ Derby Trustee Savings Bank bag. Shillings. (vg) £1 - £2

►Public Revenue cheque. 1931. (vg) £3 - £4

BANKNOTES

The collecting of banknotes is known as 'notaphily'.

This is yet another collecting area that is growing in popularity with the help of internet auctions. Banknotes are so easy to post and store.

Banknotes were first issued by The Bank of England in 1694. Country Bankers were permitted to issue their own notes, the two on this page were issued in 1821 and circa 1805.

British notes are obviously of much interest to British citizens. They form a part of our history.

The market is currently buoyant and, if notes are bought at the right price, are ideal potential investments. It really is a case of homework being essential.

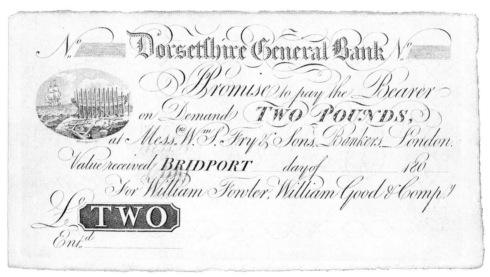

▲ Two pound note. Dorsetshire General Bank. (1805). (f-g) £100 - £110

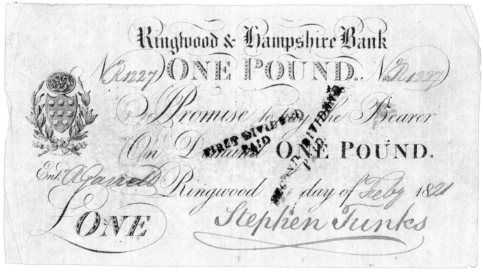

▲ One pound note. Ringwood & Hampshire Bank. 1821. (f) £100 - £110

BANKNOTES

The White Fiver

Introduced in 1793, the design and size was largely unchanged until the date of withdrawal (13 March 1961). The note was blank on the reverse and measured 212 x 134mm.

▲ White five pound note. Issued 16 February 1956. L.K. O'Brien signature. (g-vg) £120 - £140

BANKNOTES

There are countless variations to banknotes. Size of dots in the printing, large or small digits etc.... Richards Reference and Price Guide is a useful reference work.

▲ Ten Shilling note. Issued from 1919. N.F.Warren-Fisher signature. 135 x 75mm. (f) £60 - £70

▲ One Pound note. Issued from 1919. N.F.Warren-Fisher signature. Square dot. 150 x 85mm. (g) £120 - £140

BANKNOTES

▲ Ten Shilling note. 1940. K.O. Peppiatt signature. In uncirculated condition. (ex) £35 - £40

▲ One Pound note. 1940. K.O.Peppiatt signature. (f-g) £10 - £12

BANKNOTES

▲ One pound note. 1950. P.S. Beale signature. (vg) £6 - £8

▲ Ten pound note. 1971. J.B. Page signature. (vg) £25 - £30

▲ Ten shilling note. 1950. P.S. Beale signature. Uncirculated. (ex) £20 - £22

▲ Five pound note. 1957. L.K. O'Brien signature. (vg) £20 - £22

▲ One pound note. 1980. D.H.F. Somerset signature. Uncirculated. (ex) £3 - £4

▲ Five pound note. 1998. Merlyn Lowther signature. Uncirculated. (ex) £6 - £8

▲ One pound note. 1963. J.Q. Hollom signature. (vg) £3 - £5

▲ Five pound note. 1988. G.M. Gill signature. (f-g) £6 - £8

Store your banknotes flat and never fold them. Take particular care with the corners. Values depend on rarity and condition. A scruffy note is worth a fraction of a mint/excellent example. Sadly, not all notes being sold on the internet or at car boot sales are going to be genuine. Be absolutely satisfied before buying.

It is important to store your banknotes where they will not get wet and will not fade (i.e. out of direct sunlight, in a cool, dry location). It may be worth investing in specially-made banknote folders that will keep your notes free from environmental damage.

▲ Ten shilling note. 1967. J.S. Fforde signature. (vg) £3 - £4

▲ Ten pound note. 1988. G.M. Gill signature. (vg) £13 - £15

BANKNOTES - Scotland

▲ Bank of Scotland. Five pound note. 1969. (f-g) £6 - £8

▲National Commercial Bank of Scotland. Five pound note. 1963. (f-g) £8 - £10

▲Royal Bank of Scotland. One pound note. 1969. (f) £2 - £4

▲Royal Bank of Scotland. One pound note. 1993. (ex) £2 - £3

▲Royal Bank of Scotland. One pound note. 1983. (g) £2 - £3

▲Royal Bank of Scotland. One pound note. 1981. (f) £1 - £2

▲Bank of Scotland. One pound note. 1969. (f-g) £1 - £2

▲Royal Bank of Scotland. One pound note. 1967. (g) £4 - £6

◄ Clydesdale & North of Scotland Bank. One pound note. 1962. (g) £8 - £10

BANKNOTES - World

World banknotes are a good example of a collecting area that can be started at very low cost.

Many banknotes are attractively designed, giving the collection a pleasing look.

This is a great collecting idea for children, helping promote an interest in world history and geography.

Much research would be required before embarking on this hobby with serious money.

Find cheap foreign banknotes at some charity shops (particularly Oxfam specialist shops). There are plenty on the internet but do tread carefully and don't be tempted to overspend.

Some years ago, The Sunday Times gave away various world banknotes with their magazine. Needless to say they had very low face values. These are constantly cropping up and are worth pennies not pounds. The notes include the Zambia two Kwacha, and the Mozambique 100 Escudos.

▲ 50 Australes. Argentina. (ex) £1 - £2

▲ 1000 Riels. Cambodia. (g-vg) £1 - £2

BANKNOTES - World

▲ 500 Afghanis. Afghanistan. (ex) 50p - £1

▲ 1 Manat. Azerbaijan. (ex) 50p - 80p

▲ 10 Francs. Belgian Congo. (f) £2 - £4

▲ 5 Francs. Algeria. (f) 40p - 60p

▲ 1 Dollar. Bahamas. (g-vg) 40p - 60p

▲ 1000 Francs. Belgium. (f-g) £3 - £4

▲ 100 Escudos. Angola. (g-vg) 50p - £1

▲ 1 Dinar. Bahrain. (g) 50p - 80p

▲ 5 Shillings. Bermuda. (g) £70 - £80

▲ 50 Pesos. Argentina. (f) 50p - £1

▲ 10 Dollars. Barbados. (vg) £8 - £10

▲ 1 Ngultrum. Bhutan. (f) £2 - £3

▲ 2 Dollars. Australia. (f-g) 30p - 40p

▲ 1 Ruble. Belarus. (ex) 30p - 50p

▲ 1 Pound. Biafra. (f-g) £2 - £3

▲ 20 Schilling. Austria. (f) £1 - £2

▲ 1 Dollar. Belize. (ex) £10 - £12

▲ 1000 Pesos Bolivianos. Bolivia. (f-g) £2 - £3

▲ 1000 Dinara. Bosnia & Herzegovina. (ex) 50p - £1

▲ 1000 Cruzados. Brazil. (ex) 30p - 50p

▲ 100 Leva. Bulgaria. (ex) 30p - 50p

BANKNOTES - World

▲ 5 Kyats. Burma. (ex) 50p - £1

▲ 50 Pesos Oro. Columbia. (p-f) 20p - 30p

▲ 5 Kroner. Denmark. (g-vg) 50p - £1

▲ 100 Riels. Cambodia. (ex) 30p - 50p

▲ 50 Francs. Congo (Democratic Republic). (vg-ex) £1 - £2

▲ 1 Peso Oro. Dominican Republic. (vg) £1 - £2

▲ 1 Dollar. Canada. (ex) £4 - £6

▲ 5 Colones. Costa Rica. (ex) £1 - £2

▲ 5 Dollars. Eastern Caribbean. (g) £6 - £8

▲ 1 Dollar. Cayman Islands. (ex) £1 - £2

▲ 50 Kuna. Croatia. (p-f) 30p - 40p

▲ 5 Sucres. Equador. (vg-ex) £1 - £2

▲ 10 Rupees. Ceylon. (f) £1 - £2

▲ 20 Pesos. Cuba. (f-g) £1 - £2

▲ 25 Piastres. Egypt. (g-vg) £1 - £2

▲ 100 Pesos. Chile. (g) 40p - 60p

▲ 50 Cents. Cyprus. (f-g) £2 - £3

▲ 1 Kroon. Estonia. (g) 30p - 50p

▲ 10 Yuan. China (Taiwan). (vg) £1 - £2

▲ 10 Korun. Czechoslovakia. (g-vg) £1 - £2

▲ 10 Birr. Ethiopia. (p-f) 40p - 60p

BANKNOTES - World

▲ 1 Pound. Falkland Islands. (g) £12 - £16

▲1 Pound. Gibraltar. (vg) £6 - £8

▲1 Lempira. Honduras. (p-f) 50p - £1

▲ 1 Dollar. Fiji. (ex) £3 - £4

▲ 100 Drachmai. Greece. (f-g) £4 - £6

▲ 1 Dollar. Hong Kong. (g) £26 - £30

▲ 20 Markkaa. Finland. (vg) £1 - £2

▲ 1 Quetzal. Guatemala. (f) £1 - £2

▲ 10 Kronur. Iceland. (g) £2 - £4

▲ 5 Francs. France. (f) 50p - 80p

▲ 1 Pound. Guernsey. (f-g) £2 - £3

▲ 10 Rupees. India. (ex) 50p - £1

▲25 Dalasis. Gambia. (ex) £2 - £3

▲ 100 Francs. Guinea. (g) £1 - £2

▲ 100 Rupiah. Indonesia. (ex) 50p - £1

▲ 10 Deutsche Mark. Germany. (g) £1 - £2

▲ 1 Dollar. Guyana. (ex) £2 - £3

▲ 200 Rials. Iran. (ex) £1 - £2

▲ 1000 Cedis. Ghana. (g-vg) £2 - £3

▲ 1 Gourde. Haiti. (ex) £1 - £2

▲ 5 Dinars. Iraq. (ex) £2 - £3

BANKNOTES - World

▲ 1 Pound. Ireland. (ex) £4 - £5

▲0.5 Riel. Kampuchea. (ex) 50p - £1

▲100 Kip. Laos. (ex) £1- £2

▲ 1 Pound. Isle of Man. (f-g) £1 - £2

▲ 1 Tenge. Kazakhstan. (ex) £1 - £2

▲ 2 Rubli. Latvia. (vg) 10p - 20p

▲ 20 New Sheqalim. Israel. (g-vg) £2 - £3

▲ 100 Shillings. Kenya. (vg-ex) £1 - £2

▲ 5 Livres. Lebanon. (vg) 50p - £1

▲ 500 Lire. Italy. (g) 50p - £1

▲ 5 Won. Korea (North). (g) 50p - £1

▲ 2 Maloti. Lesotho. (ex) £1 - £2

▲2 Dollars. Jamaica. (f-g) 30p - 50p

▲ 1000 Won. Korea (South). (vg) £1 - £2

▲ 10 Piastres. Libya. (p-f) 50p - £1

▲ 10 Yen. Japan. (f) £1 - £2

▲ 1/4 Dinar. Kuwait. (ex) £1 - £2

▲ 1 Talonas. Lithuania. (ex) 10p - 20p

▲ 1 Pound. Jersey. (vg-ex). £1 - £2

▲ 1 Tyiyn. Kyrgyzstan. (ex) 20p - 30p

▲ 10 Denar. Macedonia. (vg) £1 - £2

BANKNOTES - World

▲ 10 Kwacha. Malawi. (p-f) £1 - £2

▲ 5 Tugrik. Mongolia. (ex) 50p - £1

▲ 1 Centavo. Nicaragua. (ex) 50p - £1

▲ 20 Cents. Malaya. (p-f) £2 - £3

▲ 10 Dirhams. Morocco. (g) £1 - £2

▲ 1 Pound. Nigeria. (f) £2 - £4

▲ 1 Ringgit. Malaysia. (vg) £1 - £2

▲ 100 Escudos. Mozambique. (ex) 30p - 50p

▲ 10 Kroner. Norway. (g-vg) £3 - £4

▲ 5 Rufiyaa. Maldives. (p-f) £1 - £2

▲ 1 Kyat. Myanmar. (ex) 30p - 50p

▲ 200 Baisa. Oman. (vg-ex) 50p - £1

▲ 10 Shillings. Malta. (f) £4 - £5

▲ 1 Rupee. Nepal. (ex) 50p - £1

▲ 5 Rupees. Pakistan. (vg) 50p - £1

▲ 25 Rupees. Mauritius. (f-g) £2 - £3

▲ 1 Gulden. Netherlands. (f) 50p - £1

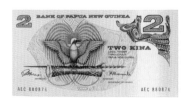

▲ 2 Kina. Papua New Guinea. (vg-ex) £1 - £2

▲ 20,000 Pesos. Mexico. (f-g) £2 - £3

▲ 1 Dollar. New Zealand. (g) £3 - £5

▲ 5000 Guaranies. Paraguay. (g) £1 - £2

BANKNOTES - World

▲ 1000 Intis. Peru. (ex) 30p - 40p

▲5,000 Francs. Rwanda. (p-f) £2 - £3

▲2 Dollars. Solomon Islands. (ex) £2 - £3

▲ 100 Piso. Philippines. (f-g) £1 - £2

▲ 2 Tala. Samoa. (ex) £1 - £2

▲ 5 Rand. South Africa. (g-vg) £2 - £3

▲ 10,000 Zlotych. Poland. (g) £1 - £2

▲ 1 Riyal. Saudi Arabia. (f) £1 - £2

▲ 100 Pesetas. Spain. (g-vg) £2 - £3

▲ 100 Escudos. Portugal. (f) £1 - £2

▲ 10 Rupees. Seychelles. (g) £2 - £3

▲ 10 Rupees. Sri Lanka. (vg) £1 - £2

▲10 Riyals. Qatar. (g) £1 - £2

▲ 50 Cents. Sierra Leone. (ex) £1 - £2

▲ 100 Pounds. Sudan. (vg-ex) £2 - £3

▲ 50,000 Lei. Romania. (g) 50p - £1

▲ 5 Dollars. Singapore. (g) £1 - £2

▲ 100 Gulden. Suriname. (ex) £1 - £2

▲ 200 Rubles. Russia. (vg) £1 - £2

▲ 10 Tolarjev. Slovenia (vg) 50p - £1

▲ 10 Kronor. Sweden. (g) £1 - £2

BANKNOTES - World

▲ 100 Yuan. Taiwan. (vg) £1 - £2

▲ 500 Shillings. Uganda. (vg) £3 - £4

▲ 200 Dong. Vietnam. (ex) 30p - 50p

▲ 10 Rubles. Tajikistan. (ex) 50p - £1

▲ 1 Karbovanets. Ukraine. (ex) 20p - 30p

▲ 5,000 Francs. West African States. (p-f) £1 - £2

▲ 200 Shilingi. Tanzania. (f) £1 - £2

▲ 5 Dirhams. United Arab Emirates. (g) £1 - £2

▲ 200 Rials. Yemen Arab Republic. (ex) £1 - £2

▲ 20 Baht. Thailand. (vg). 50p - £1

▲ 50 Nuevos Pesos. Uruguay. (vg-ex) £2 - £3

▲ 50 Dinara. Yugoslavia. (vg) 50p - £1

▲ 20 Dollars. Trinidad & Tobago. (g) £2 - £3

▲ 1 Dollar. USA (1974 series). (f-g) £1 - £2

▲ 5 Nouveaux Makuta. Zaire. (ex) 50p - £1

▲ 10 Dinars. Tunisia. (g) £1 - £2

▲ 500 Sum. Uzbekistan. (g). £3 - £4

▲ 50 Kwacha. Zambia. (g-vg) £1 - £2

▲ 50,000 Lira. Turkey. (g-vg) £2 - £3

▲ 100 Bolivares. Venezuela. (g-vg) £1 - £2

▲ 100 Dollars. Zimbabwe. (g) £2 - £3

BAODING BALLS

Originated in Baoding, China. Two balls are held in the palm of one hand and rotated repeatedly for meditation and exercise.

Balls are manufactured in pairs and normally have hollow middles containing soft sounding chimes.

▲ Pair of Baoding Balls in a decorative cloth bound box. Unknown maker. (1990). (ex) £4 - £6

BASKETBALL

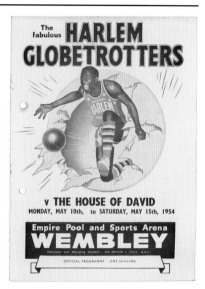

When London born Abe Saperstien formed the Harlem Globetrotters basketball team in 1927, they travelled around in a rickety old bus. Things are much different now. They travel around the world in style.

This official programme celebrated their visit to Wembley in May 1954.

▲ Empire Pool. Harlem Globetrotters programme. 1954. Hole punched but otherwise (g) £12 - £16

BAXTER PRINTS

George Baxter (1804 - 1867) is credited as the inventor of colour printing. He patented a process in 1835, which involved up to twenty processes to produce the finished article.

Amongst Baxter items collected today are needle box prints. These were produced in sheets (sets) and cut out carefully from the sheet and then individually affixed to needle boxes to make them look attractive.

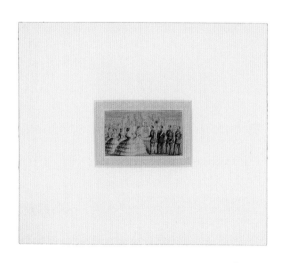

▲ George Baxter (Jnr) needle box print. (1860). Mounted on card. (vg-ex) £3 - £4

There's a collector's society which welcomes enthusiasts (www.georgebaxter.com).

BAYKO

Bayko is a construction toy (made from Bakelite) that was marketed from 1934 to 1967. It was invented by Charles Plimpton. It's an architectural building system used for constructing model houses, garages, churches, shops, stations, etc. It could be described as an early version of Lego, except it is more sophisticated.

There are bases with a matrix of holes, into which a framework of steel rods are inserted. Bricks slide into place between the rods. The building is completed with a variety of components such as windows, roof, doors, gates, fences, etc.

Plimpton Manufacturing Co. Ltd ceased trading in 1959 and Meccano carried the business on until 1967. Collectors have a greater interest in the 'Plimpton' era. In the 'Meccano' era the colour of the bases was changed from green to grey, windows and doors changed to yellow, and the roofs became green.

Finding a Bayko set with the correct original quantity of components is difficult because parts may have been lost. Also, many children had more than one set and the pieces got mixed between different boxes.

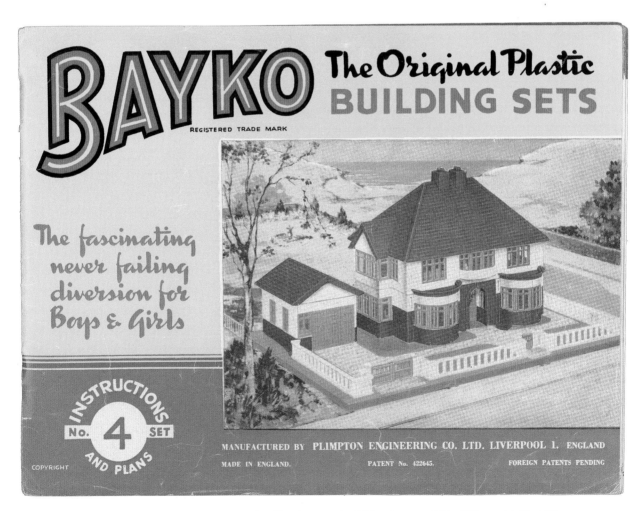

▲ Bayko Building Sets. Instruction booklet. (No.4 set). 1957. 58 pages. 245 x 185mm. (g) £8 - £12

BEANIE BABIES

Beanie Babies were the brainchild of Ty Warner, founder of Ty Inc., who was born 3 September 1944.

Ty had formed his company in 1986, using inheritance money and his life savings to get started, but it was not until 1993 that he hit upon the idea of small plush toys that children could afford to buy with their pocket money and carry around with them. The first two Beanie Babies appeared early in 1993, with a series of nine being revealed later that same year at the World Toy Fair in New York City (see The Original Nine for details). Surprisingly, they were not an immediate hit, with some critics at the Fair referring to them as "roadkill" because of their under-stuffed, slightly flattened appearance.

However, it did not take long for the toys to start being considered as collectables, and the market soared, mainly because each Beanie was available for a limited period only, before being "retired". By the end of the '90s, the world was firmly in the grip of Beanie Baby mania, with some determined collectors paying hundreds of pounds for a single Beanie. With so many people buying up the toys, envisioning huge profits later on, it was only a matter of time before the bubble burst, and it is unfortunately the case that many people who heavily invested in collections of Beanies may never recoup their expenses.

Of course, some people would never consider selling at all. Beanie Babies are great as low-value items to collect for fun. They don't take up a huge amount of space (to begin with) and they are full of character that makes them lovely display pieces. Many people still collect Beanie Babies now, but nobody does so under the illusion of turning a fast buck by reselling at profit. Now, these collectors mainly collect, for the love of collecting.

The Beanie Baby story is a timely reminder to all of us that we can never truly predict market trends. Some items are destined to be "fads" that eventually go out of fashion, and it takes a steady nerve and a quick eye to be able to hop in and out of the market at the right time to make a profit without being stung when the prices eventually crash. This is why, even if you are forming a collection (of anything) with the intention of one day selling it on for a tidy sum, always make sure you also LIKE what you are collecting. That way, if the market slumps and you can't find a buyer, you will not be left with a lot of items you can't stand the sight of.

Having said all that, there are still one or two Beanie Babies that can sell for large sums of money, and it would pay to go through your collection carefully to check for rare examples before deciding to get rid of them all for low prices. For example, if you happen to have one of the rare Beanies that were only issued to workers at Ty Inc., then you could be sitting on a real treasure that is worth hundreds of pounds.

▲ Sizzle. 2001. With tag. (vg-ex) £2 - £4

▲ Champion. 2002. With tag and Fifa badge. (vg-ex) £4 - £6

The Original Nine

In early 1993, Ty released Brownie the Bear and Punchers the Lobster (Punchers may have been a misprint of Pinchers). Later that same year, the full set of nine original beanies were released, but by that time Punchers' name had been changed to Pinchers, and Brownie's name had been changed to Cubbie. The only differences between the later beanies and the earlier ones are the names printed on the hanging tags, yet Brownie and Punchers are worth considerably more than their later counterparts due to their rarity.

BEANIE BABIES

▲ Loosy. 1998. With tag. (vg-ex) £2 - £3

▲ Inky. 1993. With tag.(vg) £2 - £3

▲ Nibbly. 1999. With tag. (ex) £2 - £3

▲ Hissy. 1997. With tag. (ex) £2 - £3

▲ Jazzy Jessie.2002. With tag. (ex) £2 - £3

▲ Smoochy. 1997. With tag. (vg) £2 - £3

▲ Peanut. 1993. With tag. (vg) £2 - £3

▲ Scurry. 2000. With tag. (vg-ex) £2 - £3

▲ Stretch. 1997. With tag. (ex) £2 - £3

The BEATLES

Unquestionably the world's biggest 1960's pop group. Their rise to fame and fortune can firstly be attributed to the Lennon & McCartney song writing team, secondly to manager Brian Epstein and thirdly record producer George Martin.

The first Beatles hit was Love Me Do (1962). Please Please Me was released in March 1963. Hit after hit followed. The Beatles finally split up in 1970.

John Lennon was born in 1940 and died from gunshot wounds in 1980. Paul McCartney was born in 1942. George Harrison was born in 1943 and died of cancer in 2001. Ringo Starr (real name Richard Starkey) was born in 1940.

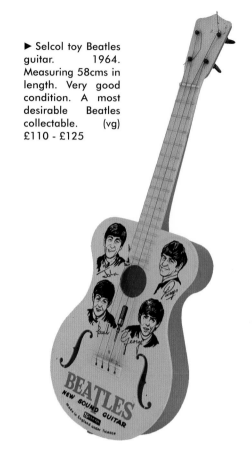

► Selcol toy Beatles guitar. 1964. Measuring 58cms in length. Very good condition. A most desirable Beatles collectable. (vg) £110 - £125

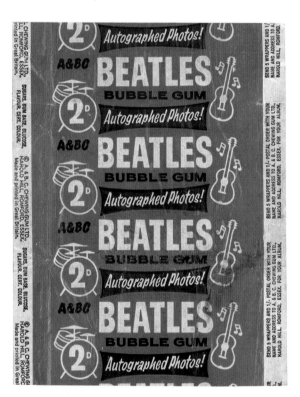

▲ Bubble Gum wrapper. 1964. From the first series of A&BC Beatles trade cards. (g-vg) £60 - £70

Amongst the truly hard to find Beatles items are the wrappers from the A&BC Gum that contained both the trade cards and pieces of bubble gum. Whilst the cards were religiously collected, the outside wrappers were normally binned.

▲ Beatles concert ticket. Original. Thursday 12 December 1963. The Odeon Theatre Nottingham. (g-vg) £70 - £90

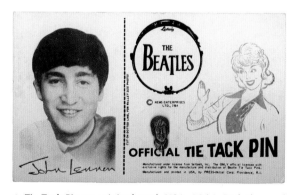

▲ Tie Tack Pin on original card. USA. 1964. Both the card and the pin are in very good condition. £25 - £30

The BEATLES

▲ Valex original photograph. No. M323. (1963)
£8 - £10

▲ Fabulous Magazine. 9 May 1964. (g-vg) £12 - £16

▲ The Beatles Show concert programme. 1963. Supporting artists (with photographs) are; The Vernons Girls, The Brook Brothers, Peter Jay & The Jaywalkers, The Kestrels and Frank Berry. (vg) £50 - £60

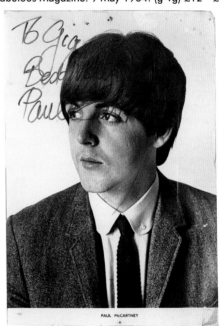

▲ Autographed photograph - Paul McCartney. Clear, black ink, 215 x 150mm. Dedicated. Circa 1964. Brian Epstein compliments slip attached to the reverse. £250 - £300

▲ Beatles Fan Club Flexi disc - The third Christmas record. 1965. Lyntone Records, LYN 948. (g). Complete with National Newsletter No.6. (g-vg) £20 - £30

The Official Beatles Fan Club secretary was Freda Kelly, although she was given much credit for the running of the Club. It was managed by Bobbie Brown, who invented the fictitious Fan Club Secretary name Anne Collingham.

The whole thing grew and grew, until the team could barely cope with the 50,000 active members in May 1964. Ashamed of the poor service offered, membership fees between May 1964 and April 1965 were waived.

The Official Beatles Fan Club eventually closed in 1972.

The BEATLES

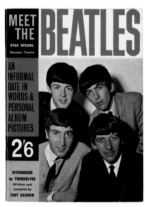

▲ Meet The Beatles. World Distributors. 1963. 44 pages. 245 x 185mm. (vg) £12 - £16

▲ The Beatles By Royal Command. Daily Mirror Publications. 1963. 32 pages. 230 x 180mm. (vg) £14 - £16

▲ Record Song Book. A McGlennon Publication. 1963. Loose cover, otherwise (g). £6 - £8

▲ NME. Summer Extra Special. 1964. (g-vg) £14 - £16

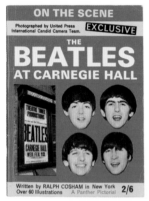

▲ The Beatles At Carnegie Hall. A Panther Pictorial. 1964. 44 pages. 250 x 185mm. (vg) £14 - £16

▲ The Beatles In America. Daily Mirror Publications. 1964. 32 pages. 230 x 180mm. (vg) £12 - £14

▲ Record Song Book. A McGlennon Publication. 1964. (g) £8 - £12

▲ Record Song Book. 1969. (vg) £8 - £10

▲ John Lennon. Brel postcard. No. CS 157. Postally unused. (vg) £4 - £6

▲ George Harrison. Star Pics. No. SP 600. (g-vg) £4 - £6

▲ Ringo Starr. Star Pics photograph. No. SP 595. 195 x 150mm. (g-vg) £6 - £8

Eskimo Foods Beatles Cards

Issued by Eskimo Foods circa 1964. They were all black and white photographs, postcard size. Some had a facsimile autograph printed at the bottom.

▲ Paul McCartney. Brel postcard. No. CS 154. Postally unused. (vg) £4 - £6

▲ Paul McCartney. Valex postcard. No. V 72. Postally unused. (g) £4 - £6

▲ Look-In. No.20. 8 May 1976. (vg) £8 - £10

▲ John Lennon. Eskimo Foods card. (1964). From a set of (8) cards. (vg) £5 - £6

The BEATLES - Original sheet music

▲I Want To Hold Your Hand. (g) £8 - £10

▲Hey Jude. (g) £6 - £8

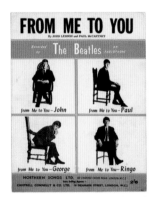

▲From Me To You. (g-vg) £12 - £14

▲Yellow Submarine. (g) £6 - £8

▲Yesterday. (f) £3 - £4

▲Paperback Writer. (g) £6 - £8

▲Michelle. (g-vg) £8 - £10

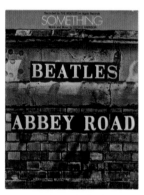

▲Something. (vg) £6 - £8

▲Ob-La-Di Ob-La-Da. (vg) £4 - £5

▲The Fool On The Hill. (vg) £6 - £8

▲You're Sixteen. (g-vg) £2 - £4

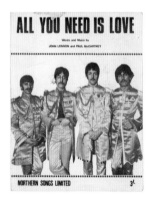

▲All You Need Is Love. (f) £3 - £5

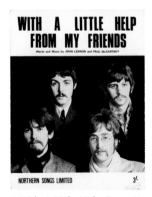

▲With A Little Help From My Friends. (g) £5 - £7

▲Roll Over Beethoven. (f-g) £7 - £9

▲She Loves You. (g) £8 - £12

▲Please Please Me. (g) £8 - £12

The BEATLES - A&BC cards

The 60 bubble gum cards in this set were produced by A&BC at the height of Beatlemania in 1964. They were hugely popular and are now much sought after. Collectors are looking for very good condition cards and are prepared to pay a premium. The expected average price for one card in very good condition is £5.

▲No.1. (vg) £4 - £5

▲No.2. (vg) £4 - £5

▲No.6. (vg) £4 - £5   ▲No.9. (vg) £4 - £5   ▲No.13. (vg) £4 - £5   ▲No.16. (vg) £4 - £5   ▲No.18. (vg) £4 - £5   ▲No.20. (vg) £4 - £5

▲No.21. (vg) £4 - £5   ▲No.24. (vg) £4 - £5   ▲No.26. (vg) £4 - £5   ▲No.27. (vg) £4 - £5   ▲No.34. (vg) £4 - £5

▲No.35. (vg) £4 - £5   ▲No.37. (vg) £4 - £5   ▲No.39. (vg) £4 - £5   ▲No.40. (vg) £4 - £5   ▲No.42. (vg) £4 - £5   ▲No.44. (vg) £4 - £5

▲No.45. (vg) £4 - £5   ▲No.46. (vg) £4 - £5   ▲No.48. (vg) £4 - £5   ▲No.50. (vg) £4 - £5

▲No.52. (vg) £4 - £5   ▲No.58. (vg) £4 - £5   ▲No.59. (vg) £4 - £5   ▲Full set of 60 cards. (vg) £280 - £320

The BEATLES - 45rpm single records

Because so many Beatles records were released, they are not as valuable as some people may imagine. The exceptions are first pressings and various quirks. Condition of the vinyl is important. The Record Collector, Rare Record Guide is an authority.

▲ A Hard Day's Night. 1964. R 5160. Vinyl (g-vg), cover (g) £6 - £8

▲ From Me To You. 1963. R 5015. Vinyl (vg), cover (g) £7 - £9

▲ Can't Buy Me Love. 1964. R 5114. Vinyl (vg), cover (g) £8 - £10

▲ Lady Madonna. 1968. R 5675. Vinyl (f-g), cover (g) £5 - £7

▲ She Loves You. 1963. R 5055. Vinyl (g-vg), cover (p-f) £5 - £7

▲ Help. 1965. R 5305. Vinyl (g), cover (g) £5 - £7

▲ We Can Work It Out. 1965. R 5389. Vinyl (vg), cover (vg) £8 - £10

▲ I Feel Fine. 1964. R 5200. Vinyl (vg), cover (g) £7 - £9

▲ I Want To Hold Your Hand. 1963. R 5084. Vinyl (g-vg), cover (g) £6 - £8

▲ Hello Goodbye. 1967. R 5655. Vinyl (f-g), cover (g) £3 - £4

▲ Ticket To Ride. 1965. R 5265. Vinyl (g), cover (g) £5 - £7

The BEATLES - Beatles Book Monthly

This monthly publication began in August 1963. The editor was Johnny Dean. The publisher was Beat Publications, Edgware Road, London. It included a page dedicated to the Official Beatles Fan Club. In the first edition, two pages (of 16) were given to 'Anne Collingham'.

The first edition is quite hard to find, particularly in very good to excellent condition. If you find a mint copy (firstly make sure it's not a fake) you have quite a valuable item on your hands, expect it to be worth around £150.

There was a reprint run of the series in 1976 (by the same publisher), of issue numbers 1 - 77. These are less valuable than the originals (probably around 35% less for issue 2 onwards and 90% less for issue 1. However, the reprints are quite hard to detect. The paper used in the originals has a slight cream tint, whereas the reprints are on whiter paper. Some of the images are slightly wider or longer in the reprints. The 1976 reprints were stapled into a new (8 page) cover and these covers are often carefully removed by canny people (see next page). However, the irony is that the reprint is worth more if the 8 page cover is kept intact.

Original issues in very good condition+ command a premium. Remember that The Beatles were so hugely popular in the sixties, these magazines were handled repeatedly, hence the average condition that can be expected is merely 'good' at best.

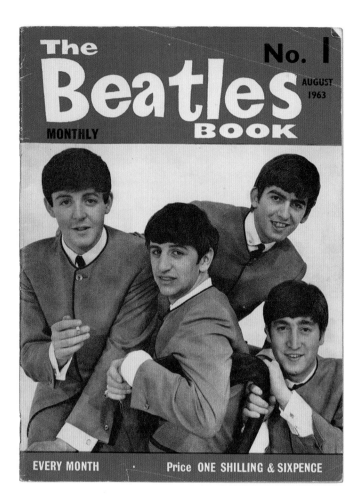

▲ Beatles Monthly. No.1. August 1963. Original issue. (g) £80 - £90

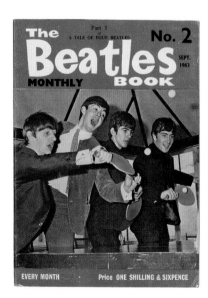

▲ Beatles Monthly. No.2. Sep 1963. Original issue. (vg) £15 - £18

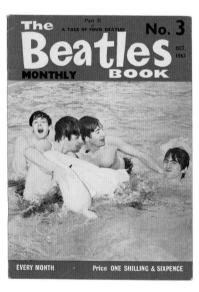

▲ Beatles Monthly. No.3. Oct 1963. Original issue. (vg) £12 - £14

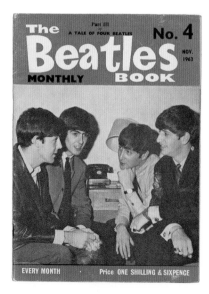

▲ Beatles Monthly. No.4 Nov 1963. Original issue. (g-vg) £7 - £9

The BEATLES - Beatles Book Monthly

▲ Dec 1963. No.5.
(g-vg) £8 - £10

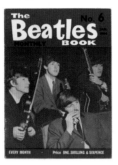

▲ Jan 1964. No.6
(g-vg) £8 - £10

▲ Feb 1964. No.7.
(vg-ex) £14 - £16

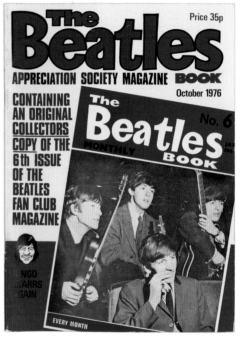

▲ Mar 1964. No.8.
(vg-ex) £14 - £16

▲ Apr 1964. No.9
(vg) £12 - £14

▲ May 1964. No.10
(g-vg) £7 - £9

▲ The Beatles Book reprint. October 1976. Issue 6 is
stapled inside. (g-vg) £5 - £7

▲ Jun 1964. No.11
(vg) £10 - £12

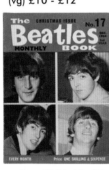

▲ Jul 1964. No.12
(vg) £10 - £12

▲ Aug 1964. No.13
(vg) £10 - £12

▲ Sep 1964. No.14
(g-vg) £8 - £10

▲ Oct 1964. No.15.
(vg) £10 - £12

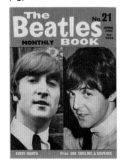

▲ Nov 1964. No.16.
(vg) £8 - £10

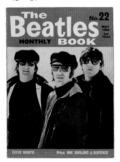

▲ Dec 1964. No.17.
(g-vg) £7 - £9

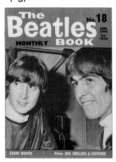

▲ Jan 1965. No.18.
(ex) £12 - £14

▲ Feb 1965. No.19.
(f-g) £2 - £4

▲ Mar 1965. No.20.
(g-vg) £6 - £8

▲ Apr 1965. No.21.
(vg) £8 - £10

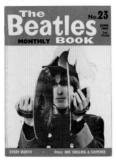

▲ May 1965. No.22.
(f-g) £3 - £4

▲ Jun 1965. No.23.
(g-vg) £6 - £8

▲ Jul 1965. No.24.
(g-vg) £6 - £8

▲ Aug 1965. No.25.
(g-vg) £6 - £8

The BEATLES - EP records

▲Magical Mystery Tour. 1967. Parlophone, MMT-B1. Vinyl copies (vg), sleeve (vg) £16 - £20

▲Beatles For Sale. 1964. Parlophone, GEP 8931. Vinyl (g), sleeve (p-f) £4 - £6

▲The Beatles No.1. 1963. Parlophone, GEP 8883. Vinyl (g), sleeve (g) £8 - £10

▲All My Loving. 1963. Parlophone, GEP 8891. Vinyl (vg), sleeve (vg) £14 - £16

▲Long Tall Sally. 1964. Parlophone, GEP 8913. Vinyl (f), sleeve (p-f) £3 - £5

▲Twist and Shout. 1963. Parlophone, GEP 8882. Vinyl (vg), sleeve (vg) £10 - £12

▲The Beatles' Hits. 1963. Parlophone, GEP 8880. Vinyl (vg), sleeve (vg) £12 - £17

▲A Hard Day's Night (sleeve only). Parlophone, GEP 8920. No vinyl, sleeve (g-vg). £4 - £6

The BEATLES - LP records

▲Beatles For Sale. 1964. Parlophone, PMC 1240. Vinyl (g), sleeve (g) £6 - £8

▲HELP! 1965. Parlophone, PMC 1255. Vinyl (g-vg), sleeve (f-g). £12 - £14

▲A Collection of Beatles Oldies. (1975). Parlophone, PCS 7016. Vinyl (g), sleeve (g-vg) £3 - £5

▲With The Beatles. 1963. Parlophone, PMC 1206. Vinyl (g), sleeve (g) £8 - £10

▲The White Album. 1968. Apple, PCS 7067/PCS 7068. Vinyl (p-f), sleeve (g) £3 - £4

▲The Beatles 1967-1970. (1990). Apple, PCSPB 718. Vinyl's (f-g), sleeve (g) £4 - £6

BEER MATS

A collector of beer mats is known as a tegestologist.

In 1960 a group of enthusiasts formed the 'British Beermat Collector's Society'. They managed to persuade comedians Morecambe and Wise to become presidents of the Society.

Some collectable beer mats can command more than £10 each and much more for the truly old and rare ones.

From time to time, you will find boxes of old beer mats for sale at car boot sales. Whilst the majority may be worth 10p each or so, your hope is to find at least a small quantity of quality collectable mats.

Because of the nature of their purpose, used beer mats often have stains and depending to what degree, will devalue them.

▲ Morecambe and Wise. Mackeson Stout. (1961). (vg) £6 - £8

▲ Beer Mat Collector's Society. Mackeson Stout. 1961. (vg) £3 - £4

▲ Beer Mat Society. Commemorative. 1961. (vg) £3 - £5

▲ Duckhams Motor Oil. (1965). (g) £3 - £4

▲ Cherry B. (1965). (g) £2 - £3

▲ Bulls Eye Brown Ale. (1960). (g) £3 - £4

▲ Brewmaster. (1970). (g-vg) £1 - £2

▲ Calypso. (1965). (g-vg) £2 - £3

▲ Abbot Ale. (1965). (g-vg) £2 - £3

▲ Pony. (1970). (vg) £1 - £2

▲ John Peel. (1970). (vg) £1 - £2

▲ Grasmere Sports. 1968. (g) £1 - £2

▲ Golden Godwin. (1960). (g-vg) £2 - £3

▲ Jubilee Stout Black Label. (1975). (vg) 30p - 40p

▲ Cameron's Strongarm. (1965). (g) £1 - £2

▲ Flowers Keg Bitter. (1975). (g) 20p - 30p

▲ Bulls Eye Brown Ale. (1970). (g-vg) £2 - £3

▲ Morland. (1980). (g) 30p - 40p

▲ Pink Lady. (1960). (g) £3 - £4

▲ Martell. (1960). (g-vg) £1 - £2

▲ England's Glory. (1965). (vg) £3 - £4

▲ Toby. (1965). (g) £1 - £2

▲ Lemon Hart Rum. (1970). (vg) £1 - £2

▲ John Courage. 1961. (g) £1 - £2

BEER MATS (1960s)

▲ Guernsey Cream. Snowball. (vg) £1 - £2

▲ Tolly Ale. (vg) £1 - £2

▲ Toby Ale. (g) £1 - £2

▲ Simpkiss. (g-vg) £1 - £2

▲ Mackeson Stout. (vg) £3 - £4

▲ Greenall Whitley. (g) £1 - £2

▲ Matthew Brown & Co. (g-vg) £1 - £2

▲ Batemans. (g) £1 - £2

▲ Baby Bubbly (f-g) £2 - £3

▲ Ch Ch Chandy. (g-vg) £2 - £4

▲ Courage. (g) £1 - £2

▲ Wilsons. (g-vg) £1 - £2

▲ Cotswold Ale. (g) £1 - £2

▲ Arctic Lite. (g) £3 - £4

▲ Cameron's. (g-vg) £1 - £2

▲ Jules Baron Brandy. (vg) £2 - £3

▲ Coates Cider. (vg) £1 - £2

▲ Roses Ales. (g) £1 - £2

▲ Worthington. (g) £1 - £2

▲ Double Diamond. (g) £1 - £2

▲ Strongarm. (g-vg) £1 - £2

▲ Wilsons. (g-vg) £1 - £2

▲ Caroni Navy Rum. (vg) £1 - £2

▲ Lemon Hart Rum. (vg) £1 - £2

▲ Merrydown. (vg) £1 - £2

▲ Worthington. (g) £1 - £2

▲ Poacher. (vg) £1 - £2

▲ Wollongong Duty Free. (g) £1 - £2

BEER MATS (1970s)

▲ Polaroid. (f-g) £2 - £3

▲ Champion. (g-vg) £1 - £2

▲ Badger Beer. (g-vg) £1 - £3

▲ Canadian Club. (g) £1 - £2

▲ Bass. (vg) £1 - £2

▲ Bullseye. (vg) £1 - £2

▲ Domingo. (g-vg) £1 - £2

▲ Dewar's Scotch whisky. (vg) £1 - £2

▲ BL. (g) £1 - £2

▲ Mackeson. (g) £1 - £3

▲ John Peel. (g) £1 - £2

▲ Vaux. (g) £1 - £2

▲ Hartleys. (f-g) £1 - £2

▲ Forest Brown. (vg) £1 - £2

▲ "take drinks home". (g) £1 - £2

▲ Nalgo. (g) £1 - £2

▲ Forest Brown. (g) £1 - £2

▲ Brakspears. (g) £1 - £2

▲ The Strathspey Malt whisky. (g-vg) £1 - £2

▲ Country Fair. (g-vg) £1 - £2

▲ Double Diamond. (vg-ex) £1 - £2

▲ Champion. (g-vg) £1 - £2

▲ KC Cyder. (g-vg) £2 - £3

▲ Coates Cider. (g-vg) £1 - £2

▲ Hartleys. (g-vg) £1 - £2

▲ John Courage. (vg) £1 - £2

▲ Merrydown. (f-g) £1 - £2

▲ Autumn Gold Cider. (vg) £1 - £2

▲ Booth's High & Dry. (g-vg) £1 - £2

▲ Taunton Cider. (vg) £1 - £2

BEER MATS (1970s)

▲ Miss Calypso. (g)
£1 - £2

▲ Bols Advockaat.
(vg) £1 - £2

▲ White Horse. (vg)
£1 - £2

▲ Britvic. (g) £1 - £2

▲ Jubilee Stout. (g)
£1 - £2

▲ Watneys Cream
Label. (g) £1 - £2

▲ Courage Tavern.
(g) £1 - £2

▲ Threlfalls. (g) £1 - £3

▲ Newcastle Blue Star.
(f-g) £1 - £2

▲ Forest Brown.
(g-vg) £1 - £2

▲ Van Dyck cigars.
(g) £1 - £3

▲ Guernsey Cream.
(f-g) £1 - £2

▲ M&B. (g) £1 - £2

▲ Ushers. (f) £1 - £2

▲ Cornhill Gin. (g) £1 - £2

▲ Double Diamond.
(g) £1 - £2

▲ Arkells.   (f-g)
£1 - £2

▲ Britvic.   (f-g)
£1 - £2

▲ Daily Record. (g)
£2 - £3

▲ Whitbread. (f-g)
£1 - £2

▲ Caroni Navy Rum.
(g) £1 - £2

▲ Makeson. (f-g) £1 - £2

BELISHA

The Belisha Beacon was invented by Leslie Hore-Belisha MP (1893 - 1957), who, as Minister of Transport in 1934, was tasked with decreasing the number of accidents on our roads.

Collectable items include the actual orange globes - these turn up at Autojumbles and on internet auctions. Matchbox and Dinky produced diecast models of Belisha Beacons.

▶ Cigarette Card no.38. From the 1935 Godfrey Phillips set of 54 titled 'In the Public Eye'. (vg) 20p - 40p

▲ Belisha - Pepys Card Game. 1938 version. Original box (damaged). Cards and rules booklet (vg) £8 - £10

BELT BUCKLES

▲ Mack Trucks brass belt buckle. (1990). 95 x 55mm. (vg) £8 - £10

Western belt buckles owe their huge popularity to the cowboy era. While there are plenty of collectors in the UK, the biggest demand is in the USA.

There's a warning notice with them. Many have been produced in recent years that are high quality and made to look old. You really do need to do your homework before you start investing in genuine antique belt buckles.

You can find plenty on the internet

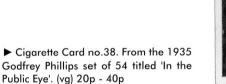

▶ Spritzer Jeans Co. (2000). 70mm diam. (vg) £3 - £4

▲ Keep On Truckin. (1995). 90 x 65mm. (vg) £3 - £4

BISCUIT TINS

Whilst they may be interesting collectables, large biscuit tins are space consuming. Sample tins (for the trade) are far smaller and very collectable items.

Huntley & Palmers, founded in 1822, was a British biscuit manufacturer originally based in Reading. They were well known for their decorative and imaginative tins. A collector would be kept very busy indeed trying to acquire an example of every kind of tin the company ever produced. Their cardboard tubes and boxes are generally much harder to find as they were less likely to be kept after the contents had been consumed. As always, look out for examples in very good condition or better as they have the potential to be real money spinners.

◀ Huntley & Palmers biscuit tin. (1920). 150 x 150 x 60mm. (f-g)   £10 - £12

Biscuit sample tins

▲ Jacob & Co's sample tin. 1924. Issued to commemorate the British Empire Exhibition. 75 x 75 x 55mm. (g) £16 - £20

▲ Peek Frean sample tin. (1950). 80 x 80 x 45mm. (vg) £14 - £18

▲ Huntley & Palmers sample tin. 1933. 35 x 35 x 45mm. (vg) £12 - £14

▶ Huntley & Palmers sample tin. (1930). 35 x 35 x 45mm. (f) £7 - £9

◀ McVitie & Price's sample tin. (1925). 85 x 85 x 30mm. (g) £8 - £12

BLACK & WHITE MINSTRELS

Although there's not a huge interest in items relating to The Black & White Minstrels, at the moment, it could be that in years to come items relating to the subject will be in greater demand.

This entertainment show featured male and female singers and dancers. The male participants (only) had their faces blacked up and this was all deemed acceptable from the first TV airing in 1958 until twenty years later when petitions were submitted to the BBC demanding an end to the show because of racist implications.

In fact the show had been one of the most successful on TV in the sixties, with audiences regularly topping 18million.

As well as the TV shows The Black & White Minstrels made several LP records (one of which reached no.1 in the album chart). They also had a very successful stage show which toured the country.

The show was created by George Mitchell (1917-2002).

▲ Souvenir brochure from the 1968 Black & White Minstrels stage show. (g) £2 - £3

BLIGHTY

Blighty was a humorous weekly magazine that was originally issued free of charge to Britain's World War I troops. It was paid for by donations and the sale of the publication to the general public.

Publication ceased after the war ended but was revived during World War II and then continued publication until 1958.

The term 'Blighty' is an endearing term for Great Britain. Troops abroad, particularly, would refer to home as "dear old Blighty".

▲ Back To Blighty postcard. (1915). Celesque Series. Postally unused. (g) £3 - £5

▲ Blighty magazine. Summer Extra. 1953. (vg) £4 - £6

BLOTTERS

Blotting paper has been around for a few hundred years, so there's plenty of scope for today's collectors.

Many companies have promoted themselves with printed advertising messages on the reverse side of blotting paper, over the years. Many of these are collectable and not expensive to acquire.

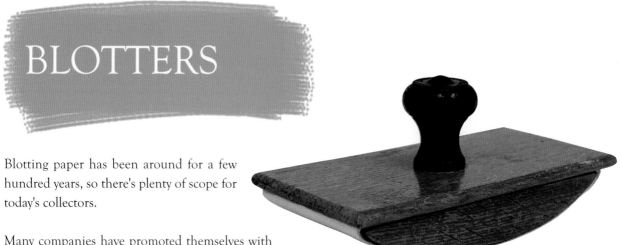

▲ Wooden blotter. (1950) 150mm long. (g-vg) £4 - £6

▲ Pirelli. C.W. Cross Motor Engineer. (1950). 145 x85mm. (vg) £3 - £5

▲ King George's Fund For Sailors. (1940). 210 x100mm. (g-vg). £4 - £6

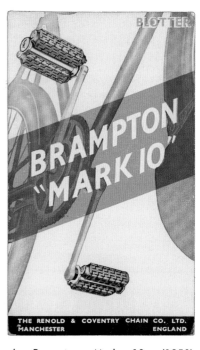

▲ Brampton Mark 10. (1950). 130 x 75mm. (g-vg) £1 - £2

▲ Roland Bellamy. 1958. 200 x 90mm. (vg) £1 - £2

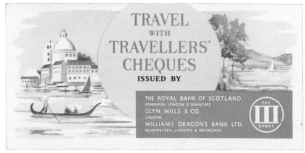

▲ Royal Bank of Scotland. Travellers' Cheques. (1950). 185 x 90mm. (g) £2 - £3

BLOTTERS

◄ Duckworth & Co., Manchester. Blotter advertising Ginger Ale extract. (1935). 150 x 95mm. (vg) £6 - £8

► Esso. Blotter advertising Extra Motor Oil. (1960). 145 x 95mm. (vg) £4 - £6

◄ Dunlop. Blotter advertising A & N Parts of Yeovil. 1959. 138 x 82mm. (vg) £4 - £6

BOARD GAMES

There's a bonus with collecting board games - they can be played with. Find a group of fellow enthusiasts and you have a formula for social gatherings. There are many active groups of board-gamers around the country. Full details can be found on the website: www.royalsocietyofgamers.com

▲ Criss Cross Quiz. Produced by Chad Valley. (g-vg) £12 - £18

▲ Scoop. Produced by Waddingtons. (1955). (vg) £5 - £7

▲ Nationwide. Produced by Omnia Pastimes. (1976). (vg) £10 - £12

▲ Gun Law. Produced by Bell Toys & Games. (1958). (g-vg) £18 - £24

▲ Wheel Of Fortune. Produced by Waddingtons. (1988). (vg) £10 - £12

▲ Take Your Pick. Produced by Bell Toys & Games. (1958). (g-vg) £15 - £20

Board games (TV related)

The popular period for TV show related board games is roughly from 1957 to 1987. A good source is internet auctions, but you do need to be sure that the game is complete and the box is in good condition. Above all, the image on the front of the box should ideally not have any damage.

One of the reasons why TV show related board games are so popular, is because of the nostalgia factor. There are also collectors of all memorabilia associated with particular TV shows, so acquiring the board game of the show becomes essential.

The BOAT SHOW

Originally held at Olympia, the (London) Boat Show later moved to Earls Court, where it stayed until moving to ExCel in 2004.

Collectors have little interest in Boat Show memorabilia; hence items such as programmes, badges, mugs etc... can be bought cheaply.

▶ The Boat Show Official Guide. 1978. 240 A4 pages. (g) £1 - £2

BOBBY BEAR

Based on the Steiff Teddy Bear, Bobby was a cartoon character featured in the Daily Herald (popular daily newspaper which eventually became The Sun).

The series began in 1919 and Bobby quickly became very popular. In 1920 the first of the Bobby Bear's Annuals was published.

Latching onto the huge success, "The Bobby Bear Club" was formed in 1930. Within two years the membership figure had risen to 400,000 members. Members had a special code and were also entitled to purchase a superbly made enamel badge.

▲ Bobby Bear Club original enamel badge. (1935). 27mm diameter. (vg) £14 - £16

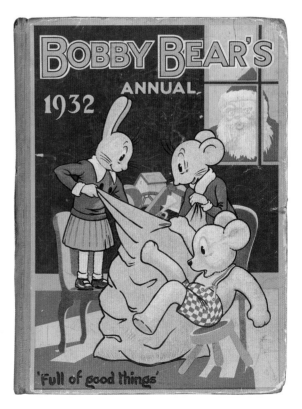

▲ Bobby Bear's Annual. 1932. Complete but only in fair condition. £4 - £6

BOOKMARKS

This is yet another collecting area that will not break the bank. You can often find some really nice examples at Collectors' Fairs and also via internet auctions. Rather craftily, some can be found at car boot sales in old books. For the price of a 50p book you might acquire a bookmark worth £5 or more.

There are plenty of variations to the theme. Collectors look out for old advertising, bookmark postcards and particularly, silks (known as Stevengraphs).

Front   Reverse

▲ Esso Extra. Advertising bookmark. Merchiston Motors, Edinburgh. (1950). (vg) £12 - £14

◄   Regal Bond Stationery. Advertising bookmark. (1935). (vg) £3 - £5

►   Fitness Wins. Information bookmark. (1945). (g) £3 - £5

▲ Book Tokens. Advertising bookmark. (1960). (vg) £1 - £2

Book tokens were created by publisher Harold Raymond in 1920. He recognised that many people were reluctant to buy books as presents because they could not be sure if the recipient would like the book or have a copy already.

Stevengraphs

Thomas Stevens (1828 - 1888) was a weaver based in Cox Street, Coventry. He invented a method for making woven silk pictures. His business quickly expanded to greetings cards and particularly, bookmarks. Other manufacturers cashed-in on the popularity of his work. These silk pictures became generally known as Stevengraphs. The genuine works of Thomas Stevens, carry his name and the place name, Coventry.

◄ To My Mother. Stevengraph silk bookmark. (1895). (vg) £25 - £35

Front

Reverse

Front

This bookmark was produced by The Ministry of Food and is a good example of how bookmarks were used by official bodies to get important messages across to the public, particularly after the traumas of war.

◄ The Bread Code. Ministry of Food. Information bookmark. 1946. (vg) £5 - £7

Reverse

BOOKMARKS

There's plenty of crossover with other collecting areas. On this page alone, there's railwayana, tobacciana, automobilia, cartophilly and deltiology.

▲ Caledonian Railway. (1910). (vg) £14 - £18

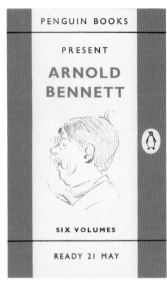

▲ Penguin Books. Arnold Bennett promotional bookmark. 1963. (vg) £2 - £4

◄ Chemins de Fer de L'Etat and Southern Railway. (1930). This was an Anglo-French railway venture. (f) £5 - £7

▶ Great Western Railway. Penzance. (1920). (g) £5 - £7

▲ Casque d'Or. French advertising bookmark. (1930). (g-vg) £5 - £7

▲ Highway Code. RoSPA promotional bookmark. 1952. (g) £4 - £6

(front)

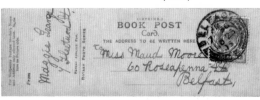

(reverse)

▲ Bookmark postcard. Rotary Series. Featuring Marie Studholme. Postmarked 1905 Belfast with half penny stamp. These bookmarks were popular between 1904 and 1914. Measurement 132 x 45mm. (vg) £6 - £8

(front)

(reverse)

◄ John Player. Bookmark (Authors) cigarette card. This is no.6 (Thackeray) from a very rare set of 10 cards dated 1902. Damage to the top left and right corner. The full set (in good condition) can sell for over £500. (f) £10 - £12

BOSSONS

W H Bossons Ltd were in production from 1946 until 1996. During that time they produced wall masks, figurines, plaques, and ornaments, all of which can accurately be called "Bossons."

The company first introduced gypsum plaster masks like the two depicted below in 1958. The first model was a Snake Charmer, and the success of the piece led to more designs being put into production. Each model was finished by hand (by trained women) so that every mask was unique.

It is important to remember that plaster is particularly fragile. Bossons should be handled with care as even the slightest knocks can cause damage. However, the fragility of the pieces often works in the favour of dealers: mint condition examples are highly prized and sell for good money, and even damaged pieces sell well as people accept a certain amount of damage as normal.

▲ "Old Salt". (1975). (vg) £15 - £20

▲ "Sikh". (1975). (vg) £15 - £20

BOTTLE OPENERS

Many of the collectable cast iron bottle openers are based on William Painter's Crown Cork invention.

Breweries (and other commercial bodies) marked their names on openers. Collectors busily seek out the more obscure breweries.

▲ Crown Cork. (1935). Marked 'Opener' on the other side. (g) £2- £3

▲ Vi-Malto. (1935). Marked 'Vi-Tonica' on the other side. (vg) £8 - £10

▲ Woodhouse. (1930). Also marked 'Woodhouse' on the other side. (g) £6 - £8

▲ Birkenhead. (1950). Marked 'Brewery Co. Ltd' on the other side. (g-vg) £2 - £4

▲ Huntsman Ales. (1950). Marked 'E.P. & Co. Ltd' on the other side. (g) £3 - £4

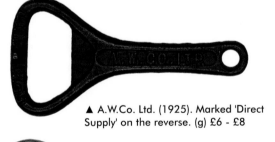

▲ A.W.Co. Ltd. (1925). Marked 'Direct Supply' on the reverse. (g) £6 - £8

▲ Fremlins Ales. (1950). Also marked 'Fremlins Ales' on the other side. (g) £3 - £5

▲ Corona. (1935). Marked 'Family Drinks' on the reverse. (g) £3 - £4

▲ Royal Crown Derby bottle opener. (1975). 150mm long. (vg) £6 - £8

▲ Brody Cider bottle opener. (1990). In the shape of a Brody bottle. 130mm long. (vg) £3 - £5

BOWLS

A popular subject under this heading is the collecting of enamel pin badges. Most bowls clubs have their own design and an interest in collecting many different ones is the enthusiast's object.

Although enamel badges are the most sought after, many clubs have issued acrylic pin badges.

In 2008 the EBA (English Bowling Association) merged with the EWBA (English Women's Bowling Association) forming the National Governing Board known as 'Bowls England'.

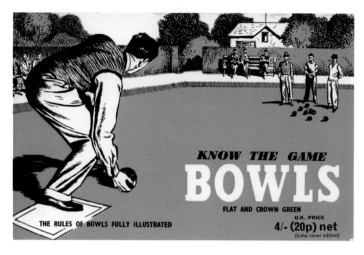

▲ Know The Game - Bowls. 1968. Published by Educational Productions. 205 x 135mm. 41 pages. (vg) £1 - £3

▲ EBA 75th Anniversary 1903-1978. (1978). (g) £1 - £3

▲ Carmarthen County. (g) £1 - £2

▲ City of London. (f-g)   £1 - £2

▲ North Thames Gas SA. (1984). (g-vg) £2 - £4

▲ Jersey. (1984). (vg) £1 - £2

▲ World Bowls Aberdeen. (1984). (vg) £1 - £3

▲ Worcs. Vice-presidents BA. (g) £1 - £2

▲ Sussex. (vg-ex) £1 - £2

▲ Lensbury BC. (vg-ex) £1 - £2

▲ Saundersfoot. (vg) £1 - £2

▲ Devonshire. (g) £1 - £3

▲ Gloucestershire. (vg) £1 - £2

▲ Oxford City & County. (ex) £1 - £2

▲ South Strathfield. (g) £1 - £2

▲ Herefordshire. (f-g) £1 - £2

▲ South Warwickshire. (vg) £1 - £2

BOXING

Like many sports, there's plenty of history and therefore plenty of collectables to look out for. Boxing offers lots of potential.

▲ The Ring magazine. USA. April 1951. Hole punched (g). £8 - £12

◄ Boxing programme. 12 May 1964. (f-g) £6 - £8

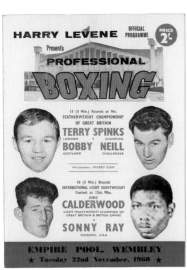

▲ Boxing programme. 22 Nov 1960. (g) £5 - £7

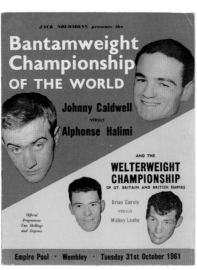

▲ Boxing programme. 31 Oct 1961. (g) £7 - £9

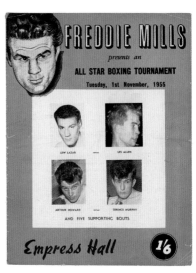

▲ Boxing programme. 1 Nov 1955. (g) £12 - £14

BOXING - Original (card) posters

Approx 365 x 545mm

The demand for boxing posters is such that there's a strong market in reproductions. Like most collectable items, copies are obviously worth a fraction of the originals.

Values of originals depend on age, condition and the names on the bill. Rather obviously, there's a big demand for Cassius Clay/Muhammad Ali. In fact these are so valuable, you do need to beware of high quality fakes being passed off as originals. Some may have been deliberately damaged or creased to give them more of an original feel.

Original posters are ideal for framing but should never be hung in direct sunlight. The idea is to protect your investment by keeping all framed items in the best condition possible.

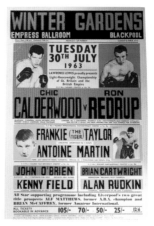

▲ Winter Gardens Blackpool. 30 Jul 1963. (g-vg) £30 - £40

▲ Corwen Pavilion. 19 Jul 1963. (f-g) £15 - £20

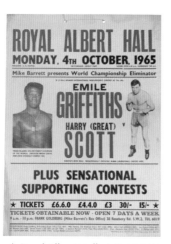

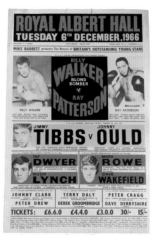

▲ Blackpool Tower Circus. 2 Feb 1965. (g) £30 - £40

▲ Royal Albert Hall. 4 Oct 1965. (g) £20 - £30

▲ Royal Albert Hall. 9 Apr 1963. (vg) £30 - £40

▲ Royal Albert Hall. 6 Dec 1966. (g) £30 - £40

◀ Empire Pool Wembley. 20 Sept 1966. (p-f) £40 - £60

▶ Winter Gardens Morecambe. 9 Jun 1964. (f) £15 - £20

◀ Belle Vue Manchester. 25 Nov 1963. (g-vg) £30 - £40

▶ Winter Gardens Blackpool. 22 Jun 1965. (p-f) £15 - £20

BOXING - Original (card) posters

Approx 365 x 545mm

▲ Royal Albert Hall. 17 Jan 1967. (g-vg) £25 - £30

▲ Empire Pool Wembley. 10 Mar 1958. (g) £30 - £40

▲ Royal Albert Hall. 10 Nov 1964. (g) £20 - £30

▲ Seymour Hall London. 5 Mar 1963. (f) £15 - £25

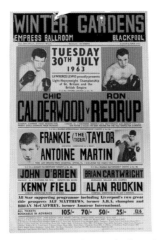

▲ Royal Albert Hall. 28 Jun 1966. (g) £20 - £25

▲ Winter Gardens Blackpool. 30 Jul 1963. (f) £10 - £15

▲ Olympia. 26 Jan 1960. (p) £8 - £12

▲ Royal Albert Hall. 12 Jan 1965. (p) £8 - £12

◄ Belle Vue Manchester. 22 Apr 1963. (f) £10 - £14

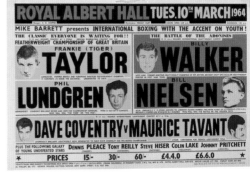

► Royal Albert Hall. 10 Mar 1964. (g-vg) £30 - £40

◄ Blackpool Tower. 6 Feb 1964. (p-f) £8 - £10

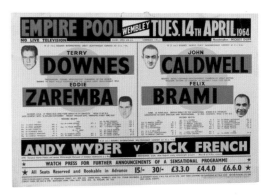

► Empire Pool Wembley. 14 Apr 1964. (g-vg) £25 - £30

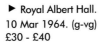

BOXING - Henry Cooper

When he was 17, he won the ABA light-heavyweight title, and he represented Britain in the 1952 Olympics where he lost on points to the Russian Anatoli Petrov in the second stage. He then did his two years National Service before turning professional under the management of Jim Wicks ("The Bishop"). Wicks was also the boxing manager for Henry's twin brother, George.

Cooper's early title challenges were unsuccessful, as he was beaten by the likes of Ingemar Johansson and Joe Erskine, but he became British and Commonwealth champion in January 1959 after beating the reigning champion, Brian London. He successfully defended his titles in bouts with Dick Richardson and Johnny Prescott. He was offered the opportunity to fight Sonny Liston, but Wicks declined the invitation.

During his career, Cooper had the honour to fight Cassius Clay on two occasions. In their first contest, in 1963, Cooper floored Clay in the fourth round with a left hook. Unfortunately for Cooper, Clay was saved by the bell, and the next round was delayed as Clay had to have a ripped glove replaced. Once the fight resumed, Clay had regained his composure, and proceeded to win the fight. Later, on television, Clay admitted that Cooper had hit him so hard that his "ancestors in Africa felt it."

The fighters met for a second time in 1966, by which time Clay had changed his name to Muhammad Ali. Ali won this fight too.

Cooper eventually won the European title in 1968 for beating Karl Mildenberger, and subsequently defended it successfully on two occasions. He had his last ever fight in 1971, when he was controversially beaten by Joe Bugner by quarter of a point and lost his titles.

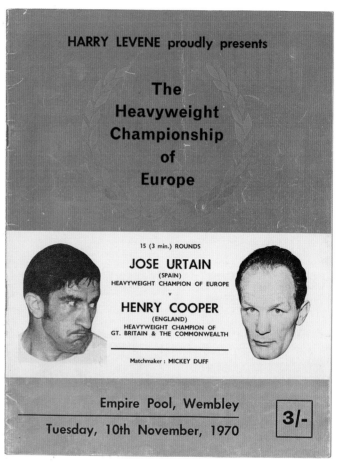

▲ Henry Cooper Wembley programme. 1970. (g) £8 - £12

▲ Henry Cooper autograph. Clear, black ink, 140 x 100mm. No dedication. £8 - £10

Cooper was awarded BBC Sports Personality of the Year twice, in 1967 and 1970, and he was knighted in 2000. He appeared on television in public service announcements encouraging people to get their flu vaccinations. The campaign was called Get Your Jab In First.

Cooper sadly passed away on 1 May 2011, after a long illness, two days before his 77th birthday.

BOXING - Muhammad Ali

▲ Muhammad Ali signed photograph. Clear, blue ink, 250 x 205mm. No dedication. £180 - £200

BREWERIANA

The collecting of items relating to breweries.

Popular collecting areas are advertising signs, bottles, pub trays, branded water jugs and ashtrays.

The landlords of traditional British pubs are often on the look-out for breweriana and provide a ready-made market.

▲ Johnnie Walker. Plastic model. 105mm high. (1960). Right arm missing (hence the value is halved) otherwise very good. £7 - £8

Ashtrays

The pub ashtray has become a 'thing of the past', thanks to the ban on smoking in public establishments. Hence ashtrays with brewery related insignia are becoming more collectable.

▲ Dry Blackthorn. Taunton Cider. Ceramic pump sign. 150mm high. (1980). (vg) £5 - £7

▲ Autumn Gold. Taunton Cider. Ceramic pump sign. 150mm high. (1980) Hairline crack. (g) £1 - £2

▲ Johnnie Walker. Wade ceramic ashtray. (1965). (vg) £8 - £12

▶ Grant's Scotch Whisky, water jug. (1985). (g) £2 - £4

◀ Goldcrest. Matchbox. (1965). (g-vg) £1 - £2

▶ Ushers. Matchbox. (1965). (g-vg) £1 - £2

▲ Worthington 'E' beer, pub tray. (1970) (g-vg) £4 - £6

▲ Whitbread. Cribbage board. In original box. (1980). (vg) £6 - £8

BREWERIANA - Ashtrays

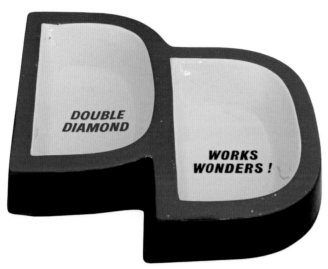

▲ Double Diamond. (1970). Bristol Pottery. 170 x 160mm. (vg) £10 - £12

▲ Burton Ale. (1980). Wade. 195 x 165mm. (vg) £6 - £8

▲ Canada Dry. (1960). Regicor ceramic ashtray. 130 x 125mm. (vg) £12 - £16

▲ Courage Tavern. (1980). Wade. 205 x 160mm. (vg) £5 - £7

▲ Budweiser. (1990). Glass ashtray. 200 x 120mm. (vg) £6 - £8

▲ Patzenhofer Lager. (1970). Solian Ware Pottery. Small chip in the ceramic. 120mm. (f) £3 - £5

BRITAIN IN PICTURES

This is a fascinating series of books (225 x 165mm) published by Collins.

The year was 1941 and Britain was embroiled in war with Hitler. It was not an inspiring time for our countrymen. Collins hit on the idea of brightening things up with various subjects that reminded everybody of our culture and heritage. They did a great job. In fact, the publications were so popular, they carried on publishing them after war ended and concluded the series in 1949.

There were 132 titles and therefore plenty for today's collectors to be excited about. They are not expensive collectables but do beware, if you start collecting them, it could be that it becomes a bit of an obsession as you strive to complete a full collection.

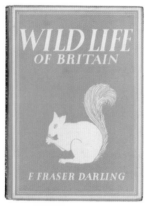
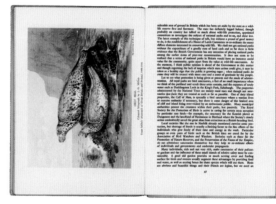

▶ Wildlife of Britain. 1943. 48 pages. No dust jacket . (g) £3 - £4

Front cover   Page 40   Page 41

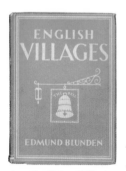
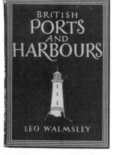

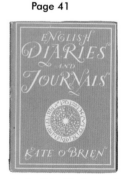

▲ English Villages. 1942. 48 pages. Dust jacket. (g) £4 - £5

▲ English Fashion. 1948. 48 pages. No dust jacket. (g) £3 - £4

▲ British Ports and Harbours. 1946. 48 pages. Dust jacket. (g) £4 - £5

▲ English Novelists. 1945. 48 pages. Dust jacket. (g) £4 - £5

▲ English Diaries and Journals. 1943. 48 pages. Dust jacket. (g) £4 - £5

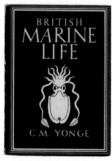

▲ British Marine Life. 1944. 48 pages. No dust jacket. (g) £3 - £4

▲ English Country Houses. 1941. 48 pages. Dust jacket. (g) £4 - £5

▲ English Inns. 1944. 48 pages. Dust jacket. (g) £4 - £5

▲ English Music. 1947. 48 pages. No dust jacket. (g) £3 - £4

▲ Battlefields in Britain. 1944. 48 pages. No dust jacket. (g) £3 - £4

BRITISH EMPIRE EXHIBITION

Held in 1924 and 1925, The British Empire Exhibition was the world's largest exhibition ever. It attracted a total of 27 million visitors. Most of the buildings were designed to be temporary structures but some were kept and indeed the most famous of them being Wembley Stadium. The iconic twin towers remained the home of British football for 75 years until it was demolished.

The purpose of the Exhibition was to promote British trade and strengthen the relationship with the 58 countries of the British Empire.

▲ Souvenir tea caddy spoon. 1924. (g-vg) £3 - £4

◄ Postcard. Malaya Pavilion. 1924. Postally unused. Creased (f-g) £2 - £3

► Postcard. Palace of Engineering. 1924. Postally unused. (vg) £2 - £4

BRITISH LEGION

The Royal British Legion is the leading charity in the UK providing support for those who have served or are still serving in the British Armed Forces.

The organisation was founded in 1921 when the Comrades of the Great War, the National Association of Discharged Sailors and Soldiers, the National Federation of Discharged and Demobilised Sailors and Soldiers, and the Officers' Association were merged together. It was awarded its Royal Charter on 29 May 1971 to mark its 50th anniversary.

▲ Haig's Fund booklet. 1937. 8 pages. 125 x 90mm. Staple rusting (g-vg) £4 - £6

BROOKE BOND

In collecting circles, it's the illustrated cards and the associated albums that Brooke Bond are most famous for. But of course, Brooke Bond are primarily tea manufacturers. The firm was started in 1869 by Arthur Brooke, who, at the age of 25, opened his first tea shop. He chose the name because he promised his customers quality tea and his word was his bond. He simply prefixed the word bond with his own name. The business flourished and quickly progressed to wholesale tea sales.

Illustrated cards (the same size and appearance as cigarette cards but classed by collectors as 'trade cards') were given away with packets of tea from the mid-1950's onwards.

Collectors prefer to collect the cards separately from the albums. Hence the reason why empty card albums (particularly the early issues) in very good condition are commanding decent prices.

There's also a demand for albums with cards glued into them but, because the market is awash with them, values are not high and condition is king. The best advice is to be patient and be highly selective by collecting tip-top condition examples. Indeed, albums in very good condition or better, have a reasonable chance of increasing in value.

In 1930, the PG Tips brand was added to the Brooke Bond portfolio. The name was derived from 'pre-gest', meaning the aiding of digestion prior to eating. Clever marketers introduced the PG Chimps to their TV advertising in 1956. Voice-overs were provided by some famous names, including Peter Sellers, Kenneth Williams and Bob Monkhouse.

PG introduced tea bags to their range in the sixties and in the nineties developed the 'pyramid bag'.

Brooke Bond's Dividend tea promotion in the 1970's was claimed to be a success. Packets included a dividend stamp which could then be affixed to a collecting card that could then be exchanged at the local grocer's shop for the princely sum of 25p, once it contained 60 stamps.

Albums

▲ Asian Wild Life. Brooke Bond album. Contains a few cards affixed. 1962. (vg) £3 - £5

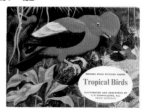

▲ Butterflies of the World. Brooke Bond album. Full set of 50 cards affixed. 1964. (g) £1 - £2

▲ Transport Through The Ages. Brooke Bond album. Full set of 50 cards affixed. 1966. (g-vg) £1 - £2

▲ Tropical Birds. Brooke Bond album. Full set of 50 cards affixed. 1961. (vg) £3 - £4

▲ Wild Flowers. Series 2. Brooke Bond album. Some cards affixed. 1959. (vg) £2 - £4

▲ British Costume. Brooke Bond album. Full set of 50 cards affixed. 1967. (g-vg) £1 - £2

▲ Wild Birds in Britain. Brooke Bond album. Full set of 50 cards affixed. 1965. (g) £2 - £3

▲ Trees in Britain. Brooke Bond album. No cards affixed. 1966. (vg) £2 - £4

▼ Packet of Brooke Bond Tea. Unopened and complete with savings stamp. This is a hard to find item (having all contents intact) and a great find for a collector of packaging. (1975). (vg) £12 - £15

▲ Brooke Bond advertisement on matchbox label. Edglets. (1950). (f) £1 - £2

▲ BT Phonecard. Advertising Brooke Bond D. 1988. Mint in original sealed pack. £3 - £4

▲ Brooke Bond Dividend savings card. With 14 stamps affixed and 1 loose. (1975). (f) £1 - £2

BUBBLE GUM WRAPPERS

Some of the most collectable bubble gum wrappers relate to the A&BC gum company.

The collecting of the cards given away with sticks of bubble gum was very popular, particularly with schoolboys, in the 1960's. The gum and the cards were wrapped in wax paper which were colourfully printed and related to particular sets of cards.

Most wrappers were simply discarded as the recipients hastily opened the packs to establish which cards from the sets, were inside. Those wrappers that survived have become the subject of intense collecting amongst enthusiasts. Some sell for £100 or more.

By the very nature of the purpose for which the wrappers were intended, it's hard to find examples in excellent condition. Indeed, if you find a rare example in excellent condition then you must ask yourself whether or not it's the genuine article.

Wrappers that have not been opened and still contain the card(s) and gum are known as 'live packs' and their value is enhanced.

The subject matter for bubble gum cards is wide ranging. Television shows and pop stars were popular themes.

Sought after examples include; The Beatles (A&BC), The Rolling Stones, Cliff Richard, The Girl From Uncle and Car Stamps.

Purist collectors like to have the wrapper with the full set of cards and where applicable, the album that was issued to hold the cards.

▲ Dollar Film Star. A&BC. (1955). (vg) £30 - £40

▲ Superman II. Topps. 1981. (g) £3 - £4

▲ Mork & Mindy. Topps. 1979. (g-vg) £4 - £5

▲ Grease. Topps. 1978. (g) £3 - £5

▲ Bay City Rollers. Topps. 1978. (vg) £7 - £9

▲ Andy Gibb. Donruss. 1978. (g) £8 - £10

▲ Saturday Night Fever. Donruss. 1977. (vg) £5 - £7

▲ The Black Hole. Topps. 1979. (f-g) £2 - £3

▲ Fright Flicks. Topps. 1988. (g-vg) £2 - £3

▲ Charlie's Angels. Topps. 1977. (g-vg) £6 - £8

▲ Three's Company. Topps. 1978. (vg) £4 - £5

▲ Batman. Topps. 1989. (g) £2 - £3

▲ Happy Days. Topps. 1976. (g-vg) £5 - £7

▲ Empire Strikes Back. Topps. 1980. (vg) £4 - £5

◄ Rambo. Topps. Live pack. 1985. (vg) £4 - £6

◄ Ghost Busters II. Topps. Live pack. 1989. (vg-ex) £5 - £7

◄ Rocky IV. Topps. Live pack. 1985. (vg) £5 - £7

◄ Magnum. Donruss. Live pack. (1985). (g-vg) £5 - £6

BUILDING SOCIETIES

Ketley's Building Society was the first Building Society. It was launched in 1775 by Richard Ketley, who was the landlord of The Golden Cross Inn, Birmingham.

Ketley's vision was to seek monthly subscriptions from the members of his Society, which in turn would be pooled in a fund for the construction of buildings to be inhabited by the members.

The formula caught on fast. However, the concept was to change fifty years later, when the funds were rolled over, rather than just being used by the Society members for their own homes. This meant that outsiders could become members of the Society, without necessarily having subscribed before.

Many years later (1980's) British banking laws were changed, permitting Building Societies to act as banks. The Abbey National Building Society was demutualised in 1989.

▲ Nationwide. Button badge. (1990). (vg) £1 - £2

▲ Gateway. Button badge. (1980). (vg) £1 - £2

▲ South of England. Button badge. (1985). (vg) £1 - £2

▲ Alliance & Leicester. Button badge. (1995). (vg) £1 - £2

▲ Abbey National. Action Savers. Cloth badge. (1995). (vg) £1 - £2

▲ Peterborough. Button badge. (1985). (vg) £1 - £2

▲ Bristol & West beer mat (square). (1965). (vg) £2 - £3

▲ Bristol & West beer mat (circular). (1965). (vg) £2 - £3

▲ Woolwich Building Society booklet. 1969. (vg) 40p - 60p

▲ Dunfermline Building Society booklet. (1960). (vg) £1 - £2

The Bristol & West Building Society opened its doors in 1850 and grew to become the 9th largest building Society in the UK. It was demutualised and sold in 1997 to the Bank of Ireland.

BUNNYKINS

Royal Doulton chinaware featuring animal characters. Barbara Vernon (Bailey) was the daughter of Cuthbert Bailey, Royal Doulton director. At the age of 19 she became a nun. She had a talent for drawing countryside animals and her father turned them into 'Bunnykins' characters. The Barbara Vernon signature appeared on the designs until 1952. Look for this name. Internet searches will help you date 'Bunnykin backstamps'.

(Front)   (Back)

▲ Royal Doulton dish (92mm diameter). (1950). (vg) £8 - £12

BUSES

The first omnibus was introduced by George Shillibeer to the streets of London in 1829.

There are plenty of enthusiasts who enjoy the nostalgia of the history of buses and therefore there's a strong market in the subject.

▲ Motor Bus At Clifton. Postcard. Postmarked Fishponds 1905 over half penny stamp. Interesting written message in pencil says 'this is one of the new motor buses at Clifton'. (g-vg) £14 - £16

▲ Southdown Leyland bus. Postcard. (1965). Postally unused. (vg) £2 - £3

▲ Trolleybus & Tram Map. 1939. London Transport. (g) £8 - £10

▲ Bus Map. Country Area. 1949. London Transport. (g-vg) £6 - £8

▲ Western National single decker. Photograph. (1965). 140 x 90mm. (vg) £2 - £3

◄ Cardiff Corporation Transport. Chrome badge. Corporate. (1960). 52 x 20mm. (vg) £6 - £8

▶ Midland Red. Accompanied luggage tag. (1945). 65 x 60mm. (g) £4 - £6

▲ Buses PHQ. 2001. (vg) 50p - 70p

BUSES

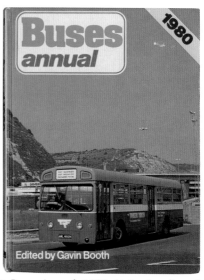

▲ The London Bus. Dryhurst Publications. 1957. 32 page booklet. (g-vg). £4 - £6

▲ The First Thirty Years. Dryhurst Publications. 1962. 40 Page booklet. (vg) £2 - £3

▲ Buses Annual. 1980. Not price clipped. Ian Allan. (g-vg) £2 - £3

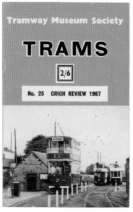

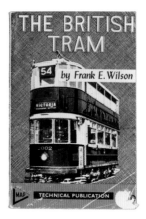

▲ Trams. 1967. Tramway Museum Society. (vg). £1 - £2

▲ Oxford South Midland timetable. 64 Pages. (vg) 1975. £2 - £3

▲ Modern Tramway. Ian Allan. Booklet 35 Pages. 1973. (f) 50p - £1

▲ The British Tram. Map Publications. (g). 1970. £1 - £2

Buses Illustrated (Ian Allan)

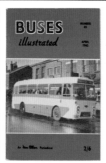

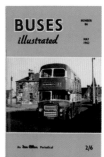

▲ January 1962. (g-vg) £1 - £2

▲ December 1962. (g-vg) £1 - £2

▲ April 1962. (g-vg) £1 - £2

▲ February 1962. (g-vg) £1 - £2

▲ December 1960. (g-vg) £2 - £3

▲ May 1962. (g-vg) £1 - £2

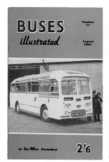

▲ August 1961. (g-vg) £2 - £3

▲ September 1961. (g-vg) £2 - £3

▲ October 1961. (g-vg) £2 - £3

▲ March 1964. (g-vg) £1 - £2

▲ October 1960. (g-vg) £2 - £3

▲ March 1962. (g-vg) £1 - £2

BUSES - PSV badges

PSV (Public Service Vehicle) badges were worn by coach and bus drivers/conductors.

When they were first introduced for horse-drawn vehicles in 1838, who would have thought that one day people would be paying relatively high sums for a PSV badge? It just proves that you should be very careful before throwing anything away!

They are certainly a fascinating collecting area and you can find them at many collectors' fairs and on internet auction sites. Although they are not so common at car boot sales, they are still worth looking out for.

The most common badges are the circular ones (red for driver and green for conductor). This style of badge was introduced in 1935 and lasted until 1991 when the EEC changed the system to PCV (Passenger Carrying Vehicles) and abolished the necessity for drivers and conductors to carry badges.

The chart on the right identifies the regional lettering codes for the badges. For example, FF 30824 was an Eastern Traffic Area issue.

▲ PSV Driver's badge. (1965). 50mm diam. (g-vg) £14 - £16

▲ PSV Conductor's badge. (1965). 50mm diam. (g-vg) £14 - £16

Regional Lettering

AA NORTHERN TRAFFIC AREA
(NEWCASTLE)

BB YORKSHIRE TRAFFIC AREA
(LEEDS)

CC NORTH WESTERN TRAFFIC AREA
(MANCHESTER)

DD WEST MIDLAND TRAFFIC AREA
(BIRMINGHAM)

EE EAST MIDLAND TRAFFIC AREA
(NOTTINGHAM)

FF EASTERN TRAFFIC AREA
(CAMBRIDGE)

GG WELSH TRAFFIC AREA
(CARDIFF)

HH WESTERN TRAFFIC AREA
(BRISTOL)

KK SOUTH EASTERN TRAFFIC AREA
(EASTBOURNE)

LL SCOTTISH TRAFFIC AREA (SUB OFFICE)
(ABERDEEN)

MM SCOTTISH TRAFFIC AREA
(EDINBURGH)

N METROPOLITAN TRAFFIC AREA
(LONDON)

BUTLIN'S

Billy Butlin (born in 1899) came from a West Country fairground family, so it was perhaps no surprise that he would follow in his family's footsteps. He started his venture into the amusement park business with the purchase of a piece of land in Skegness. Four hoopla stalls, a tower slide, a homemade haunted house, and a small track for battery operated cars were the first attractions at the "Butlin's Amusement Site". The site proved a great success and, by the 1930s, Billy had opened eight permanent amusement sites along the coast.

The first Butlin's holiday camp opened at Skegness on Easter Saturday 1936. Unfortunately for Billy, an extraordinary 'white Easter' and no heating meant the campers had to dance in their heavy overcoats, but this didn't seem to stop them having a great time and telling their friends. The first season of the camp was oversubscribed, encouraging Billy to open more holiday camps, with the next one being Clacton, which was opened in time for Christmas 1938.

In the summer of 1939, when 100,000 people were taking their holidays at the Butlin's Skegness and Clacton camps, the entertainment broadcasts on the Tannoy system were regularly interrupted to give names of men who had to report back to their hometown for call-up. Many people were told to cancel their holidays and the number of guests at the two camps was reduced to only 6,000. However, Billy refused to listen to the rumours that a war was imminent. He even included the following headline in the Butlin's Times:

"Bye-Bye Blues at Butlin's? Campers forget the crisis. Are we downhearted? No!!"

When war was declared on September 3rd, advertising posters were replaced with signs saying "Will re-open when finished with Hitler".

The camps were closed and given over for military use. The partially built camps at Filey, Ayr and Pwllheli were completed and opened as military camps.

When the War was over, Filey was the first holiday camp back in action, reopening in 1945; Skegness and Clacton re-opened in 1946 and Ayr and Pwllheli were opened as holiday camps in 1947.

Butlin's popularity continued to increase throughout the fifties and sixties. Billy decided to retire in 1968 and moved to Jersey. The company was taken over by his son Bobby, who sold the business to Rank for £43 million four years later (although Bobby remained in control).

Unfortunately, by the late seventies, foreign holidays were becoming much cheaper, meaning many people decided to take their holidays abroad. As with most British holiday resorts, Butlin's suffered badly and the number of bookings significantly dropped.

▲ Butlin's leaflet. Double sided. 1955. 152 x 102mm. (vg) £4 - £6

▲ The Butlin Holiday Book. 1949-50. Hardback book. 256 pages. 225 x 160mm. (g) £14 - £16

▲ Billy Butlin autograph. Clear, blue ink, 137 x 95mm. No dedication. £60 - £70

BUTLIN'S

▲ Entertainment programme. Filey. 1965. 24 pages. 232 x 155mm. (g) £6 - £8

◄ Bud Flanagan at Butlins. 1964. 12 pages. 135 x 105mm. (g-vg) £6 - £8

► Butlins lighter. (1975). 55 x 35mm. (vg) £6 - £8

◄ Matchbox label. Butlin's Jollidays. (1960). (f-g) 50p - 70p

► Matchbox label. Sun. (1960). (g-vg) 60p - 80p

A new beginning

Changes were made to try to modernise the camps and help them regain their appearance as a family holiday camp. The regimentation was toned down and they even began to ban single-sex bookings. Unfortunately, the number of bookings continued to decline. The low number of bookings resulted in less investment in the camps, which led to deteriorating standards. A few years later, large investments were made, but not enough to halt the decline. It was decided to scale down on the whole project and pay more attention to a smaller number of sites. Subsequently, many of the sites were closed during the '80s.

All remaining camps had huge amounts of money spent on them. A new 'Holiday World' identity was adopted for all of the camps. The camps were completely modernised and many changes were made, the words "Hi-de-Hi" were even banned from the centres (they were no longer referred to as camps) to try to help them appeal to a new market.

Visiting Butlin's is now a completely different experience to what it used to be. However, over one million people a year still enjoy their stay at Butlin's three remaining centres. The centres are set for long and prosperous futures, which has to be a good thing for all collectors of Butlin's memorabilia as there will continue to be a lot of interest in older items, and there will also continue to be a large supply of new Butlin's memorabilia to add to existing collections.

Sadly, Billy was not around to see the new modern centres as he died on 12th June 1980. His tombstone is engraved with the famous Butlin's line "Skegness is so bracing", along with an image of an amusement park, and an image of a camp scene.

BUTLIN'S - Postcards

▲ Butlin's Ocean Hotel, Brighton. Postmarked Brighton & Hove 1966. Message in ink. (g) £5 - £7

▲ Butlin's Ocean Hotel, Saltdean. Postmarked Brighton & Hove 1953. Message in ink. (vg) £6 - £8

▲ Butlin's The Rock and Twist Ballroom, Bognor Regis. (1965). The Tycoons are playing. Postmarked Bognor Regis, unclear postmark. Message in ink. (vg) £6 - £8

▲ Butlin's Redcoats Wave Goodbye, Filey. Postmarked Filey 1963. Message in ink. No stamp. (g) £4 - £6

▲ Butlin's The Sports Arena, Bognor Regis. Postmarked Bognor Regis 1969. Message in ink. (g-vg) £5 - £7

▲ Butlin's Aerial View, Skegness. (1965). Postally unused. (vg) £5 - £7

▲ Butlin's Chalets, Skegness. Postmarked Skegness 1963. Message in ink. (g-vg) £5 - £7

▲ Butlin's Pool and Theatre, Barry Island. (1968). Postally unused. (vg) £4 - £6

BUTLIN'S - Postcards

▲ Butlin's Skegness Monorail. (1975). Postally unused. (g-vg) £2 - £3

▲ Butlin's Bognor Regis. Postmarked Littlehampton 1965. Message in ink. (vg) £2 - £4

▲ Butlin's Bognor Regis. (1965). Postally unused. (vg) £2 - £4

▲ Butlin's Clacton. Postmarked Clacton-On-Sea 1963. Message in ink. (g-vg) £3 - £4

▲ Butlin's Minehead. Postmarked Minehead 1965. Message in ink. (g-vg) £3 - £4

▲ Butlin's Filey. (1965). Postally unused. (g-vg) £2 - £4

▲ Butlin's Minehead Monorail. Postmarked Exeter 1978. Message in ink. (vg) £2 - £4

▲ Butlin's Skegness Ingoldmells Hotel. Postmarked Skegness 1950. Message in pencil. (g) £6 - £8

▲ Butlin's Margate St George's Hotel. (1965). Postally unused. (g-vg) £3 - £4

▲ Butlin's Pwllheli Spanish Bar. Postmarked Pwllheli 1981.Message in ink. (g) £3 - £4

▲ Butlinland Ayr. Postmarked Ayr 1976. Message in ink. (g) £3 - £4

▲ Butlin's Clacton The Chalets. (1950). Postally unused. (g) £3 - £4

▲ Butlin's Clacton The Chalets. Postmarked Clacton-On-Sea 1962. Message in ink. (g-vg) £2 - £4

▲ Butlin's Barry Island. (1985). Postally unused. (vg-ex) £4 - £5

▲ Butlin's Minehead. Postmarked Minehead 1974. Message in ink. (g) £2 - £3

BUTLIN'S - Badges

Every visitor to Butlin's had to wear a little metal badge. The badge meant they could walk in and out of the camp freely during their stay and stopped unauthorised visitors using the free facilities. Initially, campers were asked to pay a shilling for their badge, but the badges soon became free.

The designs of the badges were initially changed annually, with a different design for each camp. It was soon discovered that some campers were re-using the badge and returning later in the year for free. To prevent this, the designs of the badges were altered slightly two or three times annually.

It became fashionable to wear a Butlin's badge both in and out of the camp (regular campers would sometimes proudly display multiple badges from all of their visits in previous years, pinned neatly in rows to their jacket).

Butlin's stopped producing the classic enamel badges in 1967 because of the high cost of production and because they believed women preferred not to have pin marks in their clothes. However, production of other badges continues to the present day.

How many badges were produced?

Many people have differing opinions as to how many Butlin's badges were produced (the figure is approximately 1,700 different designs). No accurate records have been kept, meaning it is very difficult to collect a complete set.

We know that all camps produced between one and three of the classic enamel badges each year they were open between 1936 and 1967.

As well as the general camp badges, there were numerous badges produced for other purposes (including the Beaver Club, staff badges, second week badges, the 913 Club and Christmas badges).

Collectors should note that three of the Butlin's hotels also produced the famous enamel badges. If you see a badge from Brighton, Margate or Blackpool, it is not from the holiday camp but from the hotel.

Keep a special lookout for 1965 badges from Barry Island. Although the camp didn't open until 1966, the camp was originally intended to open before this, and badges were produced for 1965. Another special badge is the 1945 Filey badge. This was produced following the War, showing a V for victory.

▲ Pwllheli. 1948. (vg) £16 - £18

▲ Skegness. 1956. (g-vg) £12 - £14

▲ Filey. 1949. (vg) £16 - £18

▲ Skegness. 1961. (vg) £4 - £6

▲ Pwllheli. 1965. (vg) £6 - £8

▲ Ayr 1965. (vg) £7 - £9

▲ Pwllheli. 1950. (g) £12 - £14

▲ Bognor. 1964. (g) £3 - £5

▲ Ayr. 1954. (vg) £15 - £17

▲ Minehead. 1966. (vg) £3 - £5

▲ Clacton. 1945. (g) £20 - £24

▲ Blackpool. 1966. (vg) £20 - £24

▲ Pwllheli. 1967. (vg) £5 - £7

▲ Margate. 1960 (g) £8 - £10

▲ Filey. 1955. (vg) £18 - £20

▲ Brighton. 1955. (g-vg) £10 - £12

BUTLIN'S - Badges (reverse side)

Collectors of Butlin's badges need to be careful to avoid purchasing a reproduction or fake badge. There are some things you can look for to help:

• The reverse of the badge is very important. The modern reproductions tend to have a secure locking mechanism to the pin on the reverse, whereas the original badges did not have this. Therefore, if you have a badge with this secure locking mechanism (see fig 2 and 3), it will almost certainly be a reproduction. The old badges regularly had the pin sticking out from the side, so you could easily cut yourself, hence why the modern reproductions have added a way of preventing this.

• Badges that are designed to be replicas (and not designed to fool people into thinking they are an original) will usually say "REPLICA" somewhere on the badge, so look very closely for this (figure 3).

• You can sometimes tell that a badge is old simply by the condition it is in. Some of the modern reproductions and fakes look very new (see fig 3). Most (although not all) old badges will show signs of ageing. If you see a 1940s badge in mint condition with a very shiny metal reverse, you should look very closely before purchasing.

• Most original badges included the maker's mark on the reverse (see fig 4). Although a fake could quite easily copy this mark, it is something else to look for.

• The old badges were all enamel. Before purchasing a badge, make sure it doesn't have a clear resin coating over the top (as these are regularly present on reproductions but were not present on originals).

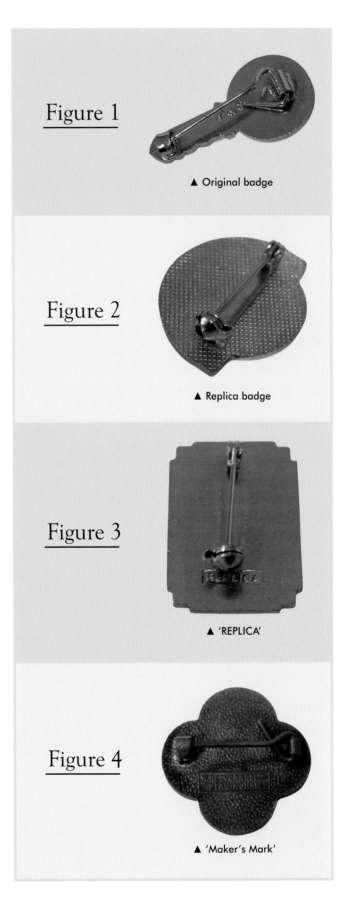

Figure 1

▲ Original badge

Figure 2

▲ Replica badge

Figure 3

▲ 'REPLICA'

Figure 4

▲ 'Maker's Mark'

CAR PARK TICKETS

Themed car park tickets (for example a closed airport) have some value, probably a little more than some may think.

Municipal car park tickets over 50 years old are becoming more collectable and are quite hard to find.

▲ Beaufort Hunt. 1972. (g) 40p - 60p

▲ Portsmouth. (1965). (g-vg) 50p - £1

▲ Doncaster. (1965). (g) 40p - 60p

▲ The British Legion. (1960). (g) £1 - £2

▲ Bridport. 1962. (g) £1 - £2

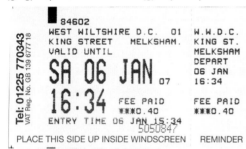

▲ Melksham. 2007. (ex) 2p - 4p

▲ Bournemouth. 2004. (ex) 5p - 10p

▲ Carlisle. (1960). (f) 30p - 50p

Parking discs

▶ French parking disc. 1960. (g) £4 - £6

◀ New Forest parking disc. 2006. (vg) £1 - £2

Parking Discs were first introduced in France in 1957. Their success led to some county councils in Great Britain introducing the scheme.

Cheltenham was the first to introduce them, in 1965. Harrogate and Devizes followed suit in 1969.

A parking disc has a rotating clock face visible through a window in the front of the disc, and the clock face could be adjusted to show your arrival time.

Discs were originally manufactured to conform with British Standard number BS4631.

The collecting of old parking discs does not appear to be the most popular hobby in the world and now could be the time to start a collection while available discs can still be purchased at relatively low prices.

CDs (MUSIC)

Whilst the CD (compact disc) is rapidly becoming an outdated format for playing recorded music, there's still a second-hand market.

It's a case of not being able to give some CDs away at a car boot sale, but there is a demand for sixties pop and particularly The Beatles.

Other CD categories to look out for are Audio Books and old radio programmes.

Overall, there doesn't seem to be much chance of CDs being a strong investment opportunity. However, if you are about to throw your music CDs away, at least keep the inlay cards, as these are very easy to store and some could just possibly be of interest to collectors in years to come.

(Note: all the CDs featured on this page are cased albums with the discs in very good playing condition).

▲The Best of Patience and Prudence. Patience and Prudence £3 - £4

▲ Eddie Fisher Early Years. Eddie Fisher £2 - £3

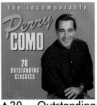
▲ Boys Cry. Eden Kane £1 - £2

▲20 Outstanding Classics. Perry Como £1 - £2

▲ Chuck Berry Greatest Hits. Chuck Berry £1 - £2

▲ Good Rockin' Tonight. Elvis Presley £1 - £2

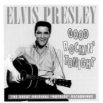
▲ Kites. Simon Dupree and the Big Sound £2 - £4

▲ Baby Call On Me. Wilson Pickett £1 - £3

▲Ray Charles. Ray Charles £1-£2

▲Great Ball Of Fire. Jerry Lee Lewis £1 - £2

▲ Birth Of The Cool. Miles Davis £1 - £2

▲The Very Best Of. The Troggs £2 - £3

▲ Little Richard. Little Richard £1 - £2

▲Heatwave. Martha Reeves & The Vandellas £2 - £3

▲The Best of Brenda Lee. Brenda Lee £2 - £3

▲ Dizzy Heights. Lightning Seeds £1 - £2

▲ Best of The Specials. The Specials £1 - £2

▲ Hold Me, Thrill Me, Kiss Me. Connie Francis £1 - £3

▲ Crazy Man Crazy. Bill Haley £1 - £3

▲ Let's Get It On. Marvin Gaye £2 - £4

▲ The Voice. Russell Watson £1 - £2

▲ The One & Only. Billy Fury £2 - £4

▲ Love Songs. Petula Clark £1 - £2

▲ The Greatest Hits. Ricky Nelson £3 - £4

▲ Don't Fence Me In. Bing Crosby £1 - £2

▲ Yakety Yak The Golden Greats Of. The Coasters £3 - £5

▲ Hey-Hey-It's The Monkees. The Monkees £1 - £2

▲ Unforgettable. Lou Rawls £1 - £2

▲ Move It. Cliff Richard. Front of case cracked £1 - £2

▲ The Very Best Of Northern Soul Volume 2 £1 - £2

▲ Reminiscing With. The Crickets £1 - £2

▲ On The Avenue. Dick Powell £1 -£2

CERAMICS

In the collectables world, ceramics are usually associated with such pottery types as porcelain, earthenware and stoneware. The big 'collectable' name is 'Clarice Cliff' (English ceramic artist).

This book breaks the trend of many books on the subject of collectable items, in as much as ceramics are not featured prominently.

Collectable traders who do most of their business on the internet are often reluctant to get involved in ceramics because the items are susceptible to breakages in transit.

Arthur Wood (Earthenware)

Arthur Wood is a significant name in the world of ceramics.

Products developed from earthenware teapots to rose bowls, vases and novelty items such as piggy banks.

Arthur Wood acquired Carlton Ware in 1967 and sold it 20 years later.

The Arthur Wood piggy banks are particularly sought after by collectors.

Coalport

The company history dates back to 1795. Production moved to Staffordshire in 1926. The company later became part of the Wedgwood group.

Many a home will have had a bowl of fruit (or similar). These ornaments were often made abroad.

▲ Basket of cherries, lemon and orange. Unknown maker. (1975). An all ceramic ornament (140 x 110mm). (vg) £4 - £6

▲ Piggy bank. Ceramic pig. Arthur Wood earthenware. (1975). (vg) £10 - £12

◄   Posy vase. Coalport 'Shrewbury' series. (1975). 160mm high. (vg) £4 - £6

CERAMICS

Homemaker

Homemaker was produced by Ridgway Potteries in Staffordshire, and was sold exclusively in Woolworths. The popular design features pieces of furniture and domestic equipment in black on a white background. The pattern was designed by Enid Seeney during 1956, and was in production from 1958 until 1970. It is still quite easy to find, but is becoming very collectable indeed.

▲ Homemaker plate. (1965). 230mm diameter. (ex) £6 - £8

Picture plates

Many ceramic items are sold as limited editions, but the number produced may not be specified. In these instances, the size of the production run is usually dictated by a time frame rather than a set amount. For example, the edition may be limited to "90 firing days". There is no way of knowing how many items can be produced in the time frame specified, and because of this, the "limited edition" may not be as limited (and therefore not as valuable) as you think it is. If you are interested in buying limited editions for their resale potential, then look for those that are numbered and clearly express the size of the edition (for example, number 1,000 from an edition of 2,500).

▲ The Flying Scotsman ceramic picture plate. 1988. Davenport Pottery Co. Ltd. 215mm diameter. (ex) £6 - £8

CHEESE LABELS

Your first impression here, could well be to dismiss cheese labels as being too obscure or of little value. Forget the first impression because this is a fascinating hobby.

The labels are incredibly easy to store, and they can be purchased inexpensively (although there are some exceptional cases of relatively valuable examples); and because they are usually colourful and varied, you can quickly build a most attractive collection.

You will quickly discover that there are thousands of variations and therefore you may wish to consider concentrating on themes.

You may consider collecting examples from as many countries as possible or maybe a theme such as "airlines." Miniature cheese packs were often made for specific airlines and carried the relevant logo. Look out for a BEA version from around 1950 among many other iconic variations.

Some of the best places to find old cheese labels are internet auction websites.

▲ France. (1950). 85 x 85mm. (vg) £3 - £4

▲ Denmark. (1960). 100mm diameter. (vg) £1 - £2

▲ Holland. (1960). 110mm diameter. (vg) £1 - £2

▲ England. (1950). 100mm diameter. (vg) £3 - £4

CHERISHED TEDDIES

Priscilla Hillman, a children's story illustrator, designed the first collection of Cherished Teddies in 1992. She had the idea while laid up in bed recovering from a back injury.

Since its launch, the collection has gone from strength to strength. There are now thousands of collectors worldwide, many of which are members of the Cherished Teddies Club, which was formed in 1994. As well as statues, the Cherished Teddies range also includes stuffed toys and decorative accessories such as picture frames, clocks, candles, and wall plaques.

When Cherished Teddies were first launched, the figurines were given a number preceded by a random letter, known as "Letter Marks." In 1993, the manufacturer, Enesco, started to add a number in front of the registration code to indicate the year of production (a 3 to represent 1993, a 4 to represent 1994, and so on). These later pieces are referred to as "3 Marks," "4 Marks," and so on. For limited edition pieces, the registration number is replaced with a unique number to identify where the model appeared in the production run.

▲ Jack and Jill. Cherished Teddy figurine. 1993. Original box. 100mm high. (ex) £5 - £7

A few examples of rare Teddies are Daisy (retired 1996), Chelsea (retired 1995), and Charity (retired 1996).

The best bargains can be found at car boot sales. There are no postage costs, and you also get the opportunity to examine the goods. Look for boxed examples in excellent condition.

◄ Christine. Cherished Teddy figurine. 1994. Original box. (ex) £3 - £5

New Teddies are added to the range each year, and in order to keep the number being produced manageable, older Teddies will be "retired" (and therefore no longer produced). This is a common practice in the collectables industry, and often results in "retired" pieces becoming much more valuable on the secondary market. However, it is important to do your homework and not to get too carried away when purchasing. Like with any collectables, some Teddies are much rarer and valuable than others.

The rarest items are those that had very limited editions, or those which were event exclusives that never went on general sale. Exclusives that were only available in certain countries will also be much more desirable in the countries where they were never available.

▲ Cub E. Bear. Cherished Teddy figurine. 1995. Original box. (ex) £4 - £6

CHURCHILLIANA

Publications or other items connected with Sir Winston Churchill. Signed items being of particular importance.

Sir Winston Leonard Spencer Churchill was born to Jennie Jerome and Randolph Churchill, in Blenheim, on 30 November 1874.

He was a British politician known chiefly for his leadership of Great Britain during World War II (he was Prime Minister from 1940 to 1945 and again from 1951 to 1955). He was also a prolific author, winning the Nobel Prize in Literature in 1953.

On 15 January 1965, he suffered a stroke. He died nine days later, aged 90, exactly 70 years after his father's death. Upon his death, the Queen granted him the honour of a state funeral, which saw one of the largest assemblies of statesmen in the world.

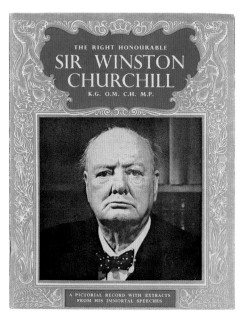

▲ Sir Winston Churchill Pitkin Publications. (1960). (vg) £2 - £3

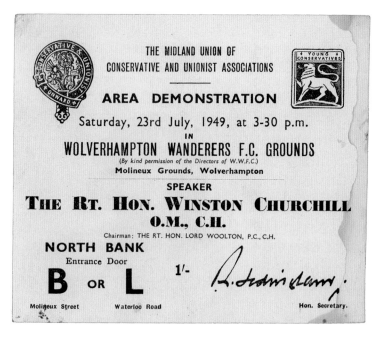

▲ Ticket for Churchill speaking at an event at Wolverhampton . 1949. Water stained. (f) £4 - £6

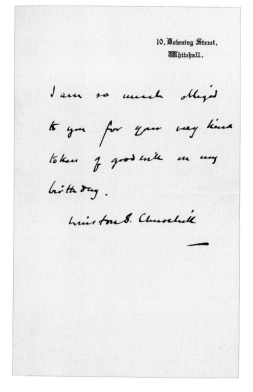

▲ Printed letter with facsimile signature. 1954. (vg) £4 - £6

CIGARETTE CARDS

▲ Notable MP's. Carreras. 1929. Full set of 50. (vg) £45 - £50

This is a huge collecting area and has been so for over 100 years.

Cards were issued in sets and inserted individually into cigarette packets.

The hobby of cigarette card collecting is known as Cartophily. A collector is known as a Cartophilist.

Cartophily also includes trade cards. These resemble cigarette cards but were issued with packets of tea, sweet cigarettes, comics, bubble gum etc... This book separates cigarette cards from trade cards.

▲ Association Footballers. Wills. 1935. Full set of 50. (vg) £30 - £34

The subject matter of cigarette cards is massive. Ranging from wild flowers to radio personalities and way beyond. It is often the case that the more interesting and obscure subjects are more sought after.

One of the big cigarette manufacturing names that collectors look out for is Taddy. Some single cards from rare sets, can command £30 or more each.

▲ Famous Minors. Godfrey Phillips. 1936. Full set of 50. (vg) £12 - £14

The collecting of old cigarette packets is closely linked to cartophily as, indeed, these were the packets that the cards were inserted in.

▲ Dandies. John Player. 1932. Full set of 50. (g-vg) £8 - £10

▲ Howlers. Churchman. 1937. Full set of 40. (vg) £10 - £12

▲ Counties & Their Industries. John Player. 1916. Full set of 25. (vg) £40 - £45

▲ Wild Flowers. Gallaher. 1939. Full set of 48. (vg) £12 - £14

▲ Cries of London. 2nd Series. John Player. 1916. Full set of 25. (vg) £10 - £12

▲ Children of All Nations. Ogden's. 1924. Full set of 50 push-out cards. (g) £20 - £25

CIGARETTE CARDS

◀ Radio Celebrities. Wills. 1934. Full set of 50. (g) £8 - £10

▲Wonders of the Ancient World. John Player. 1984. Full Set of 32. 73mm x 57mm. (vg) £4 - £6

▲Leading Lines. Kinnear's. 1900. Full Set of 1. (f-g) £15 - £18

▲Dogs. Gallaher. 1936. Full Set of 48. (g-vg) £8 - £11

▲Dogs 2nd Series. Gallaher. 1938. Full Set of 48. (vg) £6 - £8

▲Famous Film Scenes. Gallaher. 1935. Full Set of 48. (vg) £15 - £18

▲Historic Events. Wills. 1912. Full Set of 50. (g-vg) £27 - £30

▲Birds and Their Young. John Player. 1937. Full Set of 50. (vg) £3 - £6

▲Players Past & Present. John Player. 1916. Full Set of 25. (f) £6 - £9

▲Alpine Flowers. Wills. 1913. Full Set of 50. (g-vg) £17 - £20

▲Aviary and Cage Birds. John Player. 1933. Full Set of 50. (vg) £15 - £20

▲Flowers to Grow. R J Lea. 1913. Full Set of 50. (f) £80 - £95

▲Gilbert and Sullivan. John Player. 1925. Full Set of 50. (vg) £27 - £32

▲ Wonders of the World. John Player. 1916. Full Set of 25. (g) £6 - £9

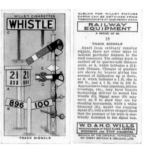

▲ Napoleon. John Player. 1916. Full Set of 25. (p-f) £9 - £12

▲Wild Animal Heads. John Player. 1931. Full set of 50. (f-g) £6 - £8

▲Roses 2nd Series. Wills. 1913. Full set of 50. (g-vg) £28 - £30

▲Railway Equipment. Wills. 1938. Full set of 50. (g) £10 - £12

CIGARETTE CARDS

▲ Garden Flowers 1st Series. Wills. Full Set of 40. 1938. 78mm x 62mm. (vg) £7 - £9

▲ Greetings of the World. Hignett Bros. & Co. Full Set of 25. 1907.(vg) £40 - £45

▲ Army, Corps and Divisional Signs 1914-1918. John Player. Full Set of 50. 1924. (g) £4 - £6

▲ Natural History. John Player. Full set of 50. 1924. (vg) £5 - £8

▲ Do You Know. Wills. Full Set of 50. 1922. (vg) £8 - £11

▲ Treasure Trove. Churchman. Full Set of 50. 1937. (vg) £5 - £7

▲ Flower Culture in Pots. Wills. Full Set of 50. 1925. (vg) £8 - £11

▲ Lucky Charms. Wills. Full Set of 50. 1923. (f-g) £3 - £5

▲ The Kings Coronation. Churchman. Full Set of 50. 1937. (vg) £4 - £6

▲ English Period Costumes. Wills. Full Set of 50. 1929. (g) £22 - £26

▲ Life In The Treetops. Wills. Full Set of 50. 1925. (vg) £8 - £10

▲ Household Hints. Wills. Full Set of 50. 1936. (g) £2 - £3

▲ Do You Know 2nd Series. Wills. Full Set of 50. 1924 (f-g) £3 - £5

▲ In Town To-Night. Churchman. Full Set of 50. 1938 (f) £2 - £4

▲ Do You Know 3rd Series. Wills. Full Set of 50. 1926. (vg) £6 - £8

▲ The Prince of Wales Empire Tour. Hignetts. Full Set of 25. 1924. (g-vg) £30 - £35

▲ ►Coastwise. Pattreioeux (Senior Service). Full Set of 48. 1939. (vg) £8 - £10

CIGARETTE CARDS

▲ Portraits Of Famous Stars. Gallaher. 1935. Full set of 48. (vg-ex) £40 - £45

▲ Association Footballers. Churchman. 1938. Full set of 50. (g) £24 - £26

▲ Regimental Uniforms. John Player. 1912. Full set of 50. (g-vg) £80 - £90

▲ Guerriers. Amalgamated Tobacco (Mills). 1961. Full set of 25. (ex) £10 - £15

▲ Cries Of London. John Player. 1913. Full set of 25. (g) £30 - £35

▲ Garden Flowers. Wills. 1933. Full set of 50. (vg) £20 - £25

▲ Famous Boys. Godfrey Phillips. 1924. Full set of 25. (vg) £50 - £55

▲ Cricketers 1930. John Player. 1930. Full set of 50. (vg) £60 - £65

▲ Flowering Trees & Shrubs. Wills. 1924. Full set of 50. (f-g) £6 - £8

▲ Old English Garden Flowers. Wills. 1910. Full set of 50. (vg-ex) £55 - £60

▲ Cinema Stars (1st Series). Wills. 1928. Full set of 25. (ex) £33 - £35

▲ Garden Flows (by Sudell). Wills. 1939. Full set of 50. (vg) £6 - £8

▲ Cinema Stars (2nd Series). Wills. 1928. Full set of 25. (vg) £24 - £26

▲ Egyptian Kings & Queens.... John Player. 1912. Full set of 25. (p) £20 - £25

▲ Cricketers 1928. Wills. 1928. Full set of 50. (g-vg) £65 - £75

CIGARETTE CARDS

▲ Leaders Of Men. Ogden's. 1924. Full set of 50. (g) £65 - £70

▲ Marvels Of Motion. Ogden's. 1928. Full set of 25. (g) £38 - £40

▲ Picturesque People Of The Empire. John Player. 1938. Full set of 25. (vg) £38 - £40

▲ Riders Of The World. John Player. 1905. Full set of 50. (f-g) £60 - £70

▲ Characters From Dickens. John Player. 1923. Full set of 50. (g-vg) £45 - £55

▲ Straight Line Caricatures. John Player. 1926. Full set of 50. (p-f) £3 - £5

▲ Ceremonial And Court Dress. John Player. 1911. Full set of 25. (g-vg) £20 - £30

▲ Wild Flowers. Wills. 1936. Full set of 50. (g) £3 - £5

▲ Coronation Series Ceremonial Dress. John Player. 1937. Full set of 50. (g) £2 - £3

▲ Radio Celebrities. Wills. 1934. Full set of 50. (vg) £20 - £25

▲ The Reign Of HM King George V. Wills. 1935. Full set of 50. (ex) £25 - £30

▲ Dogs. John Player. 1929. Full set of 50. (vg-ex) £35 - £45

▲ RAF Badges. John Player. 1937. Full set of 50. (vg-ex) £18 - £22

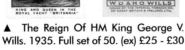 

▲ Wrestling & Ju-Jitsu. John Player. 1913. Full set of 25. (g) £35 - £40

▲ Characters From Dickens (2nd Series). John Player. 1912. Full set of 25. (g-vg) £30 - £40

CIGARETTE CARDS

▲ Trains Of The World. Gallaher. 1937. Full set of 48. (vg) £38 - £40

▲ Game Birds and Wild Fowl. John Player. 1927. Full set of 50. (g-vg) £55 - £60

▲ Modes Of Conveyance. Ogden's. 1927. Full set of 25. (g-vg) £40 - £45

▲ Curious Beaks. John Player. 1929. Full set of 50. (g) £24 - £26

▲ Arms of Foreign Cities. Wills. 1912. Full set of 50. (g) £14 - £16

▲ Aircraft of the Royal Air Force. John Player. 1938. Full set of 50. (g-vg) £35 - £40

▲ Gems of British Scenery. John Player. 1917. Full set of 25. (g) £10 - £12

▲ Aeroplanes (Civil). John Player. 1935. Full set of 50. (f) £35 - £40

▲ Colonial & Indian Army Badges. John Player. 1917. Full set of 25. (g-vg) £18 - £20

▲ Real Photographs (3rd series). Millhoff. 1932. Full set of 27. (vg) £4 - £6

▲ The Sea-Shore. Wills. 1938. Full set of 50. (vg) £6 - £8

▲ Merchant Ships of the World. Wills. 1924. Full set of 50. (f) £40 - £45

▲ Modern Railways. Ogden's. 1936. Full set of 50. (vg) £100 - £110

▲ Flags of the League of Nations. John Player. 1928. Full set of 50. (vg) £10 - £12

▲ From Plantation To Smoker. John Player. 1926. Full set of 25. (f) £1 - £2

▲ Famous Inventions. Wills. 1915. Full set of 50. (f-g) £28 - £30

▲ Naval Battles. Amalgamated Tobacco (Mills). 1959. Full set of 25. (ex) £5 - £7

▲ Drum Banners & Cap Badges. John Player. 1924. Full set of 50. (f-g) £22 - £24

▲ Life In The Royal Navy. Wills. 1939. Full set of 50. (vg-ex) £13 - £15

▲ Railway Engines. Wills. 1924. Full set of 50. (f-g) £40 - £45

▲ Real Photographs. Millhoff. 1931. Full set of 27. (vg-ex) £6 - £8

CIGARETTE CARDS

▲ Famous Beauties. John Player. 1937. Full set of 25. 80 x 62mm. (vg) £30 - £35

▲ Old Naval Prints. John Player. 1936. 80 x 62mm. (vg) £45 - £50

▲ Old Furniture. Wills (2nd series). 1924. Full set of 25. 80 x 62mm. (g) £55 - £60

▲ Celebrated Pictures. Wills. 1916. Full set of 25. 80 x 62mm. (vg-ex) £38 - £40

▲ Britain's Nocturnal Wildlife. John Player (Grandee). 1987. Full set of 30. 90 x 50mm. (vg) £3 - £4

▲ The Living Ocean. John Player (Grandee). 1985. Full set of 30. 90 x 50mm. (vg-ex) £4 - £5

▲ Winter Scenes. Pattreiouex (Senior Service). 1937. Full set of 48. 76 x 52mm. (vg) £8 - £10

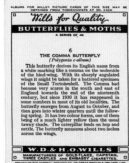

▲ Butterflies & Moths. Wills. 1938. Full set of 40. 80 x 62mm. (ex) £30 - £32

▲ Britain From The Air. Pattreiouex (Senior Service). 1939. Full set of 48. 76 x 52mm. (vg-ex) £10 - £12

CIGARETTE CARDS

▲ Dogs Scenic Backgrounds. John Player. 1925. Full set of 50. (g-vg) £28 - £30

▲ Garden Life. Wills. 1914. Full set of 50. (g-vg) £18 - £20

▲ Historie de l'Aviation (2nd series). Amalgamated Tobacco (Mills). 1962. Full set of 25. (ex) £13 - £15

▲ Ships Of The Royal Navy. Amalgamated Tobacco (Mills). 1961. Full set of 25. (ex) £6 - £8

▲ Overseas Dominions (Canada). Wills. 1914. Full set of 50. (vg) £20 - £22

▲ Britain's Defences. Carreras. 1938. Full set of 50. (g-vg) £22 - £24

▲ British Royal and Ancient Buildings. Westminster Tobacco. 1925. Full set of 48. (g-vg) £14 - £16

▲ Hints & Tips For Motorists. Lambert & Butler. 1929. Full set of 25. (g-vg) £65 - £70

▲ Ancient Chinese. Cavanders. 1926. Full set of 25. (f-g) £8 - £10

▲ Wild Birds. John Player. 1932. Full set of 50. (g) £8 - £10

▲ Kings Of Speed. Churchman. 1939. Full set of 50. (vg) £18 - £20

▲ Ships' Figureheads. John Player. 1912. Full set of 25. (g) £48 - £50

Unusual set

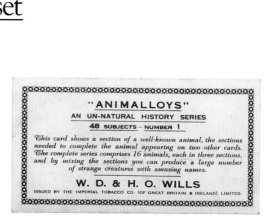

▲ Animalloys. Wills. 1934. Full set of 48. (vg) £10 - £12

CIGARETTE CARDS
(Odds)

Some sets of cards are so rare that collectors settle for incomplete sets but add to the set if they are lucky enough to find single 'odds' to fill the gaps. The reverse of very old cards are also of interest to collectors.

► Naval Skits. John Young & Sons. 1904. Single card from set of twelve. (f) £50 - £60

▲ Bewlay's War Series. (Portraits). Bewlay & Co. The King of the Belgians. 1915. Card no. 11 from 12. (f-g) £3 - £4

▲ The Great War Series. Gallaher. 1915. Distinguishing Marks On Projectiles. Card no. 1 from 100. (g-vg) £2 - £3

▲ Admirals & Generals The War Series 1. Taddy & Co. 1914. General L. Smith Dorrian. Card no.4 from 37. (vg) £7 - £9

▲ Riders of the World. John Player & Sons. 1905. Egyptian On Camel. Card no.42 of 50. (g-vg) £1 - £2

▲ Phil May Sketches. Churchman. 1912. Card no.24 of 50. (g-vg) £3 - £4

▲ Colonial Troops. W.R. Daniel. 1902. 1st Bengal Lancers. Single card from 30. (f) £20 - £30

▲ South African Football Team 1906-7. Taddy & Co. 1906. Carolin. Single card from 26. (vg) £10 - £15

 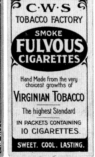

▲ Parrot Series. C.W.S. 1910. Green Leek. Card no. 11 from 25. (vg) £12 - £16

▲ Notabilities. Adkin & Sons. 1915. Joseph Chamberlain. Single card from 25. (vg) £2 - £3

▲ V.C.Heroes - Boer War. (61-80).Taddy & Co. 1902. Private J.H.Bisdee. Card no. 71 from a series of 20. (vg) £8 - £10

▲ Territorial Series (Motors Back). Godfrey Phillips. 1908. 6th Battalion The Royal Scots. Card no. 63. (g-vg) £8 - £10

▲ Colonial Troops. Roberts & Sons. 1902. An Algerian Officer. Single card from a series of 50. (g) £20 - £25

CIGARETTE CARDS - Albums
(185 x 125mm)

Newcomers to the business of buying and selling cigarette card albums can be excused for not understanding why collectors often disregard them as serious collectables.

It is true that cards permanently glued onto album pages are ruined forever. Perhaps also there's a little snobbery amongst the purist collectors. Whatever the reason may be, there's not the degree of interest you would expect. Consequently old albums in very good condition can be found at reasonable prices. The trouble is that it's getting increasingly difficult to find tip-top condition examples and that should tell you that this could be a collecting area with long-term investment potential.

Front Cover

Page 6

▲ Our King and Queen. 1937. Wills. Issued to commemorate the coronation of George VI. Album (g). Cards, full set of 50 (vg) £8 - £10

Front Cover

Page 6

▲ The Sea Shore. 1938. Wills. Album (vg). Cards, full set of 50 (vg). £14 - £16

Front Cover

Page 9

▲ An Album of National Flags and Arms. 1936. John Player. Album (g). Cards, full set of 50 (g) £8 - £10

Front Cover

Page 14

▲ An Album of Dogs. 1937. Wills. Album (g-vg). Cards, full set of 50 (vg) £6 - £10

Front Cover

Page 6

▲ An Album of Animals of the Countryside. 1939. John Player. Album (g). Cards, full set of 50 (vg) £6 - £8

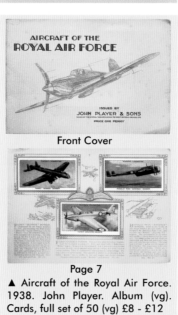

Front Cover

Page 7

▲ Aircraft of the Royal Air Force. 1938. John Player. Album (vg). Cards, full set of 50 (vg) £8 - £12

Front Cover

Page 7

▲ Cycling 1839-1939. 1939. John Player. Album (g). Cards, full set of 50 (g) £6 - £8

CIGARETTE COUPONS

▲ 7 - Player's. (vg) 50p - 60p

This must be one of the least expensive collecting areas, yet with a sprinkling of social history and colour, they take up very little space and can be displayed, imaginatively, in albums.

They were predominantly issued in the 60's and 70's.

There could be some minor investment potential, particularly where a collection contains plenty of variations.

▲ 5 - Embassy. (vg) 3p - 5p

▲ 2 - Player's No.6. (vg) 10p - 20p

▲ 10 - Cadets. (vg) 40p - 50p

▲ 2 - John Player. (vg) 20p - 30p

▲ 7 - Benson & Hedges. (vg) 10p - 20p

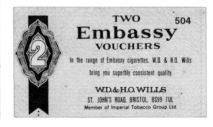

▲ 2 - Embassy. (vg) 6p - 8p

▲ 5 - Player's No.6. (vg) 3p - 5p

▲ 4 - Cadets. (vg) 50p - £1

▲ 10 - Kensitas. (vg) 20p - 30p

CIGARETTE COUPONS

▲ 7 - Carlton. (vg) 60p - 80p

▲ 2 - Park Drive. (g)
20p - 30p

▲ 1 - No.6 King Size. (vg)
5p - 7p

▲ 4 - Senior Service. (vg) 40p - 50p

▲ 1 - John Player. (g) 2p - 3p

▲ 2 - Player's No.10. (vg) 30p - 40p

▲ 2 - Cadets & Nelson. (f-g) 5p - 7p

▲ 5 - Sterling. (vg) 10p - 20p

▲ 1 - Guards. (vg) 10p - 20p

▲ 4 - Kensitas. (g-vg) 30p - 40p

▲ 1/2 - Crown Filter. (vg) 20p - 30p

▲ 4 - John Player. (vg) 20p - 30p

◄　5 - John Player. (vg)
10p - 20p

►　5 - Cadets & Nelson. (vg)
20p - 30p

CIGARETTE PACKETS

▲ Players. (1965). 5 Pack. Live with original silver foil and original slide. (g) £15 - £18

This is a wonderful collecting area and there's a plentiful supply, mainly thanks to internet auctions.

The rarer packets are commanding good money and they offer investment potential.

It's difficult to put precise dates of manufacture on cigarette packets, although the internet can offer much assistance.

▲ Clubs. (1925). Empty packet of 10. Original slide. (g-vg) £20 - £24

Collectors are always on the lookout for 'live' packets. That's a packet that still has the original cigarettes in them. These command high premiums but do be careful; some unscrupulous individuals put old cigarettes in packets to make them appear 'live'. The 'give-away' can often be that they carry no logo or indeed the wrong logo.

The next best thing to a live pack is a complete packet (the hull) with its original 'slide' (the card container that held the cigarettes and slid up and down the packet).

The best way to store and display them is to remove the slides and carefully fold the hulls, keeping the two parts flat and thereby it's less likely that the packets will get creased and damaged.

▲ Anchor. (1965). Empty packet of 10. Original slide. (g-vg) £4 - £6

Note that the first health warning to be printed on cigarette packets appeared in 1971 and stated: "Warning by H.M. Government. Smoking can damage your health." In 1976, it also became mandatory to display the cigarette tar content. Since then, the warnings have been regularly updated, and this can prove very helpful when dating cigarette packets.

▶ Sunripe. (1935). Empty packet of 10. Hull and original slide. (vg) £15 - £18

◀ Player's Navy Cut. (1955). Empty packet of 18, price marked 11½d. Original slide. (g) £12 - £14

▲ Tenner. (1935). Empty packet of 10. Original slide. (g-vg) £6 - £8

CIGARETTE PACKETS - Fronts

The lazy man's answer to collecting cigarette packets was to cut out the front of the packet. This made storage easier. However, as the hobby/business of collecting cigarette packets has grown, this practice has generally ceased.

Values depend on the condition and rarity. Some examples were not cut away from the pack neatly and this devalues the packet front. Some may actually be packet backs. Like most collectable subjects, you need to do plenty of homework before investing seriously.

Internet auctions are the best place to find cigarette packet fronts although the reduced size images may make the example look in better condition than it really is.

It is quite possible that some collectable traders at collectors fairs have been selling examples at inflated prices. In fairness to these dealers, there's no definitive value guide to work with. Generally, cigarette packet fronts can be acquired cheaply and have every chance of increasing in value over the years if bought correctly in the first place.

Hopefully the prices specified in this book will offer some guidance.

▲ Rothmans Medium Navy Cut. 50 pack front. (1950). (g-vg) £4 - £6

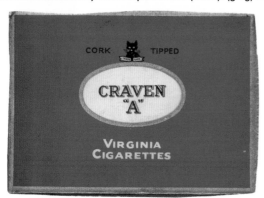

▲ Craven A. 50 pack front. (1950). (g) £2 - £4

Circa 1930-1950 (20's)

▲ Sweet Caporal. (f-g) £1 - £2

▲ Three Castles. (g-vg) £1 - £2

▲ Marino. (f-g) £1.50 - £2.50

▲ Murray's. (f-g) £2 - £3

▲ Red & White. (g) £1 - £2

▲ Kenilworth. (g-vg) £1 - £2

▲ Blue Book. (g) £2 - £3

▲ Abdulla. (g) £1 - £2

▲ Turf. (g) £1 - £2

▲ Bar One. (g-vg) £1.50 - £2.50

▲ Lorraine. (g-vg) £2 - £3

▲ Four Square. (f-g) £1 - £2

CIGARETTE PACKETS - Fronts

10's

▲ White Horse. Rothmans. (g-vg) £1.50 - £2.50

▲ Sports. Godfrey Phillips'. (g-vg) £1.50 - £2.50

▲ Robin. Ogden's. (g-vg) £1 - £2

▲ Ameer. Wills. (g) £1 - £2

▲ Grande Turque. Player's. (g) £1 - £2

▲ Anchor. Player's. (g-vg) £1 - £2

▲ The "Greys". Godfrey Phillips. (g) £1 - £2

▲ Seagirt. (f-g) £1 - £2

▲ Gold Flake. Mitchell's. (g-vg) £1.50 - £2.50

▲ 'Scotties'. (f-g) £1 - £2

▲ Walters. (g-vg) £1.50 - £2.50

▲ Scissors. Wills. (vg) £2 - £3

▲ Double Five. (g-vg) £2 - £3

▲ Double Ace (g-vg) £1.50 - £2.50

▲ Maryland. (g-vg) £1.50 - £2.50

▲ Kerry Blue. Carroll's. (g) £2 - £3

▲ Ardath. (vg) £1.50 - £2.50

▲ Sunripe. Hills. (g) £1.50 - £2.50

▲ White Eagle. Carreras. (g-vg) £2 - £3

▲ De Reszke. Millhoff. (g-vg) £1 - £2

20's

▲ Tenner. Churchman's. (g-vg) £2 - £3

▲ Top Score. Churchman's. (g) £1 - £2

▲ De Reszke. Millhoff. (g) £1 - £2

▲ Army Club. Cavenders. (g-vg) £1 - £2

▲ Golden Cross. Wills. (vg) £2 - £3

▲ Lucky Dream. (g-vg) £2 - £3

▲ Miss Blanche. Virginia. (f-g) £2 - £3

▲ Rhodian No.3. Lambert & Butler. (g) £1 - £2

▲ Gem. Richmond. (g) £1 - £2

▲ John Wood's. (g-vg) £1 - £2

▲ Spanish Shawl. (f-g) £3 - £4

▲ Sketch. Virginia. (vg) £2 - £3

▲ Gill Bros. (g) £1 - £2

▲ Ark Royal. (f) £1 - £2

CIGARETTE PACKETS - Fronts

10's

▲ Gold Leaf. Martins. (g-vg) £1 - £2   ▲ Sterling. (g) £1 - £2   ▲ Senior Service. (f-g) 40p - 60p   ▲ Everest. (g) £1 - £2

▲ Marlboro. (f) 20p - 30p   ▲ Strand. Wills (g) 30p - 50p   ▲ Jet. Ringer's (g-vg) £1.50 - £2.50   ▲ Star. Wills (f-g) £1 - £2

▲ Dunhill. (vg) 60p - 80p   ▲ Guards. Carreras. (vg) 60p - 80p   ▲ Metro Juniors. (f-g) 60p - 80p   ▲ Embassy. Wills. (g). 20p - 40p

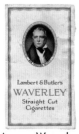

▲ Waverley. Lambert & Butler. (f) 50p - 70p   ▲ Embassy. Wills. (g-vg) £1 - £2   ▲ Three Threes. State Express. (g) £1 - £2   ▲ Envoy. (g-vg) 60p - 80p

▲ Matinee. (f) 30p - 40p   ▲ Mills. (f-g) 60p - 80p   ▲ Weights. John Player. (g) 60p - 80p   ▲ Mayfair. Benson & Hedges. (f) 10p - 20p

20's

▲ State Express. 555. (g-vg) £1 - £2   ▲ Dunhill. (g-vg) £1 - £2

▲ Wild Woodbine. Wills. (g) 70p - 90p   ▲ Vulcan. (g) £1.50 - £2.50

▲ Grosvenor. State Express. (vg) £1 - £2   ▲ Gold Flake. Wills. (vg) £1 - £2

▲ Gitanes. (vg) £1 - £2   ▲ Astor. (vg) £1 - £2

▲ du Maurier. (vg) £1 - £2   ▲ R.N. (g-vg) £1 - £2

▲ Airman. John Player. (g-vg) £1.50 - £2.50   ▲ Tradition. Ardath. (g-vg) £1 - £2

▲ Mills. No.1. (g) £1 - £2   ▲ Royalty. (vg) £1 - £2

CINEMA

There's plenty of memorabilia associated with the cinema. Some collecting areas are so big they deserve their own categories. These include film posters, lobby cards and autographs.

Cinema buildings have been featured on postcards and early examples are in demand.

▲ The Picture House at Halifax, original postcard circa 1905. Very good condition save for a crease top right. £20 - £24

Picturegoer

Published by Odhams, the first edition of Picturegoer magazine was dated January 1921 and some years later beginning in 1949 they published a series of annuals. As well as being sold via newsagents, Picturegoer was sold at cinemas but in the 1950's Odeon, Rank and ABC brought out their own publications. Picturegoer magazine ceased publication in April 1960.

Mary Pickford

One of the most important names in the history of cinema. As well as being an international film star, she was the co-founder of United Artists. She married the legendary Douglas Fairbanks. When the pair visited London, fans went crazy, causing riots in the streets. Mary died in 1979, aged 87.

▲ Mary Pickford bookmark. 1927. Advertisement for the film 'My Best Girl' at The Regent, Chatham. (g-vg) £12 - £14

▲ Picturegoer magazine. 29 May 1954. (g-vg) £3 - £4

▲ Picturegoer Film Annual. Odhams. 1949. Its particularly hard to find this first edition in such good condition. £12 - £14

▲ Mary Pickford and Douglas Fairbanks autographed photograph. With dedication to Diana Bancroft (of the famous theatrical family). £500 - £600

ABC Film Review

As the title of this magazine series suggests, this was a promotional tool for ABC cinemas. It was launched in 1950 at a cost of 3d. Two years later the popularity of the magazine had grown and the cover price doubled to 6d. It remained at this price for 16 years.

In 1972 the ABC prefix was dropped from the title and it became known as Film Review. The last edition was published in 2008.

▲ ABC Film Review magazine - November 1963. (g-vg) £3 - £5

▲ Ritz Cinema. Ticket. 1958. Leicester Square, London. Gigi - starring Leslie Caron. (vg) £2 - £3

CINEMA - Junior

The heyday of Saturday morning cinema for children was between 1935 and 1975.

Cinemas issued badges, membership cards, photographs, books, trade cards and other items that are now in much demand from enthusiastic collectors.

Many cinemas had their own songs. The classic being ABC "We are the boys and girls well known as, minors of the ABC....." This song can be heard on YouTube (ABC Minors Song).

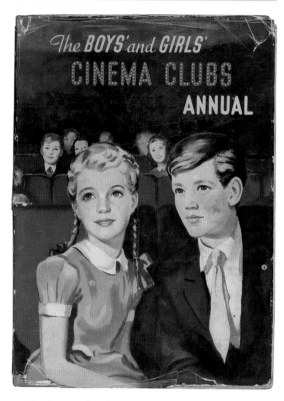

▲ The Boys' and Girls' Cinema Clubs Annual. 1949. (p-f) £3 - £4

This is simply a fantastic book with countless photographs of films and the stars who thrilled junior audiences just after World War II. The book also includes words to the songs that were sung by the audience in between the films. Kids paid sixpence to get in to the 'pictures' and were kept thoroughly entertained for several hours. ABC cinema juniors were known as ABC Minors, whilst Odeon offered the National Cinema Club, Granada Theatres offered Granadiers, and Gaumont offered Gaumont-British Junior Club.

Button badges

► Odeon. (1950). (f-g) £20 - £22

◄ Star Cinemas. (1960). (p-f) £3 - £5

► ABC Minors. (1965). (g-vg) £8 - £10

◄ ABC Minors Coronation Issue. 1953. (vg) £25 - £30

▲ ABC Cinemas trade cards. 1962. Full set of 10. (ex) £5 - £8

CINEMA - Lobby cards

Lobby Cards are small versions of film posters. Also known as 'Front of House Cards'. They generally measure 10inches x 8inches (250mm x 200mm) and were often produced in sets of 6 and sometimes 12.

Values depend on age, condition and subject matter. A 1920 original lobby card featuring Mary Pickford, could command £70 or more.

Lobby Cards are easy to store and if bought correctly, offer long term investment potential.

▲ Separate Beds. Starring James Garner. 1963. (vg) £10 - £14

▲ Up The Chastity Belt. Starring Frankie Howerd. 1971. (vg) £1 - £3

▲ The Silver Whip. Starring Dale Robertson. 1953. (f-g) £2 - £4

▲ Till Death Us Do Part. Starring Warren Mitchell. 1969. (vg) £2 - £3

▲ Station Six-Sahara. Starring Carroll Baker. 1962. (vg) £2 - £3

▲ Rich, Young And Deadly. Starring Mickey Rooney. 1960. (vg-ex) £2 - £4

▲ 30 Is A Dangerous Age, Cynthia. Starring Dudley Moore. 1968. (vg-ex) £2 - £3

▲ In Enemy Country. Starring Anthony Franciosa. 1968. (g) £1 - £2

▲ Our Miss Fred. Starring Danny La Rue. 1972. (vg-ex) £1 - £2

▲ The Likely Lads. Starring Rodney Bewes. 1976. (ex) £1 - £3

▲ Indian Paint. Starring Johnny Crawford. 1965. (g) £1 - £2

▲ Chubasco. Starring Richard Egan. 1967. (g) £1 - £2

▲ Bindle (One Of Them Days). Starring Alfie Bass. 1966. (vg-ex) £1 - £2

▲ This Other Eden. Starring Audrey Dalton. 1959. (vg) £1 - £2

▲ Jane Eyre. Starring George C Scott. 1970. (vg) £1 - £2

▲ Miss London Ltd. Starring Arthur Askey. 1943. (vg) £1 - £2

▲ The Syndicate. Starring William Sylvester. 1968. (g) £1 - £2

CINEMA

Marilyn Monroe

Norma Jeane Mortenson was born 1 June 1926, in Los Angeles. She was photographed by an Army photographer for Yank magazine while working in the Radioplane Munitions Factory during the war, and this led to a career as a model.

Eventually she came to the attention of Ben Lyon, an executive at 20 Century Fox, and was offered a six-month contract. Her name was changed to Marilyn Monroe and her first movie appearance was an uncredited role in The Shocking Miss Pilgrim in 1947.

By the mid-1950s she had become a huge star, having appeared in Gentlemen Prefer Blondes with Jane Russell, in 1953, How to Marry a Millionaire, also in 1953, and The Seven Year Itch, in 1955. She won a Golden Globe Award for her performance in Some Like it Hot, released in 1959.

Monroe passed away on 5 August 1962, aged 36, due to an overdose of barbiturates. Her death was classed as "probable suicide."

▲ Picturegoer magazine. 16 January 1954. (g) £4 - £6

John Wayne

John Wayne was born Marion Mitchell Morrison on 26 May 1907. He died of stomach cancer on 11 June 1979, aged 72.

Throughout his acting career, he was nominated for three Academy Awards, and he won one (the 1969 Best Actor Award for his performance in True Grit).

▲ John Wayne picturegoer card. (1945). (g-vg) £2 - £3

The Kinema

Picture Houses in the early days of the movies were known as Kinemas (from the word kinema – Greek for motion).

A 1929 copy of The Lounge is a wonderful piece of cinema history. Forthcoming attractions included Rose Marie with Joan Crawford.

This was the beginning of the "talkies" and the publication's editorial included a discussion on how the "talkies" were rendering the cinema orchestras redundant. It says, "There is one thing about the Talkies – they can never be unspeakably bad."

CINEMA - LP records

Recorded works of the soundtracks of movies on vinyl (LP Records) offer a triple collecting option. They will interest collectors of LP records but are unlikely (generally) to be of much value. Collectors with an interest in specific movies or film stars are another. The third is the framing option for the LP cover. Many of the covers are colourful, interesting and will look great in a picture frame.

▲ The Young Ones - Cliff Richard with The Shadows. 1962. Columbia, 33SX 1384. Vinyl (g), sleeve (g) £4 - £6

▲ GI Blues - Elvis Presley. 1960. RCA, RD 27192. Vinyl (f), sleeve (p) £3 - £5

▲ Chitty Chitty Bang Bang - Original cast soundtrack. 1968. United Artists, SULP 1200. Vinyl (f-g), sleeve (g) £2 - £4

▲ Grab Me A Gondola. 1956. HMV, CLP 1103. Vinyl (f-g), sleeve (f) £2 - £4

▲ Casino Royale. 1966. RCA, RD 7874. Vinyl (g-vg), sleeve (f) £3 - £4

▲ A Hard Day's Night - The Beatles. 1964. Parlophone, PMC 1230. Vinyl (f), sleeve (g) £8 - £10

▲ Wonderful Life - Cliff Richard with The Shadows. 1964. Columbia, 33SX 1628. Vinyl (g), sleeve (vg) £8 - £10

▲ Midnight Cowboy. 1969. United Artists, UAS 5198. Vinyl (f), sleeve (g-vg) £3 - £5

▲ Air America. 1990.MCA, MCG 6112. Vinyl (g-vg), sleeve (g-vg) £3 - £5

▲ Help - The Beatles. 1965. Parlophone, PMC 1255. Vinyl (f), sleeve (g) £8 - £10

▲ Love Story. 1970. Paramount, SPFL 267. Vinyl (g), sleeve (f-g) £2 - £3

▲ Beat Girl. 1960. Columbia, 33SX 1225. Vinyl (f), sleeve (f) £8 - £12

▲ The Woman In Red. 1984. Motown, ZL72285. Vinyl (g), sleeve (g) £2 - £4

▲ The Glenn Miller Story. 1961. Ace Of Hearts, AH 12. Vinyl (f), sleeve (vg) £2 - £4

▲ Superman The Movie. 1978. Warner Bros, K 66084. Vinyl 1 (g), vinyl 2 (g), sleeve (g) £2 - £4

▲ Deep In My Heart. 1955. MGM, MGM-C-755. Vinyl (g), sleeve (f) £2 - £4

▲ Expresso Bongo - Cliff Richard. 1980 reissue. EMI, K052Z-07329. Vinyl (g), sleeve (g-vg) £2 - £3

▲ International Velvet. 1978. MGM, 2315400. Vinyl (g), sleeve (vg) £3 - £5

CINEMA

Tyrone Power

Tyrone Edmund Power was born 5 May 1914, in Cincinnati, Ohio. He moved to Hollywood in 1936 in search of movie work following a series of roles in theatre productions, and he was signed to 20th Century Fox. He attracted some attention in minor roles in Girls' Dormitory and Ladies in Love, but it looked like his career was going to falter until he fought for a star-making role in Lloyd's of London. Even though he did not receive top-billing for his role in the movie, he gained great critical acclaim and his success in Hollywood was assured.

Throughout his career, Power was a huge box-office draw, and he appeared in many successful movies, such as Blood and Sand, The Rains Came, Rose of Washington Square, and Jesse James. He was an exceptional swordsman, and is particularly well remembered for his appearances in swashbucklers such as The Mark of Zorro and The Black Swan.

Sadly, on 15 November 1958, Powers died of a heart attack that he suffered during a strenuous duelling scene he was filming for the movie Solomon and Sheba.

▲ Tyrone Power Picturegoer photogragh. (vg) £2 - £3

James Mason

James Neville Mason was born 15 May 1909, in Huddersfield.

From the mid-30s until his death he starred in some hugely successful movies, including Troubled Waters (1936), Fire Over England (1937), Return of the Scarlett Pimpernel (1937), The Patient Vanishes (1941), The Seventh Veil (1945), Julius Caesar (1953), 20,000 Leagues Under the Sea (1954), North by Northwest (1959), Journey to the Centre of the Earth (1959), Lolita (1962), and Genghis Khan (1965).

Mason was also considered for the role of James Bond in Dr No, a part that was eventually played by Sean Connery.

Mason had a heart attack and passed away 27 July 1984, aged 75. He is buried in Switzerland close to his good friend Charlie Chaplin.

▲ James Mason signed publicity photograph. Clear, black ink. (g) £20 - £24

CINEMA

▲ Palace Cinema, Devizes card poster. 1982. 395 x 255mm. (vg) £6 - £8

CIRCUS

The colour, the glamour, the nostalgia, all contribute to making this collectable subject so appealing to collectors.

There have been plenty of circus companies trading over the years and therefore a wide variety of collectables to seek out.

▶ Billy Russell's Circus. Souvenir programme. 1957. Hard to find. (g) £12 - £14

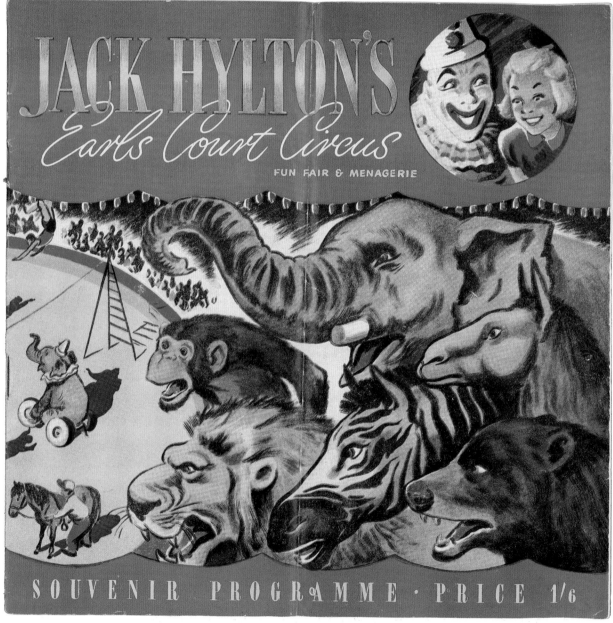

▲ Jack Hylton's Earls Court Circus. Souvenir Programme (folded). 1952. Hard to find. (g) £14 - £16

CIRCUS - Billy Smart's

▲ Billy Smart's Circus programme. 1958. With Billy Smart on the front cover. 245 x 185mm. (g-vg) £8 - £10

▲ Billy Smart Junior publicity photograph. As Wyatt Earp. (g-vg) £6 - £8

Billy Smart began his world famous circus in 1946. The show went on until the huge cost of travelling a six thousand seater Big Top, fifty horses, fifteen elephants, lions and tigers plus a company of almost 200 people, proved too much and the era came to an end in November 1971.

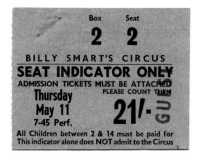

▲ Billy Smart's Circus ticket. 1967.   (g-vg) £8 - £10

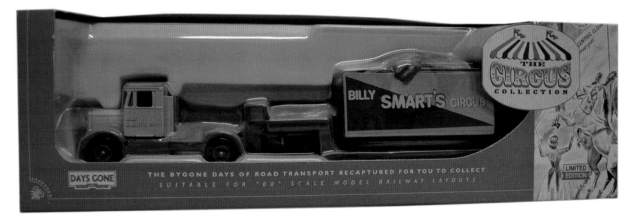

▲ Days Gone Billy Smart's Circus tractor with low loader. 2001. Mint in pack. £6 - £8

CIRCUS - Bertram Mills

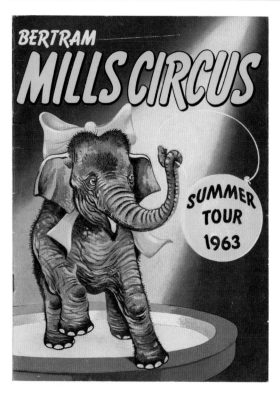

Bertram Wagstaff Mills (1873 - 1938) was born in London, the son of an undertaker (who had the distinction of being a pioneer of embalming).

Bertram's interest in performing with animals began when he rode horses as a child.

The first Bertram Mills circus was held at Olympia, London in 1920.

After Bertram's death, the family kept the name for the circus and it became one of the most famous in the world.

◀ Bertram Mills circus programme. 1963. (vg) £6 - £8

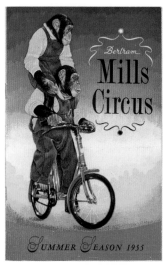

◀   Bertram Mills circus programme. 1955. (g) £6 - £8

▶   Bertram Mills circus programme. Olympia. 1950. (p-f) £3 - £4

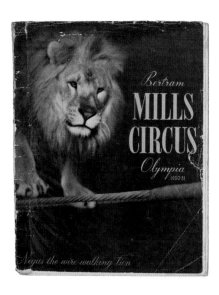

Coco the Clown (Nicolai Poliakoff 1900 - 1974) was brought to this country by Bertram Mills in 1929. He became one of the best known and most loved clowns of all time.

◀ Coco The Clown autograph. With an ABC Cinemas card 95 x 65mm in fair condition, circa 1955. Clear, blue ink. No dedication. £35 - £40

▶ Bertram Mills button badge. (1960). (vg) £10 - £12

CIRCUS - Chipperfield's

Chipperfield's Circus was the name of a British family circus that dated back to 1684, when James Chipperfield first introduced performing animals to England. However, despite having several generations of animal trainers and circus performers, it was not until the 1930s that the Chipperfield family became well established in the traditional circus business.

By the end of World War II, the circus had become one of the biggest touring circuses in Europe, and by the end of 1953, Chipperfield's Circus was bigger than its closest rivals, Bertram Mills and Billy Smart. Chipperfield's had a big top (that could sit 6,000 people), 200 horses, and 16 elephants, plus a huge menagerie with more than 200 other animals.

The circus finally ceased touring in the late 1980s, but the name was briefly revived for a touring circus in the late '90s.

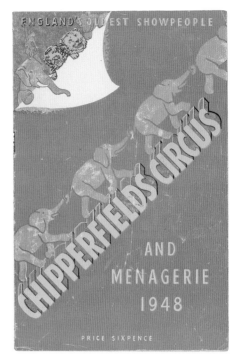

▲ Chipperfields programme. 1948. (f) £5 - £6

◄ Chipperfields programme. (1955). (g-vg) £6 - £8

► Chipperfields programme. (1950). (f) £3 - £4

Jimmy Chipperfield started out as an acrobat and clown, but eventually he left the circus and began providing animals for film work. In the 1960s he pioneered the first drive-through safari parks outside of Africa at Longleat and Woburn Abbey.

▲ Chipperfields horse transporter. Corgi model no 1130. (1965). (g) £15 - £18

COAT HANGERS

Most people in Britain will have amassed a collection of coat hangers, but they are usually just seen as a necessity of modern life, rather than a "collectable". However, collectors of coat hangers are now beginning to become slightly more common, and values seem to be increasing. As well as being a very interesting (and still slightly unusual) area to specialise in, they are obviously very easy to store.

Coat hangers were first used in the 1870s, reported to have been inspired by a coat hook invented by O.A. North of Connecticut in 1869. Originally hangers had a central bar attached to them, but they quickly became more 'shoulder-shaped' (they were occasionally known as "clothes shoulders").

In terms of storage, coat hangers really are fantastic and they follow the principle of collecting items that are easy to store. Today, most people use standard plastic hangers to hang up their clothes. Collectors of coat hangers simply replace these with much more interesting vintage wooden hangers.

Old wooden hangers will often have an interesting advert across the top, meaning they will also appeal to collectors of advertising items.

The advert is very important to the value of the hanger. A special advert (maybe a famous company or event) will mean the hanger can be worth relatively high sums.

Older wooden hangers tend to be very long, and were predominantly designed for suit jackets (with a bar sometimes added to hold trousers). The ever-changing world of fashion has led to the introduction of a number of new hangers in a wide variety of shapes and sizes. You may not think it at first, but a collection of hangers really can be quite varied!

It helps prove the theory that you don't need to spend a lot of money or need a lot of space to start a collection!

▲ Butlin's. (1970). (vg) £5 - £6

▲ London Opera Centre. (1935). (g-vg) £4 - £5

▲ Kilgour French & Stanbury. (1950). (vg) £4 - £5

▲ T.E.Box, Outfitter, Penarth. (1930). (g-vg) £3 - £5

COCOCUBS

▲ Gussie Robin. 1934.
(g-vg) £16 - £18

Cococubs first appeared as promotional toys inside tins of Cadbury's Bournville Cocoa in 1934. They were small hollow cast lead figures, produced by Britains (famous manufacturer of toy soldiers).

In total, between 1934 and 1936, 32 Cococubs were produced in a number of different colourways. Most of the figures represent anthropomorphic animals in clothes, similar to the kind seen in the works of Beatrix Potter. This comparison is unsurprising, as all of the characters were invented by celebrated artist Ernest Aris, who was famous for his illustrations of children's books.

▲ Mr Pie Porker. 1934.
(g-vg) £16 - £18

At a time when the majority of people did not have a huge amount of money to spend on toys, the Cococubs were a huge incentive to buy Cadbury's products. Indeed, the campaign was so successful that, for a short period, demand outstripped supply and the tins with the free toys were unavailable for several months while Cadbury restocked.

In 1936, Cadbury also started to distribute a free monthly magazine called Cococub news, and they created a collectors club with an enamel badge. They also issued a Leader's Bar to add to the badge to anyone who managed to "recruit" five new club members. During this time, Ernest Aris produced games and a range of cut-out houses: These toys could be acquired by collecting coupons.

▲ Granny Owl. 1934.
(g-vg) £16 - £18

The whole phenomenon came to an end in 1939, when the outbreak of war meant production of the toys ceased, and the club was closed.

Although there were only 32 Cococubs, collecting a full set is not easy. Certain figures were produced in different colourways (for example, Nutty Squirrel is available with at least three different scarves) and certain figures were only produced for a limited amount of time. One of the rarest figures is the little boy Jonathan eating a bar of chocolate, which can easily sell in excess of £200 at auction.

It is worth noting that while most of the Cococubs are hollow cast, there are examples of solid lead figures as well. These solid figures were produced by an unknown company when the promotion was at its peak and Britains were unable to keep up with demand. Some people mistake these solid figures for forgeries.

▲ Cococubs enamel badge. (1935). 25mm diam. (vg) £18 - £20

▲ The Cococub News. No.9, Nov 1936. (f) £8 - £12

COMEDIANS

This subject matter is quite absorbing. Many comedians, past and present, led very different lives to their stage persona. The great and brilliant Tommy Cooper, for example, portrayed a carefree existence with his stage act but in the real world, suffered from depression and turned to alcohol for comfort.

Frankie Howerd
1917-1992

Frankie began his career during his World War II service. When the war ended he joined a touring company performing a show called 'For the Fun of it'. He was quickly signed up by BBC Radio for the programme 'Variety Bandbox'. He played his first movie role in 1954, playing opposite Petula Clark, in The Runaway Bus.

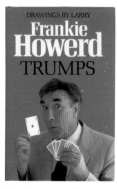

In the sixties and seventies, Frankie was constantly on television. He was best known for his role in the comedy 'Up Pompeii'. He had become a household name.

During a trip to the River Amazon in December 1991, Frankie contracted a virus and he died of heart failure a few months later. He is buried at St.Gregory's Church, Weare, Somerset.

▲ Frankie Howerd. Trumps. Hardback book. First edition. 1982. (vg) £4 - £6

Les Dawson
1931-1993

His big break was on the TV show Opportunity Knocks in 1967. His act revolved around playing the piano and interspersing it with deadpan humour.

In 1971 and in 1992 he was the subject of the TV show 'This Is Your Life'. Les died of a heart attack in June 1993.

◄ When You're Smiling. The Illustrated biography of Les Dawson. First edition, 1999. Hard back book. (vg) £3 - £5

► Les Dawson. Autographed publicity photograph. Clear, black ink, 177 x 126mm. Dedicated. (vg) £20 - £25

◄ Les Dawson PHQ card. 1998. (ex) £1 - £2

Jethro
1948-

Real name Geoffrey Rowe, he was born in St.Buryan, Cornwall. In the late sixties he adopted the stage name 'Jethro' and began his comedy career by touring Cornish pubs.

He got a break when signed up by Westward Television for the programme 'Treasure Hunt'. This lead to national television appearances on the Des O'Connor Show. Other TV credits include The Generation Game.

In December 2001, he appeared in front of Her Majesty The Queen, in The Royal Variety Show.

▲ Jethro. Autographed publicity photograph. Slightly faded, blue ink, 148 x102mm. No dedication. £3 - £4

Ken Goodwin
1933-2012

Before his starring role on the TV show, 'The Comedians', Ken played the Club circuit with his stand-up routine.

He was a great fan of George Formby and took up the ukulele, becoming a proficient player and then included it in his act.

His catchphrase was "settle down now".

He appeared on the Royal Variety Show in 1971.

▲ Ken Goodwin. Autographed publicity photograph. Clear, black ink, 148 x 100mm. Dedicated. £10 - £12

COMEDIANS

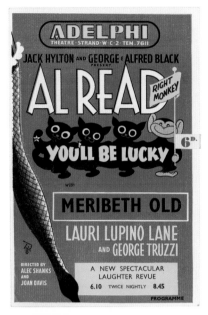

Al Read

Legendary comedian, Al Read (his real name) made his first BBC Radio broadcast in 1950. It became one of the most popular radio shows in the 1950's.

Al had two catchphrases that just about everybody knew, "You'll Be Lucky" and "Right Monkey". He ventured into television in the 1960's but it was as a radio comedian that he will be best remembered.

In 1954, he was one of the stars of the Royal Variety Show at the London Palladium.

Al Read died in 1987, aged 78.

◀ Al Read theatre programme. Adelphi London. 1954. (vg) £5 - £8

◀ Al Read publicity photograph. (vg) £4 - £6

▶ Al Read autograph. Clear, blue ink, 135 x 95mm. Dedicated. £30 - £35

Benny Hill

Alfred Hawthorne Hill, known to comedy-lovers around the world as Benny Hill, was born 21 January 1924, in Southampton. After gaining work as an assistant stage manager, he was inspired to become a comedian, and he changed his first name in homage to his idol, Jack Benny.

Hill moved from stage to radio and then made his first television appearance in 1949 on a show called Hi There; however, it was not until he starred in the Benny Hill Show in 1955 that he became a household name. The show ran (mostly) on the BBC, until moving to Thames Television in 1969, where it remained until cancellation in 1989. Hill also had a radio show from 1964 until 1966 called Benny Hill Time, and a short-lived sitcom anthology called Benny Hill.

Hill was in demand for movie work, with one of his most famous roles being that of the Toymaker in 1968's Chitty Chitty Bang Bang, and he recorded several hit songs, including Harvest of Love and the 1971 UK Christmas number one Ernie (The Fastest Milkman in the West).

Benny Hill's health began to decline in the mid-80s. He passed away on 20 April 1992, aged 68. The official cause of death was coronary thrombosis.

▲ Benny Hill autograph on publicity photograph. With a handwritten message on the reverse. Clear, black ink 150 x 100mm. Dedicated. £30 - £35

COMICS

When you collect comics, you are collecting a piece of social history. Many of us grew up on comics. They fired imagination and helped our reading skills. They were one of the top entertainments for children, particularly in a time before television.

They date back over 100 years and there are hundreds of titles to collect. The rarer the title, the higher the value and, of course, some first editions sell for thousands of pounds. For example, in February 2010 a copy of Action Comics issue one (the first comic to feature Superman) was sold in America for $1 million.

There's plenty of information on the internet to help you learn all about the history of a particular title and this adds so much more to the collecting hobby.

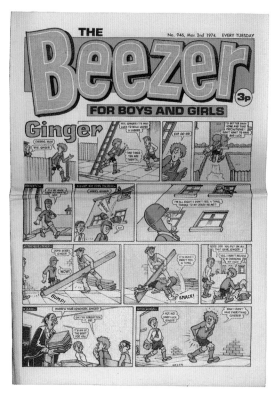

▲ Beezer. 2 March 1974. (g) £1 - £2

▲ The Modern Boy. 19 June 1937. (g) £3 - £4

▲ The Beano. 30 August 1958. (f) £2 - £3

▲ Sports Budget. 22 March 1930. (f) £2 - £4

▲ Sergeant O'Brien. May 1952. (vg) £8 - £10

▲ Wonder. 4 February 1950. (g) £2 - £3

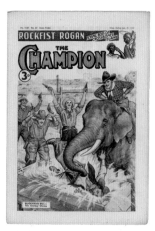

▲ The Champion. 21 July 1951. (g-vg) £2 - £4

COMICS

The Dandy

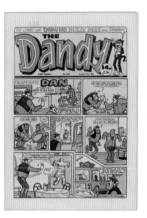

▲ 9 Mar 1963. (g) £2 - £4   ▲ 24 Mar 1973. (g-vg) £1 - £2   ▲ 17 Aug 1985. (g-vg) £1 - £2   ▲ 3 Jun 1995. (g-vg) 40p - 60p

Jack And Jill

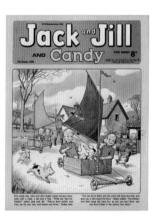

▲ 16 Sep 1967. (g) £1 - £1.50   ▲ 20 Jul 1968. (vg) £2 - £3   ▲ 10 May 1960. (g) £1 - £1.50   ▲ 7 Mar 1970. (vg) 60p - 80p

The Funday Times

▲ 10 Dec 1989. (g-vg) 30p - 40p   ▲ 17 Sep 1989. (g) 20p - 30p   ▲ 18 Nov 1990. (g-vg) 30p - 40p   ▲ 16 Dec 1990. (g-vg) 30p - 40p

COMICS

The Hotspur

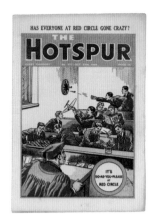

▲ 29 Oct 1949. (g-vg) £3 - £4   ▲ 8 Jul 1961. (f-g) £1 - £2   ▲ 16 Mar 1968. (g) £1 - £2   ▲ 5 Feb 1977. (g) £1 - £2

The Schoolgirl's Own

▲ 19 May 1923. (f) £1 - £2   ▲ 24 Nov 1923. (f) £1 - £2   ▲ 27 Aug 1932. (f-g) £1 - £2   ▲ 4 Aug 1934. (f-g) £1 - £2

Adventure

▲ 15 Dec 1951. (g-vg) £2 - £3   ▲ 15 Aug 1953. (g-vg) £2 - £3   ▲ 22 Aug 1953. (g) £1.50 - £2.50   ▲ 23 Jan 1954. (f-g) £1 - £2

COMICS

Robin

▲ 5 May 1956. (f-g) 50p - 80p   ▲ 11 Aug 1956. (vg) £1.50 - £2.50   ▲ 25 Aug 1956. (g) 70p - £1   ▲ 6 Oct 1956. (g-vg) £1 - £2

The Gem

▲ 14 Jan 1928. (f) £2 - £3   ▲ 24 Jun 1939. (g) £1 - £2   ▲ 5 Aug 1939. (f-g) 70p - £1   ▲ 30 Sep 1939. (f) 50p - 80p

Knockout

▲ 10 Aug 1946. (f) £2 - £3   ▲ 15 Jun 1957. (f) £1 - £2   ▲ 8 Jan 1972. (g) 70p - 90p   ▲ 15 Apr 1972. (g-vg) 90p - £1.20

COMICS

Judy

▲ 9 Dec 1961. (f). 50p - £1

Bonnie

▲ 8 Feb 1975. (g). 60p - 80p

Cracker

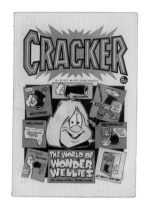

▲ 4 Oct 1975. (g). £1 - £2

Debbie

▲ 28 Aug 1976. (g). £1 - £2

Playhour

▲ 27 Mar 1976. (g-vg) £1 - £2

Donald & Mickey

▲ 23 Mar 1974. (p) 10p - 20p

Champ

▲ 19 Oct 1985. (g) 50p - £1

Cheeky

▲ 8 Jul 1978. (f-g) 30p - 40p

Victor

▲ 8 Sep 1984. (f) 40p - 60p

Toby

▲ 24 Apr 1976. (g-vg) £1 - £2

Tammy

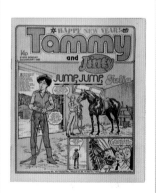

▲ 2 Jan 1982. (g-vg) £1 - £2

Roy Of The Rovers

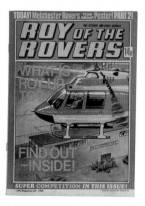

▲ 18 Oct 1980. (g). 50p - £1

COMICS - TV Tornado

This comic was published by City Magazines between 1967 and 1968.

The no.1 edition was dated 14 January 1967 and contained a free gift (Batchute). If you find a very good+ copy complete with the free gift in very good condition+ expect to pay £200 or more.

TV Tornado is quite sought after by collectors (the iconic images of TV characters helps enormously) and therefore, well worth looking out for at car boot sales and collectors fairs.

▲ No.26. 8 Jul 1967. (g) £6 - £8

▲ No.36. 16 Sep 1967. (g-vg) £8 - £10

▲ No.38. 30 Sep 1967. (g-vg) £8 - £10

▲ No.39. 7 Oct 1967. (f) £4 - £6

▲ No.41. 21 Oct 1967. (f-g) £6 - £8

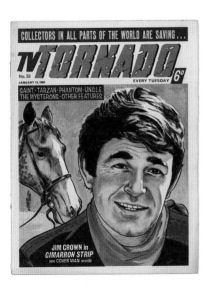

▲ No.53. 13 Jan 1968. (g-vg) £8 - £10

▲ No.75. 15 Jun 1968. (g) £6 - £8

▲ No.82. 3 Aug 1968. (g) £6 - £8

COMICS - No.1 editions

▲ Buddy. No.1. 14 Feb 1981. Without free gift. (vg) £8 - £10

CONCERT TICKETS

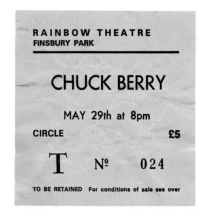

RAINBOW THEATRE
FINSBURY PARK

CHUCK BERRY

MAY 29th at 8pm

CIRCLE £5

T Nº 024

TO BE RETAINED For conditions of sale see over

▲ Chuck Berry. 29 May 1976. (g) £2 - £4

This is a collecting area with investment potential. The general rule is to look for tickets over 25 years old and then 'the bigger the artiste, the more valuable the ticket', however, there are exceptions. Find a ticket for the sixties pop group The Undertakers, for example and you could be looking at around £50. The condition of concert tickets is important but not crucial.

WEMBLEY ARENA

PHILIPS COMPACT DISC
BY ARRANGEMENT WITH OUTLAW PRESENT

DIRE STRAITS
LIVE IN '85

Thursday, 11th July, 1985
at 8.00 p.m.
There will be no interval

UPPER TIER SOUTH

£10.75

TO BE RETAINED   See conditions on back

JULY
11
1985
ENTER AT
SOUTH DOOR
ENTRANCE
62
ROW
A
SEAT
121★

▲ Dire Straits. 11 Jul 1985. (f) £4 - £6

ODEON THEATRE, Birmingham

M.C.P. presents—
A Flock of Seagulls
PLUS SPECIAL GUESTS
Tuesday, 19th April 1983
Evening 7.30
FRONT STALLS
£3.50
G   10
No Ticket Exchanged nor Money Refunded
This portion to be retained   (P.T.O.)

▲ A Flock Of Seagulls. 19 Apr 1983. (g-vg) £1 - £3

EARLS COURT, LONDON
(Opposite Warwick Road Exit, Earls Court Tube Station)

Harvey Goldsmith and Kennedy Street
proudly present

ROD
STEWART
WORLD TOUR 1983
PLUS SUPPORT
Saturday 25th June, at 8 p.m.
Doors open 6.30 p.m.

No cameras, tape recorders or
bottles allowed in the
Auditorium
WARNING: Official souvenirs are
on sale within the Auditorium
only
For conditions see over

STALLS
£10.00
inc. VAT

BLOCK
5
ROW
A
SEAT
89
TO BE RETAINED

▲ Rod Stewart. 25 Jun 1983. (g-vg) £5 - £7

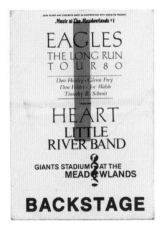

JOHN SCHER AND CONCERTS WEST IN COOPERATION WITH WNEW-FM PRESENT
Music at The Meadowlands #1

EAGLES
THE LONG RUN
T O U R 8 0

Don Henley • Glenn Frey
Don Felder • Joe Walsh
Timothy B. Schmit

HEART
LITTLE
RIVER BAND

GIANTS STADIUM AT THE
MEADOWLANDS

BACKSTAGE

▲ Eagles. Backstage pass. 1980. The Long Run Tour. (g) £10 - £12

The GATEHOUSE

STAFFORD

MON., 17th SEPTEMBER, '84
at 7.30 p.m.

MLA & Stafford Borough Council
present

THE CULT
PLUS SUPPORT

TICKETS UNRESERVED
£3.00 each (IN ADVANCE)
£3.50 each (ON THE DOOR)
(Standing only)

Nº   **174**

NO TICKET CAN BE EXCHANGED OR
MONEY REFUNDED ONCE PURCHASED.

Cameras & Recording
Equipment will not be
admitted to the Hall.

The Management
reserve the right to
refuse admission

▲ The Cult. 17 Sep 1984. (g) £1 - £3

PLANET PROMOTIONS PRESENT

Icicle Works

+ SUPPORT
SUNDAY 18th MARCH 1984
at the NEW OCEAN CLUB
Rover Way, Cardiff

8.00 p.m. – 12.00 p.m.

£3.00 Advance   £3.50 on Door

No. 101

Transport available to show from
7.30 p.m. outside Cardiff mainline
station entrance. Return trip also
available.

▲ Icicle Works. 18 Mar 1984. (g-vg) £1 - £3

M.A.M. in association with TRIGRAM
presents

STEVE HARLEY and
COCKNEY REBEL
in concert

THE APOLLO
Renfield Street, Glasgow

TUESDAY, 10th FEBRUARY, 1975
from 8 p.m. — Doors open 7.30 p.m.

STALLS

R   Nº   24

TICKET £2.50 inc. VAT
TO BE RETAINED
This Ticket is not transferable

▲ Steve Harley and Cockney Rebel. 10 Feb 1975. (f) £2 - £4

REGULAR MUSIC
presents

BBM

featuring GINGER BAKER, JACK BRUCE
and GARY MOORE
at BARROWLANDS, GLASGOW
on MONDAY, 23rd MAY, 1994
Doors open 7.30 p.m.

Ticket £12.00
plus booking fee

A   Nº   454

Management reserves the right of admission.
Over 18's only. I.D. may be required.
This ticket cannot be exchanged or refunded.

▲ BBM. 23 May 1994. (f-g) £10 - £15

BARRY CLAYMAN CONCERTS and KENNEDY STREET
Proudly Presents

MICHAEL
JACKSON
ROUNDHAY PARK
LEEDS
SUNDAY AUG 16th 1992
(SUBJECT TO LICENCE)
TICKETS **£21.50**
(SUBJECT TO BOOKING FEE)
GATES OPEN 4.30 PM

Issued subject to conditions on reverse
No Alcohol, Bottles or Cans Permitted

PEPSI   epic

024190

TO BE RETAINED
USE ENTRANCE GATES 1-3

▲ Michael Jackson. 16 Aug 1992. (vg) £12 - £14

MADONNA
THE
GIRLIE
SHOW

doors open at 4.30pm

Sunday 26th September

Enter by TURNSTILE   C

No   Price
010030   22.50

▲ Madonna. 26 Sep 1993. (g) £5 - £7

CONFECTIONERY

Just about every one of us has childhood memories of visiting the local sweet shop and buying our favourite confectionery.

Some of the 1960's favourites included, Black Jacks, Fruit Salad, sweet cigarettes, Jelly Babies, Sherbet Fountains, Jamboree Bags and Spangles.

▶ New Berry Fruits. Meltis Ltd. Empty box. (1955). 125 x 90mm. (g-vg) £3 - £4

▲   CWS Silvertown Sweets. Original advertising postcard. Postmarked Bodmin 1917. (g-vg) £12 - £14

Button badges

▲ Mars. (1970). (f) £1 - £2

▲ Sharps Toffee. (1935). (f) £6 - £8

▲ Rolo. (1990). No pin. (g-vg) £2 - £3

▲ Toffo. (1985). (vg) £3 - £4

▲ Cadbury's Chocolate Break. (1980). (f-g) £2 - £3

▲ Curly Wurly. (1980). (vg) £3 - £4

▲ Haribo. (1990). (vg-ex) £1 - £2

▲   Moore's shop front unknown location. Original postcard. (1910). Postally unused. (g) £8 - £10

▲ Wispa. (1985). (vg) £2 - £3

▲ Animal Bar. (1990). (vg) £3 - £4

▲ Wagon Wheels. (1990). (vg) £3 - £4

▲   Rowntree's packet front. 1935. (g) £8 - £10

CONFECTIONERY - Fry's

Joseph Fry started manufacturing chocolate in 1759. Two years later he joined forces with John Vaughan and they bought-out chocolate manufacturer Walter Churchman. When Fry died in 1787 the business name was changed to Anna Fry & Son. The firm was later taken over by Joseph Storrs Fry and renamed J.S. Fry & Sons. The famous Fry's Chocolate Cream was created in 1866. Turkish Delight came along in 1914. Amongst dozens of other products, Fry's Five Centre was produced in the 1930's.

Five Boys was claimed to be the most famous chocolate bar in the world (1902). The famous boy (Lindsay Poulton) was captured with five expressions; Desperation, Pacification, Expectation, Acclamation and Realization.

At one time, Fry's was one of the biggest employers in Bristol. The move to Somerdale, Keynsham came in 1923 and the Fry's name was maintained there until 1981.

▲ Fry's Five Boys. Original postcard. (1910). Postally unused. (vg) £18 - £24

▲ Fry's souvenir tin. (1950). (g) £12 - £14

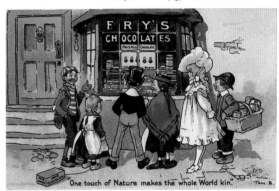

▲ Fry's Chocolate. Original postcard. With strong 1918 postmark 'Arnhem'. Message in ink. (vg) £14 - £18

▲ Fry's souvenir tin. Commemorating the opening of the Royal Edward Dock in Bristol by Their Majesties King Edward VII and Queen Alexandra on 9 July 1908. Empty. (g-vg) £20 - £26

▲ Somerdale Works. Original 'House of Fry' postcard. (1930). Postally unused. (g) £5 - £8

▲ Coronation souvenir tin. J.S. Fry & Sons. 1911. With images of King George V and Queen Mary. Empty. (g) £14 - £18

▲ Fry's Cocoas and Chocolates. Original postcard. (1915). Includes an extract from an article in The Times newspaper. (g-vg) £6 - £8

CONFECTIONERY

▲ Matchbox Convoy CY24. (1995). With original box. 165 x 45mm. (mnt) £4 - £6

► Barratt. Bright Babies. Empty trade box (100 x 1p). (1975). (g-vg) £6 - £8

▲ Twix. Card. (1970). (vg) £2 - £3

PEPPERMINT CREAMS
12 a 1d.

▲ Peppermint Creams. Card. (1935). (vg) 30p - 40p

ROWNTREE'S
Plain Chocolate Vanilla Flavour
walnut whips
4p

▲ Walnut Whips. Card. (1975). (vg) 60p - 80p

Jelly Babies were created in 1864 by Fryers of Lancashire but were called 'Unclaimed Babies'. In 1918 they were produced by Bassett's (Sheffield) but the name was changed to 'Peace Babies' to mark the end of World War I. The product was ceased altogether during World War II and wasn't re-launched until 1953, when the name was changed again, to 'Jelly Babies'. In 1989, Bassett's were taken over by Cadbury-Schweppes.

▲ Hillabys Pontefract Cakes tin. (1935). Empty. 100 x 80mm. (g) £6 - £8

▲ Maynards sugar matches. (1950). Empty box. (g-vg) £8 - £10

CHERRY GENOA CAKE
CONTAINS BUTTER
PER **2/-** LB.

▲ Cherry Genoa Cake. Plastic. (1950). (g) £1 - £2

▲ Thorne's Toffee. (1925). Empty tin. (f-g) £6 - £8

► Kiddicraft sweets. Small sugar sweets in a miniature Robinson's cereal box (Groats). (1950). With original sweets, but not suitable for consumption. (vg) £6 - £8

Rowntree
BLACK MAGIC
11/6 (57½p
ONE POUND
NET

▲ Black Magic. Card. (1970). (vg) £1 - £3

CONFECTIONERY - Chocolate dummy bars

Many a sweet shop had an attractive shop window. Amongst the displays were chocolate bars, which, for obvious reasons could not be real chocolate and therefore manufacturers produced 'dummy bars' usually made of wood and shaped to the exact size of the real thing and with the real wrapper.

Dummy chocolate bars are widely collected and represent a truly fascinating area of our social history - a great excuse for nostalgic indulgence.

You would be lucky to find good examples at a car boot, so be prepared to pay a premium via collector's fairs or auctions.

▲ Needler's Kreema Orange. (1965). (vg) £10 - £12

▲ Cadbury's Bar Six. (1965). (vg) £8 - £12

▲ Cadbury's Fruit & Nut. (1965). (vg) £8 - £10

▲ Caley Tray (A.J.Caley Ltd. Norwich). (1965). (vg) £8 - £10

▲ Cadbury's Turkish Delight. (1965). (g) £7 - £9

CORGI

Corgi Toys was founded in 1956 by Mettoy Toys. They competed with the giant of the industry - Dinky and scored an immediate advantage by introducing window glazing to their model vehicles. Corgi took their logo and name from the Welsh breed of dogs.

Whilst generally, Corgi model vehicles are of less interest to diecast collectors than Dinky, there's not a lot in it and a mint boxed Corgi toy can command serious money.

▲ Fordson Power Major Tractor. No.55. 1962 - 1964. Silver seat and steering wheel. Model (ex), original box (vg) £180 - £200

► Vanwall Racing Car. No. 50. 1957 - 1961. Green body. Large Corgi Toys Vanwall across base. Model (ex), original box (g-vg) £80 - £90

▲ Bedford 12cwt Van 'Daily Express'. No. 403. 1957 - 1960. Model (ex), original box (vg) £110 - £120

► Mobile Cement Mixer. Corgi Juniors. No.30. 1973. Unopened pack. Model (mnt), pack (g-vg) £8 - £10

▲ Ghia L.6.4. No. 241. 1963 - 1969. Model (vg), original box (g-vg) £45 - £55

◄ Corgi enamel badge. (1960). 20 x 15mm. (g) £8 - £10

CRICKET

Whilst the roots of the game of cricket go back hundreds of years, it is widely acknowledged that the legendary amateur cricketer W.G.Grace (1848 - 1915) played an important role in the development of the game as we know it today.

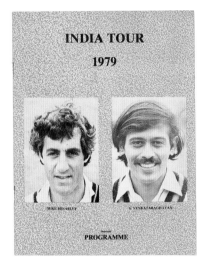

◀ India Tour Programme. 1979. David Gower has signed on the page containing a photograph of the England party. Clear, blue ink. No dedication. (vg) £8 - £10

David Ivon Gower (born 1 April 1957, in Tunbridge Wells, Kent) is a television personality and former English cricketer.

Throughout his cricketing career he played 117 Test matches, scoring 8,231 runs. He retired in 1993 and began working on television, appearing as a team captain in the comedy panel show They Think It's All Over from 1995 until 2003. He also presented Gower's Cricket Monthly from 1995 to 1998, and has been a commentator for the BBC and Sky Sports.

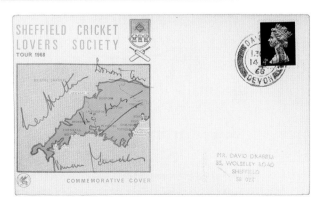

▲ Commemorative postal cover issued by The Sheffield Cricket Lovers Society in 1968 to celebrate the tour of Devon and Cornwall. Signed by Len Hutton, Donald Carr, Vic Wilson and Norman Yardley. Clear, blue ink. No dedication. (vg) £8 - £12

▲ Slazenger cricket bat. Impressed 'Australia v England / Test / Series / 1975'. Signed in ink to the face by seventeen Australian team members. (vg) £120 - £140

CYCLING

The ultimate collectable in this category surely has to be a bicycle and even Victorian examples are not totally beyond reach. Perhaps the most satisfying purchase for the collectables addict, is a 1950's model. They can often be picked up at large car boot sales or collectors fairs for around £60 - £80 in good condition and therefore suitable for daily use.

There's plenty of memorabilia to satisfy the cycling enthusiast. For example; advertising signs, bells, pumps, oil cans, saddle bags, lights, club ephemera, badges etc...

Cycling publications complement collections. As well as the features, the manufacturers' advertisements paint an historic picture of a century+ of the rise and fall of bicycle sales.

▲ The Bicycle newspaper. Issue dated 30 January 1952. (vg) £3 - £4

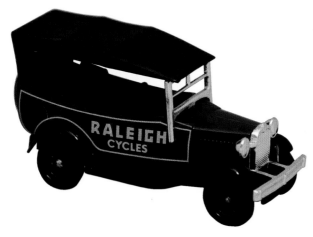

▲ Day's Gone Diecast model. Model 'A' Ford car. Raleigh Cycles. Boxed. (mnt) £3 - £4

The Raleigh Bicycle Company, which took its name from the street in Nottingham where it was situated, was formed in 1890. It was founded by Frank Bowden, and is one of the oldest bicycle manufacturers in the world.

Interestingly, from 1929 to 1935, the company also made motorcycles and automobiles. When production was ceased in order to focus on bicycles, the leftover equipment and parts were used as the basis for a new company. As the parts from Raleigh were branded with an R, the new company needed a name that also began with an R, and thus Reliant was formed, the company that produced the wellknown three-wheeler, the Reliant Robin.

▲ Cycling newspaper. Issue dated 3 April 1952. (vg) £3 - £4

DARTS

There's not a massive amount of scope for collectors of darts memorabilia, however, it's out there if you look in the right places.

Autographs and photographs of star players, programmes, tickets, old darts, old dart boards and other associated ephemera are all on the radar.

JOCKY WILSON
PLAYS WITH AND ENDORSES
DATADART PRODUCTS
Tel: 091 – 2374471
Fax: 091 – 2374472

◀ Dart board eraser. 64mm diam. Unused. (ex) £1 - £2

▲ Jocky Wilson. Autographed photograph. Clear, black ink, 210 x 150mm. No dedication £15 - £20

John Thomas 'Jocky' Wilson, Fife, Scotland, was one of the top darts players. He won the British Professional Championship four times. He retired from the game in 1995, withdrawing from public life and rarely made public appearances until his death in 2012.

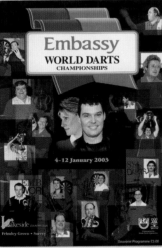

▶ Embassy World Championship 2003. Programme with autographs of six of the players. Tony David, Shaun Greatbatch, Tony O'Shea, Dennis Harbour, Colin Monk and James Wade. (g) £14 - 16

◀ Alan Evans darts case. (1975). (g-vg) £6 - £8

Alan Evans was one of the first stars of televised darts. He died aged 49 in 1999.

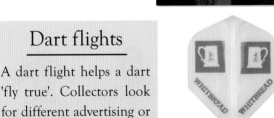

Dart flights

A dart flight helps a dart 'fly true'. Collectors look for different advertising or images on the flight. The older the better.

▲ Whitbread. (1980). (g) 20p - 30p

▲ Datadart (Tony O'Shea). (2005). (g) 5p - 10p

▲ Carlsberg. (1975). (g) 20p - 30p

▲ Adkin's Nut Brown. (1935). (g) £3 - £4

▲ Mackeson. (2000). (f) 1p - 5p

▲ British Darts Organisation. (1995). (vg) 10p - 20p

▲ Walker's Beers. (1935). (g) £3 - £4

DEL PRADO

Del Prado is a company that produces "partwork" magazines. "Partworks" are simply regularly produced magazines, each issue of which is accompanied by something collectable like an episode of a cult television show on DVD, a painted toy soldier, or a piece of a model kit. Many companies are currently working on such magazines, including Hatchette and De Agostini.

Del Prado are known for producing "partworks" for detailed, hand-painted pewter soldiers. Usually, the first few issues of a "partwork" are available in shops, and they will be heavily advertised on television to encourage subscriptions. From about issue three onwards, the magazines will only be available by subscription. This means that the collectable figures begin to become collectable almost instantly, because they are not widely available. As a series continues, more and more people will cancel their subscriptions, so later issues will be produced in fewer numbers and therefore will generally be rarer and more valuable than early ones.

Be warned that such models are usually rather delicate and the paint is prone to flaking off. Mint condition examples will obviously be worth more than damaged examples, and models that are in the original boxes with the accompanying magazine will command a premium.

▲   Tirailleur, senegalais (France - 1914).   (vg) £2 - £3

▲ General Joffre, French Army (France - 1914). (vg) £1 - £3

▲ English Knight, 1250.   (g-vg) £1 - £2

▲ Viking Warrior, Norway, c. 872. (vg) £2 - £3

▲ Irish Sub-King, 7th - 8th century. (vg) £2 - £3

▲ Trooper, Belgian 5th Light Dragoons, 1815. (vg) £2 - £3

▲   Venetian Sailor, c. 1320. (vg)   £2 - £4

▲ Mongol Archer, Kalka River, 1223. (vg) £2 - £3

▲ Don Cossack, (White Army), Russia - 1918. (vg) £1 - £3

▲   Spanish guerrilla chief, c. 1812. (vg) £2 - £3

▲ Richard I's Lieutenant. Third Crusade, 1189. (vg) £2 - £3

▲   General Lasalle, 1806-7. (vg)   £2 - £3

DEXTERITY PUZZLES

Dexterity puzzles are handheld games that became popular towards the end of the nineteenth century. The market was quickly cornered by Robert Journet, a London toy shop owner. Robert's father made the puzzles by hand. The puzzles were popular in Britain but by 1918 the puzzles were truly big business (including exports to the USA).

Dexterity puzzles quickly caught-on in the USA and that's where you can now obtain some great examples.

The trouble is that these puzzles were not originally purchased with the view to storing them in the hope that mint condition examples would become serious investments. Consequently they were much played with and finding puzzles in excellent condition now is rather difficult.

Robert Journet died around 1935 and the business was taken over by his son Frederick. The business was eventually sold in 1965 to Abbey Corinthian Games.

Imagine a world without handheld computer games and you can imagine how popular these games were with children (and adults) particularly between 1915 and 1955.

It may be a good idea to concentrate your collecting on Journet puzzles. Nice old examples are becoming increasingly popular with collectors and they are commanding more and more money. If you find one at a boot sale for £1 or so, then snap it up fast. Realistically, you are not going to find many Journets at boot sales. However, you will find a steady supply on internet auction websites but at much, much more than boot sale prices.

(Front)

(Reverse)

▲ The Beacon puzzle. (1935). 120 x 100mm. (g-vg) £18 - £22

DEXTERITY PUZZLES - Journet

▲ Golden Rod Puzzle. (1950). (g-vg)
£14 - £16

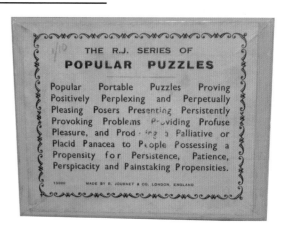

The "Golden Rod" Puzzle. Manufactured by R. Journet & Co. (1950). The aim is to roll the golden rods into their respective positions.

▲ The Divers Puzzle. (1950). (g) £10 - £12

▲ The Queen Mary Puzzle. (1950). (g) £16 - £18

▲ The Cog Wheel Puzzle. (1950). (g-vg) £18 - £20

▲ The Lucky Seven Domino Puzzle. (1960). (f-g) £7 - £9

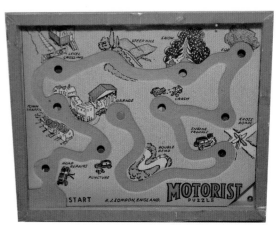

▲ Motorist Puzzle. (1955). (vg) £16 - £18

DINKY

Dinky is one of the best known names in the world of toys. Created by Frank Hornby (1863 - 1936) as an extension of his Meccano business. The first model was produced in 1933 and some of the early rare examples now sell for more than the price of a real new motor car.

Identifying the most desirable models is a bit of a science and no-one should start investing large sums of money until they fully understand market values. The best advice for any newcomer to Dinky, is to attend toy fairs. Then perhaps, venture to some serious collectors auctions.

You do need to tread carefully when buying Dinky. Boxed examples are most sought after. However, there are many reproduction boxes available via the internet and a repro' box does not enhance the value of a model as much as the real thing. Many original boxes are damaged to some extent. Quite often a mint condition box will give the game away. Make sure you establish if the box is an original.

Condition of the model is critical and is devalued if they have been repainted. Top prices are achieved when the model is a mint example with original paintwork and in an original mint box.

Ramsay's Catalogue of British Diecast is regarded by many experts as the 'bible' for values of Dinky and other Diecast models. It is published by Swapmeet Publications.

▲ Trojan Van. Chivers. No. 31c. 1953 - 54. Original paint. Unboxed. (g-vg) £45 - £55

▲ Fordson Thames Flat Truck. No.422. 1954 - 60. Original paint. Unboxed. (g-vg) £55 - £65

▲ Armstrong-Siddeley. No. 36a. 1947 - 50. Original paint. Unboxed. (vg) £95 - £115

▲ Taxi with driver. No.36g. 1947 - 50. Original paint. Unboxed. (g-vg) £40 - £50

▲ Daimler Ambulance. No.253. 1954 - 58. Original paint. Unboxed. (g) £18 - £22

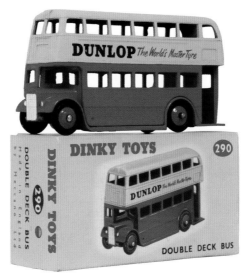

▲ Double Decker Bus. No. 290. 1954 - 59. Original paint. Very good original box, (ex) £100 - £120

▲ Cooper-Bristol Racing Car. No. 23g. 1952 - 54. Original paint. Very good original box. (ex) £80 - £90

▲ Fiat 600. No. 183. 1958 - 60. Original paint. Good original box. (vg) £65 - £75

▲ Bedford CA Van. No.481. 1955 - 60. Original paint. Unboxed. (g) £18 - £22

▲ UK Catalogue. No.14. 1978. (vg-ex) £6 - £8

▲ Centurion Tank. No. 651. 1954-70. Original paint. Unboxed. (f-g) £12 - £16

▲ Standard Vanguard. No. 153. 1954 - 60. Very good repaint. Unboxed. (g) £10 - £12

DINKY

Some collectors/dealers specialise in restoring Dinky toys and are therefore looking for poor condition/damaged/ incomplete models. Look out for them at car boot sales. As long as you buy correctly, there's a good profit to be made on these.

◀ Coles Mobile Crane. Dinky Supertoys. No. 571. 1949-54. Length 116mm. Original paint. Very good original box. (ex) £80-£90

▲ Rover 3500. No. 180. 1979-80. Original paint. Unboxed. (g) £10 - £15

▲ Austin Wagon. No. 30J. 1950-54. Original paint. Unboxed. (g) £40 - £50

▲ Armoured Car. No. 670. 1964-70. Original paint. Unboxed. (g) £8 - £10

▲ Rover 75 Saloon. No. 140b. 1951-53. Original paint. Unboxed. (f-g) £35 - £40

▲ Jaguar XK120. No.157. 1954-57. Original paint. Unboxed. (f-g) £40 - £50

▲ Aston Martin DB5. No. 110. 1966-67. Original paint. Unboxed. (vg) £30 - £40

▲ Ford Fordor Sedan. No. 170. 1956-58. Original paint. Unboxed. (g) £50 - £60

▲ Ford Taunus 17M. No. 154. 1966-69. Original paint. Unboxed. (vg-ex) £8 - £10

▲ Austin A105 Saloon. No. 176. 1958-59. Original paint. Unboxed. (f-g) £35 - £40

▲ Range Rover Ambulance. No. 268. 1973-77. Original paint. Unboxed. (ex) £8 - £10

▲ Land Rover. No. 340. 1954-66. Fairly good repaint. Unboxed. (g) £5 - £8

▲ Hudson Sedan. No. 171. 1956-58. Complete fairly good repaint. Unboxed. (g) £4 - £7

▲ Express Dairy N.C.B. Electric Van. No. 30V. 1949-54. Fairly good repaint. Unboxed. (g) £5 - £8

▲ Volkswagen Saloon. No. 181. 1956-70. Original paint. Unboxed. (g) £12 - £15

▲ Studebaker Land Cruiser. No. 172. 1954-56. Original paint. Front tyres flat. Unboxed. (vg) £20 - £22

▲ Cadillac Eldorado. No. 131 1956-61. Original paint. Windscreen broken. Unboxed. (f) £15 - £20

▲ Jensen FF. No. 188. 1968-74. Original paint. Unboxed. (ex) £18 - £20

▲ Aston Martin DB6. No. 153. 1967-71. Original paint. Unboxed. (vg) £25 - £30

▲ Estate Car. No. 344. 1954-61. Good repaint. Unboxed. (g) £6 - £8

▲ Lamborghini Marzal. No. 189. 1969-76. Original paint. Unboxed. (g-vg) £12 - £15

▶ Tank Transporter. No. 660. 1956-61. Original paint. Unboxed. (g) £15 - £20

DISC JOCKEYS

The term 'disc jockey' was created by American broadcaster Walter Winchell in 1935. He combined the word 'disc' (record) and 'jockey' (operator of a machine).

Radio Luxembourg was responsible for introducing the 'disc jockey' to the masses in the late 1950's.

In the 1960's disc jockeys were so popular, they became stars of radio and TV.

Mobile discotheques enabled almost anyone to become a DJ. The rest as they say, is history.

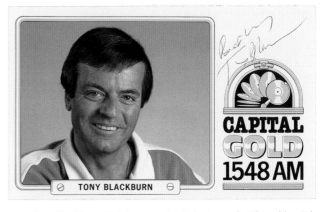

We cordially invite you to our

TOP LUXEMBOURG RECORD SHOW

with Star Disc Jockey

PETER ALDERSLEY

in the

"POP AROUND" SHOW

FRIDAY, MAY 8th, 1964 at

ST. ANSLEM'S HALL, HATCH END

(Two shows: 7.30 p.m. - 9 p.m.)

ADMISSION FREE **7.30 p.m.** BY THIS TICKET ONLY

Giles   389, UXBRIDGE ROAD, HATCH END

▲ Pop Around Show ticket. 1964. Signed on the reverse by Radio Luxembourg DJ Peter Aldersley. Clear, black ink. No dedication. (g) £1 - £2

▲ The late Ray Moore. DJ. Autographed photograph. Clear, red ink, 150 x 100mm. No dedication. £6 - £8

▲ The late Alan (Fluff) Freeman. DJ. Autographed photograph. Very slightly smudged, black ink, 150 x 100mm. No dedication. £6 - £8

▲ Tony Blackburn. DJ. Autographed photograph. Clear, blue ink, 165 x 100mm. No dedication. £3 - £4

▲ Simon Bates. DJ. Autographed photograph. Clear, blue ink, 155 x 105mm. No dedication. £3 - £4

▲ Simon Mayo. DJ. Autographed photograph. Clear, black ink, 150 x 100mm. No dedication . £3 - £4

Antony Kenneth (Tony) Blackburn. Born 1943. Began his career as a disc jockey when he joined the pirate radio station Radio Caroline.

He joined the BBC and became the very first DJ to present a show on Radio 1, when it was launched in 1967.

DOGS

There are plenty of dog-related collectables to choose from. Most people specialise in particular areas, for example, ceramics. Even then, collectors of ceramics may concentrate on one particular maker.

If you are interested in dogs and looking for an area with investment potential, we highly recommend collecting dog licences. Previous prices achieved in Collecticus auctions prove the interest factor. Interestingly, the cost of a dog licence did not keep in line with inflation.

Dogs have been featured on many matchbox labels. The Bryant & May 'Top Dogs' matchbook series is one of the most popular among collector.

"SCOTTIE."

▲ Valentine's postcard. "Scottie". (1910). Postally unused. (vg) £6 - £8

No. 43B—(Farmer).   DOGS.   No. 40 30

CERTIFICATE OF EXEMPTION FROM DUTY.
41 & 42 Vict., cap. 15.

I hereby certify that Mr. *Thomas Pither*,

of *Woodley*, in the Parish of *Sonning*,

in the County of *Berks*, has delivered a Declaration under the above-mentioned Act, stating that he is a **Farmer,** and that *two* Dogs *are* kept by him solely for use in tending sheep or cattle on his farm, and I hereby further certify that he is exempt from Licence Duty in respect of such Dog*s* while so kept and used until the 31st day of December next inclusive.

Dated this *6th* day of *February*, 1*902*.

_____ . Supervisor of Inland Revenue.

Reading

NOTE.—This Certificate will become void and must be exchanged for a Licence if the dog ceases to be used for the purpose stated, or is used in taking rabbits or game, or, in the trade of a butcher or drover. A Declaration must be delivered and a fresh Certificate obtained in the month of January next, if required.

This Certificate must be produced, when required, to any Officer of Inland Revenue or Police, under a penalty of £5.

M. & S. Ltd. 3265. 8757—250,000 5/99 [**38**]

▲ Certificate of Exemption From Duty. 1902. (g) £12 - £14

DOGS - Licences

Many people kept their dog licences in memory of pets departed and simply as hoarded items. Consequently, licences over 100 years old are not impossible to find (but are rare).

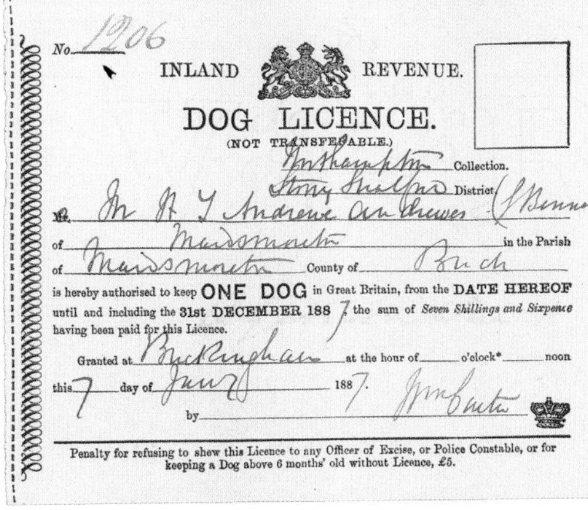

Licences make an unusual and interesting collection. The last dog licences issued in Great Britain were in 1987 (price 37p). The price dropped from 37½ p in 1984 when the ½p was abolished.

INLAND REVENUE.

LICENCE—to expire 31st Dec., 1878—for ONE DOG.

(NOT TRANSFERABLE.)

No. 136 Bangor Collection.

Holyhead District.

Mr. William Williams

of Caer brynian in the Parish

of Llanfaethlu County of Anglesea

is hereby authorized to keep ONE DOG in Great Britain, from the date hereof, until the 31st December, 1878, the Sum of Five Shillings having been paid for this Licence.

Dated at Llanfachreth this 8 day of February 1878.

Granted by H Williams

This Licence must be shown to any Officer of Excise, or Police Constable, on request, and should be renewed in January. Penalty for keeping a Dog above 6 months old without Licence £5.

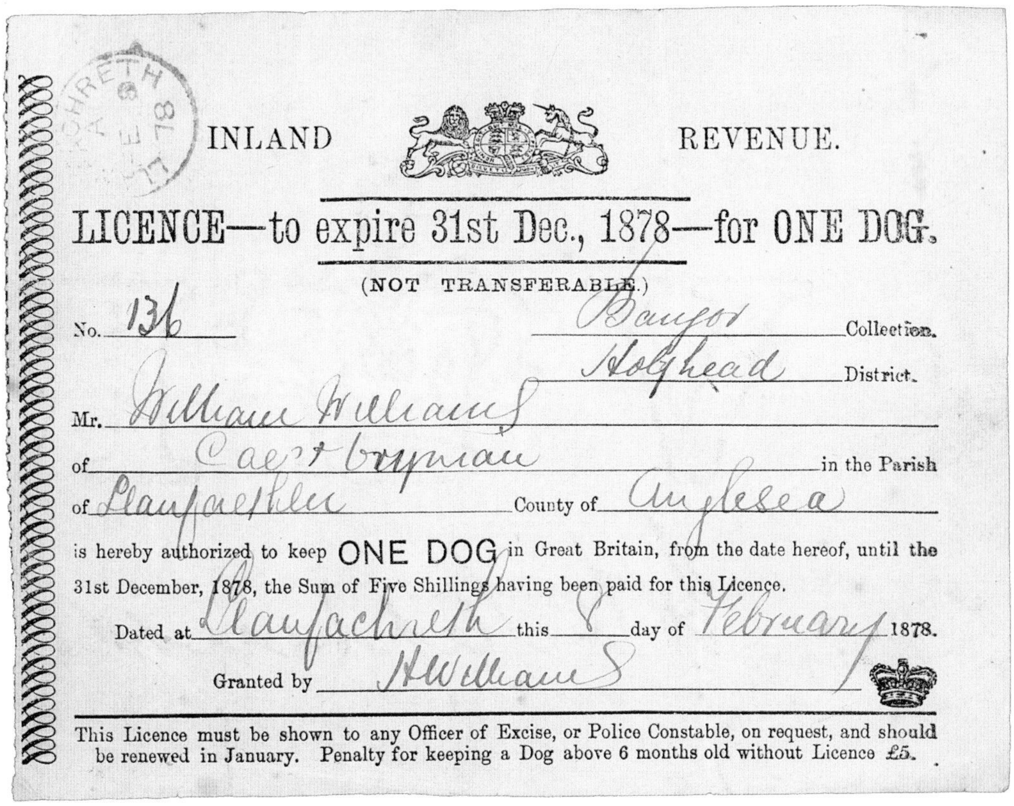

(Actual size)

▲ 1878. (g) £40 - £50

No. 1206

INLAND REVENUE.

DOG LICENCE.

(NOT TRANSFERABLE.)

Northampton Collection.

Stony Stratford District.

Mr. N. J. Andrews

of Maidsmorton in the Parish

of Maidsmorton County of Bucks

is hereby authorised to keep ONE DOG in Great Britain, from the DATE HEREOF until and including the 31st DECEMBER 1887 the sum of Seven Shillings and Sixpence having been paid for this Licence.

Granted at Buckingham at the hour of ____ o'clock* ____ noon

this 7 day of June 1887.

by ____

Penalty for refusing to shew this Licence to any Officer of Excise, or Police Constable, or for keeping a Dog above 6 months' old without Licence, £5.

▲ 1887. With VR Watermark. (g-vg) £35 - £40

THIS LICENCE EXPIRES ON THE 31st DECEMBER OF THE YEAR WHEN ISSUED.

7s. 6d. DOG LICENCE. (NOT TRANSFERABLE). CY 08460

† Alfred Henry Cooper Esq.

of ____ in the

Civil Parish or Township of Long Stratton St Peter within the

Administrative County* of Nfk

is hereby authorized to keep ONE DOG in Great Britain, from the *date hereof* until and including the *31st day of December next following*; the sum of SEVEN SHILLINGS and SIXPENCE having been paid for this Licence.

Granted at Long Stratton at 11 hours 57 minutes a.m.

o'clock this 7th day of January 1914.

by R. E. Bungard

Penalty for refusing to shew this Licence to any duly authorized Officer, or Police Constable, or for keeping a Dog above 6 months old without Licence £5.

†Insert full Christian Name and Surname.

*If the residence is within a County Borough strike out "Administrative" and insert "Borough" after "County".

S. D. 1913.

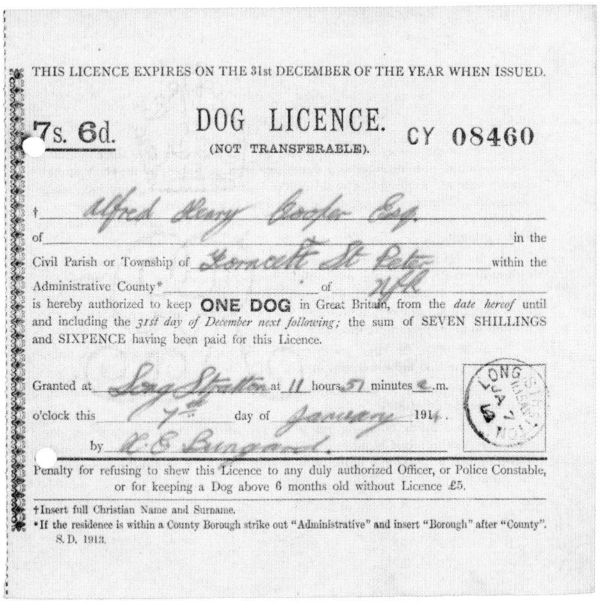

▲ 1914. Hole punched. (g) £25 - £30

DOGS - Licences

▲ 1927. (g) £20 - £25

▲ 1943. Scotland. (g-vg) £20 - £25

▲ 1945. (g) £12 - £16

▲ 1947. (g-vg) £14 - £18

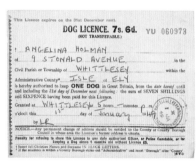

▲ 1949. (g-vg) £14 - £18

▲ 1952. (g-vg) £10 - £12

▲ 1957. (f-g) £5 - £7

▲ 1975. (vg) £4 - £6

▲ 1979. (vg) £4 - £6

▲ 1980. (f) £1 - £3

▲ 1983. (g-vg) £3 - £5

DOLLS

Dolls as miniature representations of people have existed since the time of the ancient Greeks and Romans, and probably before. They serve several purposes, but most commonly are the loved playthings and companions of children. It is sometimes the rediscovery of an old childhood friend that inspires an adult to begin a collection. As dolls have been made (and continue to be made) all over the world, in all sizes, shapes and varieties, the choice is vast and though many dolls are very expensive, others are not, so there are many dolls available to suit all pockets.

Whatever you decide to buy, be sure that you understand what you are buying, especially if a large price is involved. There are many pitfalls waiting to catch out the unwary. Consider first whether the doll is what it purports to be, making sure that the head is appropriate to its body. For example, when the doll is undressed, does the head look overly large or small in proportion to its body? If it does, it could be a replacement. The best way to learn about dolls is to look at, and handle, as many of them as possible and become familiar with all the many different methods of construction.

If you are considering buying a hard plastic doll, look carefully at the condition of the plastic. If any part of it appears to be too pink and a bit shrivelled, do not buy it as this is an indication that the chemicals in the plastic are starting to break down and the doll will only deteriorate more. With vinyl dolls, avoid those which have been scribbled on with ball point pens or lipsticks as stains on vinyl are very hard to remove. Fabric dolls with dirty faces do not respond well to washing as water can remove all the stiffening in the fabric as well as the features, and you could end up doing more harm than good.

Once you have collected a few dolls, they need to be stored or displayed correctly. Always store dolls with weighted eyes face downwards. Ideally each doll, wrapped in tissue, should be stored in its own box. This is particularly important with wax dolls, celluloid dolls and those with glue stiffened fabric faces, all of which are prone to being damaged by crushing.

Displaying dolls is very much a matter of personal choice but however you decide to store or display them, check regularly for insect damage. This is especially important with fabric dolls, which are prone to damage by moths.

With such a wide range of dolls available, you can choose dolls that you really like, and create your own personal collection that can be treasured for many years to come.

▲ Rosebud doll. (1945). Made of composition. 175mm tall. Arms included but no longer attached. (g) £28 - £32

▲ Qantas doll. (1980). In original box, 295 x 90 x 45mm. (ex) £15 - £20

DOLLS - Postcards

▲ (1920). Postally unused. (vg) £3 - £5

▲ (1910). Postally unused. Message in pencil. (g-vg) £4 - £6

▲ 1910. Postmark illegible. Message in ink. (g-vg) £4 - £6

▲(1920). Postally unused. Message in ink. (g) £2 - £4

▲ Postmarked Hull 1912. Message in pencil. (g-vg) £3 - £5

▲ (1923). Postally unused. Message in ink. (g-vg) £3 - £4

▲ Postmarked Manchester 1910. Message in ink. (g) £3 - £5

▲ (1925). Postally unused. (g-vg) £3 - £5

▲ (1910). Postally unused. Message in ink. (g-vg) £3 - £5

EDUCATION

The majority of Britain's population were educated at schools and colleges and for many people; their school days are full of mainly happy memories. Consequently, there's a great deal of nostalgia linked to the subject of education.

Collectables include postcards, school text books and exercise books, examination papers, uniforms, photographs, school magazines etc...

▲ The Colston School, Bristol postcard. Postmarked Bristol 1905. Message in ink. (vg) £5 - £7

Taunton's School, Southampton, has a long history (from 1864). The first Taunton's School Journal was published in 1895. It included news, events and examination results.

◄ Taunton's School Journal. June 1924. (g-vg) £6 - £8

GCE

GCE (General Certificate of Education) examinations were first introduced in England, Wales and Northern Ireland in 1951. They replaced the SC (School Certificate) and HSC (Higher School Certificate).

▲ GCE Examination Paper. General Science 1951. The introductory year and therefore an interesting piece of social history. (g) £2 - £4

Singing Together

Singing Together was a BBC Radio schools broadcast (began in 1939) that was enjoyed by schoolchildren for over sixty years.

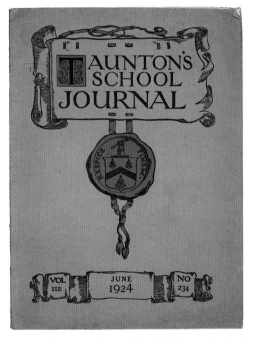

◄ Singing Together 24 page publication. 1952. 210 x 130mm. (g) £6 - £8

► Singing Together 16 page publication. 1965. 215 x 140mm. (g) £3 - £5

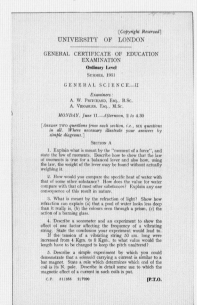

EGG CODDLERS

▶ Egg Coddler. (1990). Royal Worcester. Porcelain. (ex) £4 - £6

Egg coddlers are used in the 'coddling' (cooking process) and are generally made of porcelain.

Royal Worcester have been manufacturing egg coddlers for over 100 years.

EGG CUPS

Collecting egg cups is known as pocillovy, and a collector is known as a pocillovist (pronounced po-sil-o-vist).

There is much more interest in the subject than you might at first realise. Novelty egg cups are particularly in demand; but, of course, egg cups shaped like chickens and other fowl are rather common.

Egg cups can often be picked up at relatively little expense, and it is easy to get a large collection; just remember that storage can become a problem, especially if you want your collection on display.

▲ The Magic Roundabout. Ceramic. (1995). (vg-ex) £2 - £3

▲ Duckula. Ceramic. (1995). (vg-ex) £1 - £2

▲ Cowabunga. Ceramic. (1995). (vg) £1 - £2

▲ Tweenies. Ceramic. (1995). (vg-ex) £1 - £2

▲ Donald Duck. Ceramic. (1995). (f-g) £1 - £2

▲ Postman Pat. Ceramic. (1995). (vg-ex) £1 - £2

▲ Thomas The Tank Engine. Ceramic. (1995). (g) £1 - £2

▲ Teletubbies. Ceramic. (2000). (vg) £1 - £2

▲ Little Bunnies. Ceramic. (2000). (vg) £1 - £2

ELVIS

Elvis Aaron Presley was born in Tupelo, Mississippi, USA. He was known as 'The King' and acquired cult status, becoming a major influence on the rock and roll era of the late 1950's and early 1960's. British pop stars such as Cliff Richard, Adam Faith and Billy Fury successfully styled themselves on Elvis.

Expect to pay more than £2500 for an Elvis autograph (in clear ink). However, be warned, there are many forgeries being sold via internet auctions.

There's a mountain of Elvis memorabilia, some of which was manufactured to cater for the collecting market after his death in 1977.

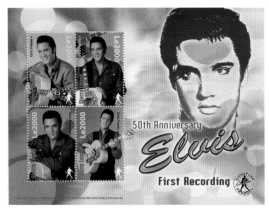

▲ Sierra Leone. Stamp sheet. 2004. (mnt) £4 - £6

▲ Meet Elvis. Star Special. 52 pages. 1962. (g) £6 - £8

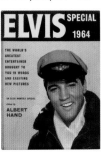

▲ Elvis Special 1964. Hardback book. 112 pages. (f) £8 - £10

▲ Surrender. Original sheet music. 1960. (g-vg) £10 - £12

▲ Such A Night. Original sheet music. 1964. (vg) £14 - £18

▲ I Don't Care If The Sun Don't Shine. Original sheet music. 1959. (p-f) £10 - £12

► Donruss. Empty bubble gum wrapper. 1978. (g-vg) £5 - £7

Colonel Parker
1909 - 1997

Thomas Andrew Parker was a Dutch-born impresario, whose real name was Andreas Cornelis van Kuijik. In 1955 he was introduced to a young chap named Elvis Presley and became his manager. Parker famously became known as 'The Colonel'. He was responsible for Elvis signing the recording deal with RCA. When Elvis died, The Colonel was asked what he would do now, to which he replied "I shall carry on managing him".

▲ Autographed 10 x 8in photograph of The Colonel. Clear, black ink. Dedicated. £125 - £150

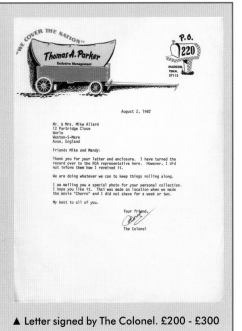

▲ Letter signed by The Colonel. £200 - £300

ELVIS - Records

You are likely to find Elvis records at just about every large car boot sale, however, the majority are likely to be of very little value.

The Rare Record Price Guide (published by Record Collector) lists the rare and more valuable varieties. Even if you are armed with this mine of information, an understanding of the current market is recommended before investing in rare Elvis Records.

Surprisingly, generally, 78rpm shellac Elvis records are not overly rare or valuable. A good condition example of Hound Dog (HMV POP 249) released in 1956 is likely to make around £10.

Buying 78rpm records through the post is fraught with danger and not recommended unless you can rely on the seller to pack extremely well. Shellac records break very easily.

The release of Elvis records in 1956 and 1957 coincided with the release of the new format 45rpm vinyl single records and many of these are rarer than their 78rpm counterparts.

A 78rpm version of 'All Shook Up' is likely to sell for around £20 if in very good condition, whereas the 45rpm version (HMV purple label, push-out centre, with gold print) can make around £150 (vg).

Elvis EP and LP records were reproduced by the truck load. It's the original issues that you need to look out for.

▲ California Holiday - Elvis Presley. (LP record). 1966. RCA, Mono, Red Spot label, RD-7820. Vinyl (vg), sleeve (f-g) £12 - £14

▲ Elvis Is Back - Elvis Presley. (LP record). Original. 1960. RCA, Mono, RD-27171. Vinyl (g), sleeve (f) £12 - £14

▲ Blue Hawaii - Elvis Presley. (LP record). 1966. RCA, Mono, Red Spot label, RD-27238. Vinyl (vg), sleeve (vg) £8 - £10

▲ Peace In The Valley - Elvis Presley. (EP record). 1957. RCA, RCX-101. Vinyl (vg), sleeve (g) £25 - £30

▲ Peace In The Valley - Elvis Presley. (EP record). 1969 re-pressing. RCA, RCX-101. Vinyl (vg), sleeve (vg) £12 - £15

▲ Kid Galahad - Elvis Presley. (EP record). 1962. RCA, RCX-7106. Vinyl (g-vg), sleeve (g) £6 - £8

▲ Follow That Dream - Elvis Presley. (EP record). 1962. RCA, RCX-211. Vinyl (vg), sleeve (g) £6 - £8

▲ Love Me Tender - Elvis Presley. (EP record). 1957. HMV, 7EG 8199. Vinyl (g-vg), sleeve (g) £40 -£50

▲ Such A Night - Elvis Presley. (EP record). 1960. RCA, RCX-190. Vinyl (vg), sleeve (g) £15 - £18

▲ Christmas Album - Elvis Presley. (LP record). Original. 1957. RCA, RD-27052. Vinyl (f), sleeve (f) £20 - £30

▲ All Shook Up - Elvis Presley. Single. Original. 1957. HMV, 45-POP 359. Vinyl (p-f), sleeve (vg) £40 - £50

▲ Hard Headed Woman - Elvis Presley. Single. Original. 1958. RCA, 45-RCA 1070. Vinyl (f-g), sleeve (g-vg) £5 - £7

▲ It's Midnight - Elvis Presley. Single. Re-pressing. 1980. RCA, PB-10074. Vinyl dinked (vg), sleeve (g) £1 -£2

▲ My Boy - Elvis Presley. Single. Original. 1974. RCA, RCA 2458. Vinyl (g), sleeve (vg) £2 - £3

ELVIS - Elvis Monthly

This magazine series was launched in 1960 by publisher Albert Hand, Heanor, Derbyshire and was printed by Arthur Gaunt, Heanor. It was a huge success. After just one year, every newsagent wholesaler in Great Britain distributed it. The publisher also sold it by postal subscription.

As you may expect, Series 1, Number 1 commands a premium and can fetch around £100 for a genuine original copy in good+ condition. Numbers 2 - 11 of the first series are much harder to find than the second series, which in turn is harder to find than the third series.

The annual Series numbering system was changed after Series 6, Number 9, the next one became no.69 and then so on, up to the last issue of Elvis Monthly, which was no. 483.

In 1977, issue number 1 was reprinted with a special wraparound cover.

▲ Series 1. No.6. July 1960. (g-vg) £20 - £30

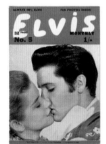

▲ Series 3. No.5. May 1962. (vg) £3 - £5

▲ Series 3. No.7. July 1962. (f-g) £2 - £3

▲ No.160. May 1973. (vg) £1 - £2

▲ No. 138. July 1971. (vg) £1 - £3

▲ Series 3. No.4. April 1962. (f) £1 - £2

▲ Series 3. No.8. August 1962. (g) £2 - £3

▲ Series 4. No.11. November 1963. (vg) £2 - £3

▲ Series 2. No.12. December 1961. (g-vg) £6 - £8

▲ On Tour Special. Published 1973. Souvenir issue commemorating the film 'Elvis On Tour'. (vg) £4 - £6

▲ Series 2. No.8. August 1961. (f) £2 - £3

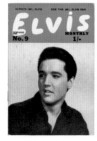

▲ Series 4. No.9. September 1963. (vg) £2 - £3

▲ Series 2. No.11. November 1961. (f-g) £4 - £6

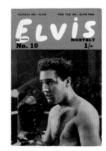

▲ Series 3. No.10. October 1962. (vg) £3 - £5

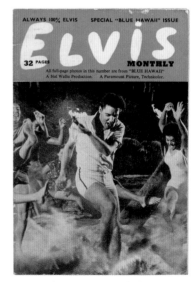

▲ Series 3. No.1. Special 'Blue Hawaii' Issue. (f-g) £2 - £3

ENTERTAINERS

One definition of an 'entertainer' is a person who combines two or more of the following; an actor, a comedian, a singer, a musician or a variety artist.

Hoagy Carmichael

Born Howard Hoagland Carmichael in 1899 (Bloomington, Indiana, USA) he was best known for being the composer of the song 'Georgia On My Mind'. He was an all-round entertainer with a career spanning six decades. He appeared in a number of feature films, often playing the role of a musician. The height of his fame was in the 50's and 60's when he became a household name. He died of heart failure in 1981.

▲ Hoagy Carmichael autograph on a publicity photograph. Clear, blue ink, 140 x 90mm. No dedication. £40 - £50

◄ London Casino programme. 1948. With ticket. Bernard Delfont production. Hoagy Carmichael top of the bill. (g-vg) £6 - £8

Front   Page 5

Edmund Hockridge

Canadian born Edmund James Hockridge had a long and varied career. He was renowned for his baritone voice. In 1986 he played alongside Suzi Quatro in a London production of Annie Get Your Gun. He died in 2009 aged 89.

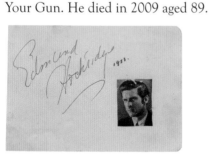

▲ Edmund Hockridge autograph. Clear, pink ink, 160 x 110mm. No dedication. £7 - £9

▲ The Music Man. Edmund Hockridge. EP record. 1961. Pye label, NEP 24135. Vinyl (vg), sleeve (g-vg) £4 - £6

Danny Kaye

Born David Kaminsky, Danny Kaye was an all-round entertainer who starred in 17 movies and countless stage appearances.

Amongst the many songs he recorded were; The Ugly Duckling, The King's New Clothes and Hans Christian Andersen.

▲ Danny Kaye autograph on a publicity photograph. Clear, black ink, 175 x 125. No dedication. £40 - £50

▲ Hans Christian Andersen. Sheet music. Loose sheets otherwise in good condition. £1 - £2

▲ The Five Pennies. LP Record. 1959. London Records HA-U 2189. Vinyl (g), sleeve (f-g) £2 - £4

ENTERTAINERS

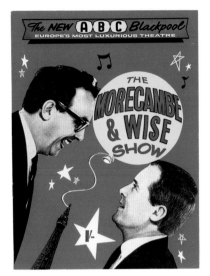

▲ ABC Blackpool Theatre programme. 1965. The Morecambe & Wise Show. The guest star was Mark Wynter. (vg) £12 - £14

Morecambe & Wise

Morecambe & Wise, also known as Eric & Ernie were one of Britain's best loved entertainers of all time. The famous double act began in 1941 when they were both booked separately to appear in a Revue at the Nottingham Empire Theatre. Then war intervened and the lads went their separate ways until meeting by chance at the Swansea Empire Theatre in 1946 when, once again they were booked separately. They then trod the boards at venues across the country until getting their big break on television in 1954, but the critics hammered them. In 1956 they were back on the TV screens with an appearance on the popular Winifred Atwell Show. They never looked back.

Eric Morecambe (real name John Eric Bartholomew) was born in 1926. He died of a heart attack in 1984.

Ernie Wise (real name Ernest Wiseman) was born in 1925. He died from a chest infection and heart failure in 1999.

▲ Bring Me Sunshine. Original sheet music. (1970). (g-vg) £6 - £8

▲ Embassy Theatre (Peterborough) programme. October 1950. A nice piece of Morecambe & Wise history, as they were yet to acquire top of the bill status. (vg) £6 - £8

▲ Flexi disc in picture cover. Mars confectionery promotional record. 1974. (g) £4 - £6

▲ Morecambe & Wise autographs on a single page with the date, 1953. Clear, black ink, 125 x 80mm. No dedication. £12 - £14

▲ A pane of 4 x 26p postage stamps featuring Eric Morecambe. 1999. Unused, with gutter. (vg) £1 - £2

ENTERTAINERS

Eamonn Andrews

Possibly one of the all-time most popular stars of television, Eamonn Andrews began his illustrious career with Radio Éireann as a sports commentator.

In 1950 he moved to the BBC as host of the radio programme Ignorance Is Bliss. He then became host of the TV show What's My Line. Soon after (in 1955), he hosted the legendary children's show Crackerjack (inventing the game 'Double or Drop').

Perhaps his most remembered role will always be as the host of TV show This Is Your Life. The first recipient of the big red book was originally meant to be Stanley Matthews but the secret leaked out and the producers of the show switched it to Eamonn himself.

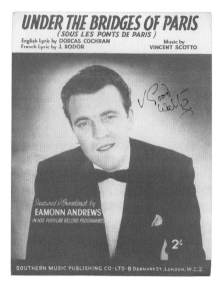

▲ Under The Bridges Of Paris - Sheet music. (1955). With Eamonn Andrews on the cover. (vg) £2 - £3

In 1964 he moved from BBC to ITV and became the presenter of World of Sport.

He had his own TV chat show, The Eamonn Andrews Show (1964 – 1969). Guests included Noel Coward, Lee Marvin, and The Beatles.

In 1969, he once again became host of This Is Your Life. The show ran for 18 years until illness prevented him from carrying on.

Eamonn died of heart failure on 5th November 1987, aged 64.

Russ Abbot

Russell A Roberts, more commonly known as Russ Abbot, was born 16 September 1947 in Chester. He is a well loved musician, actor, and comedian, who has been awarded the title of Funniest Man on Television on five occasions.

▲ Russ Abbot autograph. Clear, blue ink, 97 x 70mm. No dedication. £3 - £4

Despite a run of high-profile stage performances (in well-loved shows such as The Producers and Chitty Chitty Bang Bang) he is probably best known for his old television series, The Russ Abbot Show, in which, with the assistance of Les Dennis, he brought to life many memorable characters, including Basildon Bond, and Scottish icon C U Jimmy.

Russ has also had some success as a recording artist, with his single Atmosphere reaching number six in the charts in 1984. However, Russ personally loathes this song, and now that he has bought the performing rights to it, he refuses to allow it to be played on the radio.

▲ Let's Go To The Disco - Russ Abbot. 45rpm single record. 1985. Spirit Records, FIRE 9. Vinyl (vg), sleeve (g) £2 - £3

EPHEMERA

Ephemera refers to anything designed to be used and then eventually thrown away so, as you can imagine, it is a subject area that covers an incredibly diverse range of items: train and bus tickets, concert tickets, football programmes, First Day Covers, stamps, telegrams, postcards, birthday cards, and even newspapers are all forms of ephemera.

Collecting ephemera is actually a lovely hobby to get involved in. Collections can normally be built at little expense as they will often consist of items that other people discard after use, and because a lot of the items are made of paper, they don't take up a lot of space, and can be stored with ease in drawers or box files. The sheer diversity of available ephemera means you are also able to tailor a collection to whatever your interest might be. In fact, because ephemera is such a general topic, it really is recommended that you collect to a theme in order to keep your collection under some kind of control.

However, above and beyond all these other benefits, one of the most exciting aspects of the hobby is learning about 'social history' through the items you find. Postcards are a particularly good example of this, as they may contain images of buildings or places that were demolished many years ago.

Social history is absolutely fascinating, and collectors of ephemera help preserve it for generations to come.

▲ Cow & Gate Baby's Weight. 4 page card. 1949. 110 x 70mm. With records of a baby's weight written in ink. (g-vg) £4 - £6

The back page of the card, advertised three Cow & Gate products of the day. Milk Food to build bone, flesh and muscle. Brestol for backward and underweight children. Cerex Vitamin D for extra nutrition.

► Teignmouth Visitor's Guide. 1959. 100 pages. 210 x 135mm. Published by The Urban District Council of Teignmouth. (g-vg) £2 - £3

EPHEMERA

Starting an ephemera collection can be quite daunting, and without some self-imposed guidelines, you may end up buying (or saving) every piece of ephemera you find. You can possibly end up with a rather random and not particularly interesting array of items.

Here are a few tips that may help you stay focused, and acquire a collection of quality that might even offer some investment potential:

Only buy or keep items that are in very good condition. Rips, stains, and folds will all devalue an item. Normally, the older the item is, the more damage it can have suffered thereby significantly harming the value. The exception here is if you need a certain piece of ephemera to complete a collection, in which case you can consider buying inferior quality as a "stop-gap" while you look for a nicer example. Just make sure the price is right, and never spend more than you can afford. This is particularly relevant if you are bidding on items in an auction. It can be very easy to get carried away in all the excitement, and the desire to be the winner. Always set yourself an upper limit for any item you are trying to purchase, and do not be tempted to exceed that price. Of course, only you can decide what your maximum price limit should be, but be sensible about it.

If auctions aren't your thing, and you would rather go around collectors' fairs and car boot sales, remember that it doesn't hurt to haggle. At worst your negotiations will be rejected; at best, you could pick up a bargain.

There are so many types of ephemera, you should settle on a strong idea for a theme to your collection so that you can keep it manageable. For example, you may specialise in items relating to railways.

The content of ephemera is important. Letters are a good example of this. For example, a letter sent from or to someone famous would be incredibly interesting. Similarly, a telegram from a soldier about to go into battle is likely to attract a lot more interest from collectors than a telegram wishing someone a happy birthday. Always do your research. If you find an interesting letter, try to find out about the sender and the recipient. You may discover you have happened across a fascinating piece of history that becomes the centrepiece of your collection.

Remember that wherever there is a market, there will be fraudsters. Some people make fake ephemera (particularly wartime items), and some companies make legitimate reproductions that eventually find their way onto the secondary market where sellers pass them off (ignorantly, or purposefully) as originals. Make sure you do your homework before buying.

It seems obvious, but once you have gone to all the effort of amassing a nice collection, do take the time to store your items properly. Keep them in cool, dry locations where they are not going to be nibbled on by mice or rats. Damp is a big problem, so make sure air can circulate around your items with ease.

▲ National Health card. 1931. (vg) £3 - £4

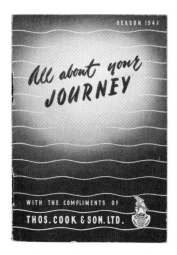

▲ Thomas Cook International Journey booklet. 1948. 16 pages. 125 x 90mm. (g-vg) £2 - £4

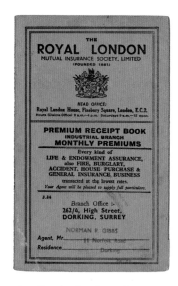

▲ Royal London Insurance Premium receipt book. 1952. 24 pages. 170 x 105mm. (f-g) £2 - £3

EPHEMERA

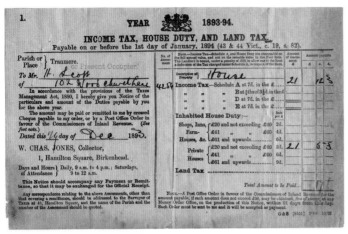

▲ House Duty invoice. Birkenhead. 29 December 1893. (f) £2 - £3

▲ Commando Shoes. Soles and Heels guarantee. 1968. (g) 50p - £1

▲ Hoover repair invoice. 9 Nov 1959. (g) 20p - 40p

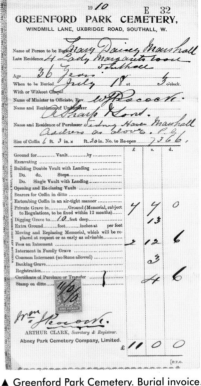

▲ Greenford Park Cemetery. Burial invoice. 18 July 1910. (g-vg) £2 - £4

▲ South Eastern Gas Board. Unused £5 silver (heavy duty paper) bag. 1965. (vg) £1 - £2

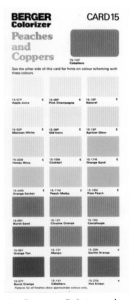

▲ Berger Paints colour chart. (1975). (vg) 10p - 20p

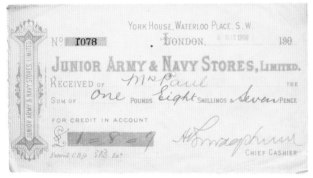

▲ Junior Army & Navy Stores. Receipt. London. 8 March 1909. (g) £1 - £3

▲ Receipt with one penny revenue postage stamp. 1 April 1909. 30p - 40p

◀ SCC Transport. Invoice. For livestock transportation. 31 October 1956. (f-g) 20p - 30p

▶ Bristol's Own Fund. Receipt for £50. World War II charity collection. (f-g) £1 - £3

EPHEMERA

In 1939 UK citizens were required by law to carry identity cards. This requirement ceased in 1952. The card had to be produced to a police officer or uniformed member of H.M. Armed Forces. Nowadays, it's hard to find one of these identity cards in excellent condition and tip-top examples command a premium.

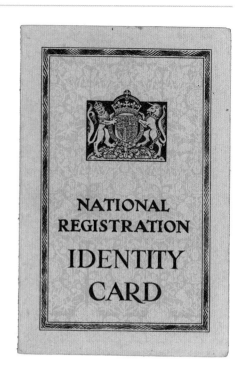

▶ National Registration Identity Card. Issued June 1943 to a lady living in Helston. With three circular (National Registration Office) date stamps '43, '47, '50. (vg-ex) £6 - £8

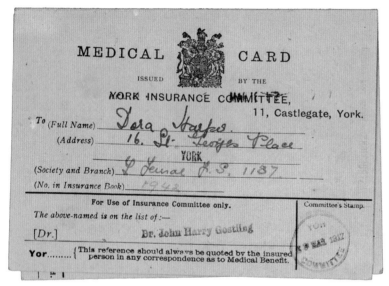

The National Insurance Act of 1911 provided a medical scheme for workers. Anyone who earned less than £160 a year was required to pay four pence, whilst the employer paid three pence. The Act is widely regarded as the foundation for modern social welfare.

◀ Medical Card. Date stamped 1917. (vg) £2 - £4

▶ National Rose Society receipt. Dated 1961. For the sum of half a guinea. (vg) 5p - 10p

Nº 4312

National Rose Society,

Telephone No. St. Albans 50461

Chiswell Green Lane,
St. Albans,
Herts.

17 5 1961

Received of G. White. Esq

the sum of Half-a-Guinea as a Subscription to the above Society for the year ending December 31st, 1961.

£ . 10 . 6

HON. TREASURER.

EPHEMERA

The National Anti-Vaccination League was founded in 1866 by Richard Gibbs. The purpose was to oppose compulsory vaccination, particularly smallpox. In Victorian times there was a widespread belief that vaccinations did more harm than good. This receipt dated 1940, proves that belief and support was still there over 50 years later.

▲ National Anti-Vaccination League. A receipt for a donation of £2.2.0d. 1940. 175 x 95mm. Some rust marks on the paper, otherwise in good condition. £2 - £3

▲ National Council for the Abolition of the Death Penalty. Receipt for a donation of ten shillings. 1935. 140 x 100mm. (vg) £4 - £6

The National Council for the Abolition of the Death Penalty was founded in 1925. They had a number of successes prior to the total abolition in 1969.

In 1933 the minimum age for trial for murder was raised to 18.

In 1938 The Infanticide Act was extended which meant that the killing of a baby up to one year old, by its mother, was no longer a capital offence.

TRADE AND COLLECT
EPHEMERA

68 page book (limpback)

Full colour throughout

This book has been written as a comprehensive introduction to the world of ephemera collecting. It covers a wide range of the types of item that can form part of a collection, and we hope that it will inspire you to start a collection of your own.

Price £2.95

Order from: Collecticus

Tel: 01380 811750

Internet: www.collecticus.co.uk

By post: Collecticus, P.O.Box 100, Devizes, Wiltshire, SN10 4TE

(Cheques/Postal Order's payable to 'Hartley Publications Ltd')

EPHEMERA

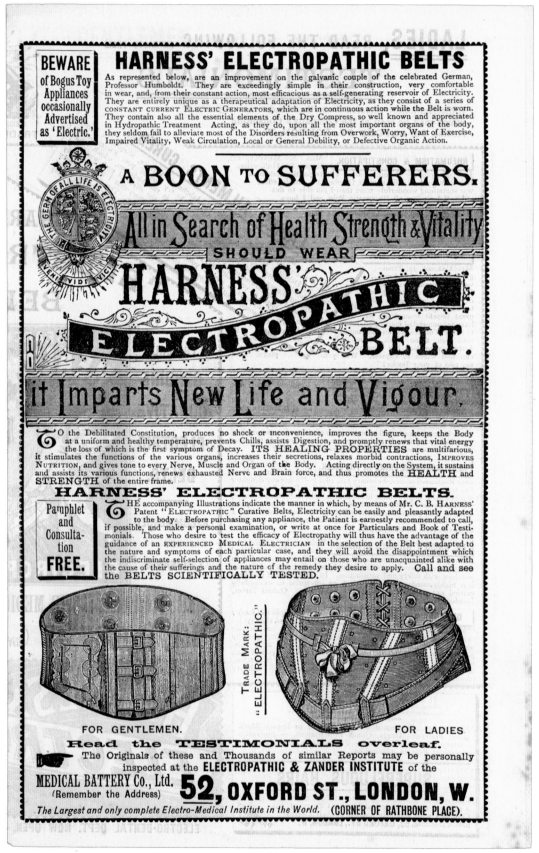

(Shown actual size)

▲ Harness Electropathic Belt 4-page leaflet. 1891. 225 x 150mm. £4 - £6

A fascinating insight into a therapeutic device. Claimed to aid certain medical conditions.

ERASERS

Novelty shaped erasers are collectable. The subject has an entry in the Guinness Book of World Records, with a German lady holding the record at over 19,000 non-duplicate shapes. She started her collection over 25 years ago.

Erasers should never be used, otherwise they will lose value (not that they are worth much individually). A collection should be stored in a cool place, in an appropriate box, perhaps something like an old fishing tackle box.

Novelty erasers can be purchased at a number of outlets. Internet auctions are a good source.

Standard erasers (not novelty shapes) can include promotional items advertising products, services etc....

▲ Tulip. (vg) 60p - 80p   ▲ Ice Cream Cornet. (vg) 60p - 80p

▲ Rock. (vg) £1 - £1.50

▲ Mouse. (vg) £1 - £2

▲ Boombox radio. (g) £80p - £1

▲ Sure Aerosol. (g) £1 - £2   ▲ Fresh Milk Carton. (vg) £1 - £2   ▲ Strawberry deodorant stick. (vg) 60p - 80p

▲ 5 Mark coin. (vg) 60p - 80p   ▲ Half Dollar coin. (vg) 60p - 80p   ▲ 2 Franc coin. (vg) 60p - 80p   ▲ Dog. (vg) 70p - 90p

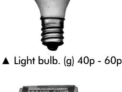

▲ Light bulb. (g) 40p - 60p

▲ Phonebox. (vg) 70p - 90p   ▲ Toilet. (vg) 60p - 80p   ▲ Roll of film. (g) 50p - 70p   ▲ Lion 3D framed picture. (vg) 80p - £1

FESTIVAL OF BRITAIN

The Festival of Britain was a national exhibition that opened 3 May 1951.

After World War II, much of Britain required redevelopment; the Festival was a means of boosting morale, by giving Britons a sense of recovery and declaring "belief and trust in the British way of life" (as put by the Archbishop of Canterbury). Furthermore, the Festival was intended to promote better quality design when rebuilding towns and cities, as well as being a celebration of the centenary of the 1851 Great Exhibition.

One of the most important parts of the Festival was The South Bank site, a 27-acre public space that contained the majority of the exhibition and was used to showcase the design principles that would be adopted when rebuilding London.

▲ Festival Of Britain Guide. 1951. 54 pages. (g) £3 - £5

▲ Festival Of Britain postcard. Postmarked London 1951. Message in ink. (g) £2 - £3

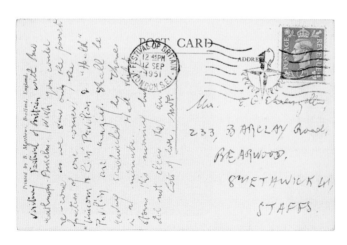

◄   National Gallery postcard. Carrying a message referring to time spent at the Exhibition. Postmarked with a Festival of Britain cancellation over a 2d postage stamp. 12 September 1951. Message in ink. (vg) £1 - £2

FESTIVAL OF BRITAIN

(Obverse)

(Reverse)

◄ Crown coin commemorating the 1951 Festival Of Britain. (ex) £3 - £5

(Front cover)

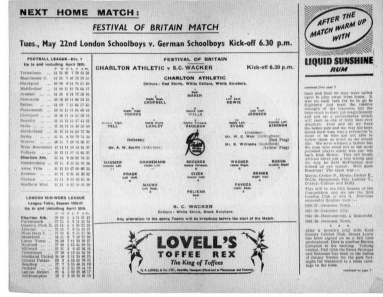
(Centre pages)

▲ Festival Of Britain football match programme. Charlton Athletic v S.C. Wacker (Germany). Wed 13 May 1951. (f) £3 - £4

(Front)

(Reverse)

◄ London Transport special bus service ticket. (vg) £2 - £3

► Bryant & May matchbook. Empty. (f-g) £2 - £3

FILM CELLS

Film cell collecting is big business. The practice is to cut a small quantity of cells from the reel of a well known movie and then mount the strip of cells on a board. Then add a picture from the movie and a small plaque specifying the name of the film.

There is a fair chance that the phasing out of 35mm film from the movie industry will help film cell values rise in the distant future. However, for the moment, the supply is so plentiful that realistically this does not appear to be the best of investments.

A collection of mounted film cells (with photographs) can be quite colourful and attractive. Above all they can be fun to collect and are ideal for the movie enthusiast.

▲ Rocky V. Framed cells. (vg) £6 - £8

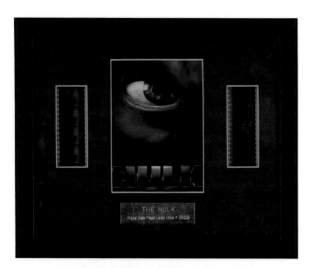

▲ The Hulk. Framed Cells. (vg) £6 - £8

▲ Sin City. Framed cells. (vg) £6 - £8

▲ i, Robot. Framed cells. (vg) £6 - £8

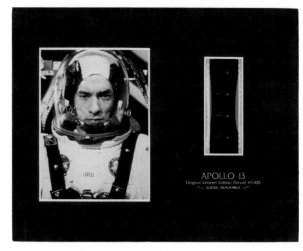

▲ Apollo 13. Mounted film cells. (ex) £6 - £8

FILM POSTERS

Yet another subject that requires research and specialist knowledge before you start investing large sums of money. The best tip for the beginner is to start with lower value posters, understand how condition affects values, study values on internet sales sites.

Many large collectors' fairs often have a serious trader just selling film posters (usually quad size). It's big business. It's a great learning exercise to examine serious stock, in person.

In 1990 a collection of 271 posters were sold by auctioneers Christies for $935,000. In 2005 a poster for the 1927 film Metropolis sold for $690,000.

The majority of quad posters being sold by traders today are far more affordable and can be purchased from around £10 for a very average example.

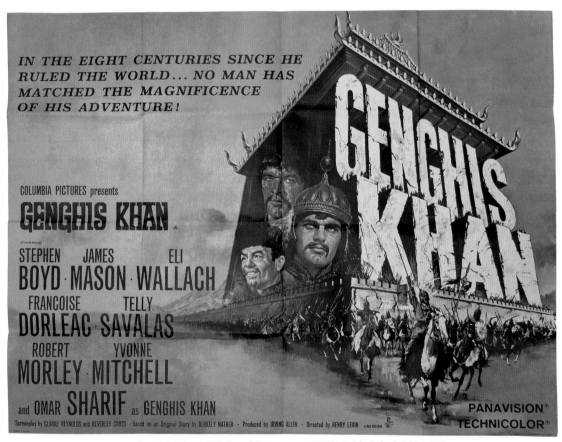

▲ Genghis Khan. UK Quad film poster. 1975. Folded. (vg) £40 - £50

(UK) film poster sizes

Quad: Size 30 inches by 40 inches (762 x 1020mm), landscape format	One-sheet: Size 27 inches by 40 inches (686 x 1020mm), portrait format
Double crown: Size 20 inches by 30 inches (508 x 762mm), portrait format	Three sheet: Size 40 inches by 81 inches (1020 x 2060mm), portrait format

FILM POSTERS

▲ The Taming Of The Shrew. UK Quad film poster. 1967. Folded. (vg) £80 - £100

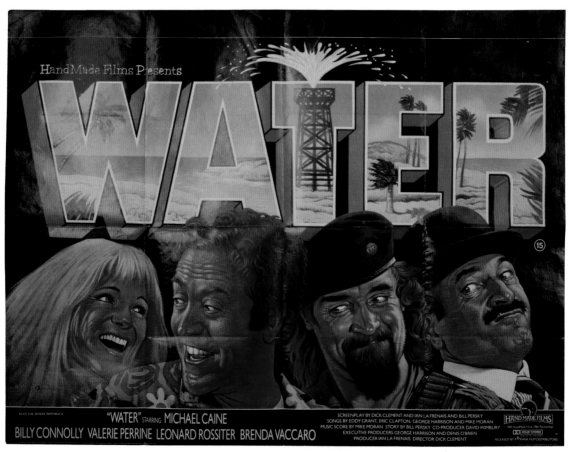

▲ Water. UK Quad film poster. 1985. Folded. (g) £25 - £30

FILM POSTERS

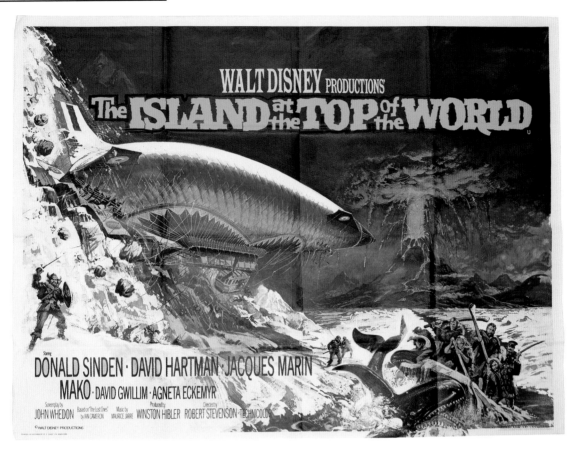

▲ The Island At The Top Of The World. UK Quad film poster. 1974. Folded. (vg) £40 - £50

▲ The Plainsman. UK Quad film poster. 1966. Folded. (vg) £30 - £40

FILM POSTERS

▲ Goodbye Mr. Chips. UK Quad film poster. 1969. Folded. (g-vg) £40 - £50

▲ Matilda. UK Quad film poster. 1978. Folded. (g) £30 - £40

FIREWORKS

Fireworks can be a nice theme for a collector to focus on, and there are some really lovely old items relating to fireworks and bonfires available. Collecting old fireworks can be extremely dangerous and we would suggest you only purchase used (dead) fireworks (never store live fireworks as collectables!). Used fireworks can be cleaned of any remaining gunpowder. Old examples are very collectable but they are extremely hard to find. It's a lot easier to find old items of ephemera relating to the evening of 5 November and such items, especially ones relating to firework safety, can sometimes prove to be very interesting indeed.

▲ Standard Fireworks. Empty box. (1960). 270 x 130mm. (g) £8 - £10

◄ Fireworks advertisement. Overprinted on the reverse of a circa 1925 picture postcard (yachting scene). (g) £4 - £6

▲ Excelsior Sparklers. (1955). Pack of 12 with 10 remaining. (g) £10 - £12

▲ Stella Sparklers. (1960). Pack of 12 with 4 remaining. A Brocks Fireworks product. (g) £3 - £5

▲ Brocks Fireworks model van. Days Gone model. 2002. Box (vg), model (mnt) £3 - £4

▲ Standard Fireworks model van. Days Gone model. 2002. Box (vg), model (mnt) £3 - £4

FOOTBALL

With over 100 years of history of the modern game of football there's a mountain of memorabilia, some of which now commands decent sums of money. It's basically a case of choosing what level you wish to buy into. Some football programmes around 50 years old can still be bought for just a few pounds.

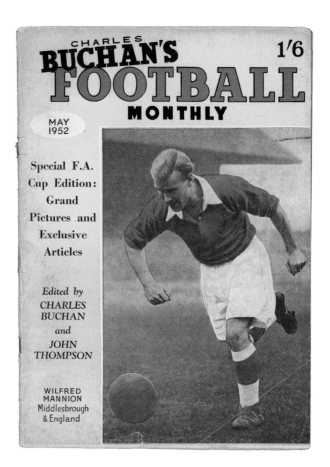

▲ Charles Buchan's Football Monthly magazine. May 1952. (g) £3 - £4

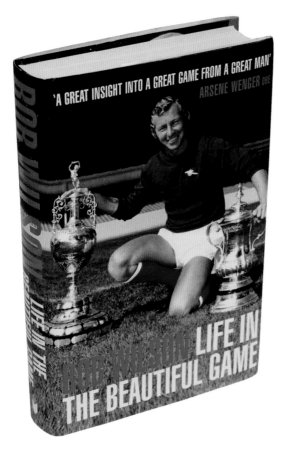

▲ Life In The Beautiful Game - Bob Wilson. Hardback book. 472 pages. Signed (with dedication to an Arsenal fan) by Bob Wilson. Clear, blue ink. (ex) £4 - £6

◀ Dave Mackay button badge. 32mm diameter. (g) £3 - £4

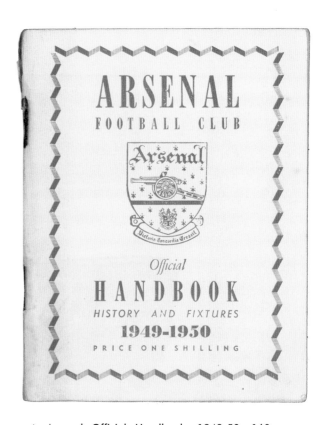

▲ Arsenal Official Handbook. 1949-50. 160 pages. 135 x 105mm. (g) £10 - £14

FOOTBALL - George Best

George Best was born in Belfast in 1946. He was talent spotted at the age of 15 by a Manchester United talent scout. He became one of the most talented players of the 20th century. George died in 2005.

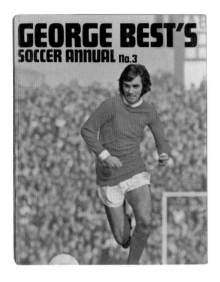

▲ George Best's Soccer Annual. No.3. 1970. (vg) £4 - £6

► George Best limited edition signed photograph. Clear pencil, 420 x 295mm. No dedication. £80 - £90

George Best

George Best turns to celebrate scoring Manchester United's second goal in the1968 European Cup Final at Wembley. United go on to beat Benfica 4-1 after extra time.

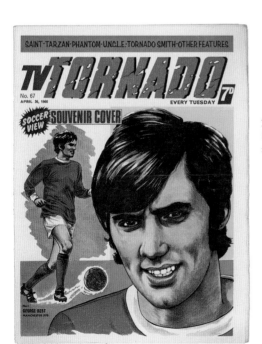

◄ TV Tornado magazine. 20 April 1968. George Best on the cover. (vg) £6 - £8

► Charles Buchan's Football Monthly. May 1966. George Best on the cover. (g) £4 - £6

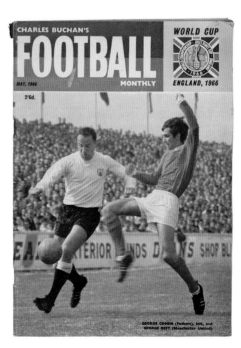

FOOTBALL - Sir Stanley Matthews

Stanley Matthews was born in 1915 and died in 2000. He was one of the greatest English football players of all time. He was many a schoolboy's super hero, particularly in the 50's and 60's. He played at the top level until the age of 50. A remarkable feat.

▶ Stanley Matthews C.B.E. Biography by Anthony Davis. Hardback. 1962. First edition. 119 pages. 190 x 125mm. (vg) £10 - £12

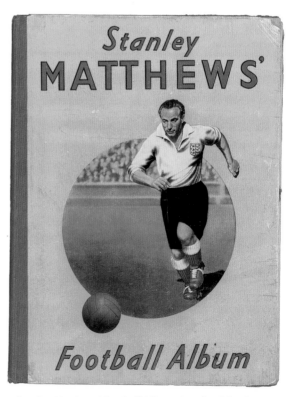

◀ Stanley Matthews autographed commemorative cover. 1993. Clear, black ink, 160 x 115mm. No dedication. (vg) £14 - £16

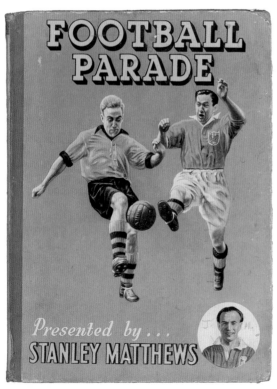

▲ Football Parade hardback book. 1950. 275 x 205mm. (p-f) £2 - £3

▲ Stanley Matthews' Football Album. Hardback book. 1950. 275 x 210mm. (p) £2 - £3

FOOTBALL

Brian Clough

Footballer and manager Brian Howard Clough was born 21 March 1935, in Middlesbrough. He started his professional career playing for Middlesbrough in 1955, and he stayed with them until 1961, making 213 league appearances and scoring 197 goals. He subsequently played for Sunderland, before hanging up his boots.

As a manager he helmed Hartlepool United (1965-1967), Derby County (1967-1973), Brighton & Hove Albion (1973-1974), Leeds United (1974), and Nottingham Forest (1975-1993).

Sadly, Clough was diagnosed with stomach cancer and passed away on 20 September 2004, aged just 69. A memorial service was held for him on 21 October 2004 and was Attended by more than 14,000 people.

▲ Brian Clough Testimonial Match programme. 27 October 1965. (g) £6 - £8

Billy Wright

William Ambrose "Billy" Wright (born 6 February 1924) was an English footballer who started out at Wolverhampton Wanderers in 1939 and stayed with them for the entire span of his 20-year career.

From 1946 until 1959 he also made 105 appearances for England (including a record 90 times as captain), making him the first player to have ever earned 100 caps for his country. After retiring from the pitch, he managed Arsenal from 1962 until 1966.

▲ TV Tornado. Issue no.61. 9 March 1968. Billy Wright featured on the front cover. (vg) £3 - £5

He died on 3 September 1994, aged 70, as a result of the stomach cancer he had been diagnosed with in 1994.

Asa Hartford

Manchester City	
Asa Hartford	
International Appearances	20
International Goals	2
League Appearances	331
League Goals	37
Height	5'7"

▲ Asa Hartford. Top Trumps trading card. 1978. 90 x 60mm. (vg) 20p - 40p

Richard Asa Hartford (born 24 October 1950) is a retired Scottish international footballer who was capped for Scotland 50 times between 1972 and 1982.

He began his professional career in 1967, playing for West Bromwich Albion. A high-profile transfer to Leeds United in 1971 was cancelled when a medical examination revealed a potential hole-in-the-heart condition; but this discovery did not prevent Hartford from going on to have a long and successful career with other clubs, including Manchester City (1974 - 1979 and 1981 - 1984), Everton (1979 - 1981), Norwich City (1984 - 1985), and Bolton Wanderers (1985 - 1987). The last team he played for before finally hanging up his boots in 1991 was Shrewsbury Town.

He has since managed several teams, including Blackburn Rovers and Manchester City.

FOOTBALL - World Cup 1966

The eighth staging of the World Cup was held in England throughout July of 1966. England had been chosen as hosts by FIFA in August 1960 as a celebration of the centenary of the standardisation of football in England.

In total, 70 nations took part, and it would have been even more if 16 African nations hadn't boycotted the tournament in protest of a controversial FIFA ruling that meant teams from Africa, Asia, and Australia would all need to fight it out for just a single place in the finals.

England eventually won the tournament, beating West Germany, 4-2, in the final and becoming the first host nation to win since Italy in 1934. Three of England's goals were scored by Geoff Hurst (the only player to have ever scored a hat trick in a World Cup final) and one was scored by Martin Peters.

Of course, the final moments of the competition have gone down in footballing history. The game had gone into extra time, when Hurst scored his second goal, making the score 3-2. With seconds left on the clock, fans invaded the pitch, and BBC commentator Kenneth Wolstenholme declared, "Some people are on the pitch. They think it's all over..." At that exact moment, Hurst found the back of the net once again, making the score 4-2, and Wolstenholme cried, "It is now!"

Off the pitch there was some excitement prior to the first round when the Jules Rimet trophy was stolen and a replacement was made while a nationwide search was undertaken. The trophy was sniffed out just in time by a dog called Pickles, and the replacement was not required. Sadly, Pickles died when his lead got snagged on a tree branch while he was chasing a cat and he choked to death.

▲ Look and Learn Magazine. 3rd June 1967. Featuring 'Pickles' the 'World Cup dog' on the cover. 315 x 250mm. (g) £4 - £6

▲ World Cup Final Programme. Original. 1966. (g) £70 - £80

World Cup Willie

▲ Original button badge. 1966. 25mm diam. (vg) £15 - £18

▲ Soccer Review. Volume 1, Number 26, 1966. With World Cup Willie sweets advert. (vg) £3 - £4

The 1966 World Cup was the first to have an official mascot. The mascot in question was World Cup Willie, a cartoon lion in a Union Jack jersey. He was drawn by Reg Hoye, and was chosen over a bulldog character because of the link with the three lions that appear on England's crest.

Willie was used as a way of generating funds to support the World Cup, appearing on clothes, toys, mugs, badges, posters, key rings, pennants, comics, cloth patches, flags, and even sweets. The official World Cup Willie song (which surprisingly failed to chart in the UK) was performed by Lonnie Donegan.

World Cup Willie memorabilia is very desirable right now, and mint condition pieces can be expected to sell well at auction.

FOOTBALL PROGRAMMES

The first football programmes were produced in the 1870s. They were extremely basic (usually a single sheet) and were used to enable fans to identify the players and notify them of forthcoming fixtures. At this time, players did not have names and numbers on the back of their shirt, meaning there had to be other ways for fans to identify the players, usually the colour of their stockings or the type of cap they wore.

In the 1900s, football clubs began to realise that a profit could be made from programmes and cover prices began to rise. To justify the price increase, the quality had to be increased too, meaning programmes were no longer single sheets and they began to resemble the programmes we are used to today, with editorial content on the club, news, and more detailed information on the players.

Rising popularity in football meant more people attended the games, leading to a higher circulation of the programme. By the 1920s, programmes were used by the vast majority of clubs and they were proving very popular with fans.

▲ England v Scotland programme. 14 April 1951. England's line-up included Alf Ramsey, Jack Froggatt, Billy Wright, Stanley Matthews, Wilf Mannion and Tom Finney. (f) £12 - £16

When Wembley opened in 1923 the quality of programmes dramatically increased and the covers began to be produced in colour. The first FA Cup Final programme at Wembley from 1923 is a highly desirable programme and is one of the most famous available. It is sometimes referred to as the "Penny Black" of football programmes, and it has been known to sell for four figure sums (it sold for £1,100 at an auction in 2007). Not bad for something with a cover price of 3d!

The quality of football programmes suffered a major setback after World War II (predominantly due to paper rationing). During (and for a few years after) the War, they began to resemble the original programmes from the 1870s.

The 60s saw the very interesting introduction of small programmes. Many collectors believe this was due to the popularity of "mini" items (such as the popular car and the fashionable skirt). Others believe it was simply because fans wanted to be able to fit the programme into their pockets!

The success of the 1966 World Cup increased the nation's interest in football and programmes were completely modernised (graphic designers were used for the first time).

In the 1970s, programmes began to look more like magazines (some clubs even referred to the programmes as "matchday magazines"). Glossy paper was common and photographs (some in colour) were used.

Today's programmes have fullcolour pages throughout and look very much like magazines (often in A5 size). Practically every club uses the programme as a way of gaining extra revenue (through the cover price and advertising) and to keep fans informed of the latest happenings at the club, although the programme is also a good way for the club to advertise other areas they are involved in (such as merchandise).

The majority of football programme collectors are also big football fans. Some of these collectors tend to focus their collecting to their favourite club. The top clubs have millions of fans throughout the country so if you are selling a programme from one of these clubs, you will have a huge market.

Other collectors choose to specialise in particular areas of football programmes. For example, they may try to collect the programmes from all FA Cup Finals or collect one from each English and Scottish team (or sometimes one per season per club).

FOOTBALL PROGRAMMES

▲Derby County v Arsenal. 10 May 1947. (f-g) £20 - £24

▲Manchester United v Blackpool. 2 Sep 1950. (f-g) £12 - £14

▲Rangers v Airdrieonians. 12 January 1952. (f-g) £8 - £10

▲Chelsea v Clapton Orient & Crystal Palace. 11 and 13 February 1911 (single issue). Volume 6. No.29. (f) £175 - £200

▲   Shelbourne   v Waterford. 16 January 1955. (f-g) £2 - £4

▲Chelsea v Arsenal. 24 August 1949. (p-f) £6 - £8

▲Schools' International. England v Scotland at Wembley.   15 April 1950. (f) £3 - £5

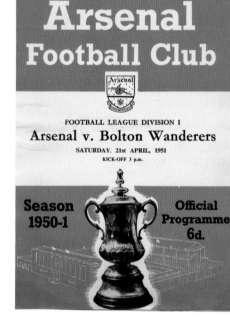

▲Arsenal v Bolton Wanderers. 21 April 1951. (g-vg) £12 - £16

▲Leicester   City   v Manchester   City.   4 September 1954. (g) £8 - £10

▲Arsenal v Liverpool. 24 May 1947. (f-g) £6 - £8

▲Chesterfield v Notts County. 8 May 1948. (f-g) £8 - £12

◄ Charlton Athletic v Arsenal.   27 August 1947. (f) £8 - £12

►Chelsea   v Preston   North End.   27   March 1948.   (g-vg) £15 - £18

◄   Arsenal v Manchester   City. 6 December 1947. (g-vg) £15 - £18

►   Blackpool v Everton. 10 Dec 1955.   (g-vg) £10 - £12

FOOTBALL PROGRAMMES

▲ Norwich City v Manchester Utd. 10 Jan 1959. (g-vg) £1 - £2

▲ York City v Shrewsbury Town. 8 Nov 1958. (g) £2 - £4

▲ Finchley v Southall. 24 Apr 1954. (f-g) £3 - £5

▲ Airdrieonians v Ayr Utd. 23 Feb 1957. (vg) £2 - £4

▲ Chester v Luton. 11 May 1966. (g) £1 - £2

▲ Stockport Cty v Managers & Ex - Internationals. 28 Apr 1952. (f) £4 - £6

▲ Chelsea v Middlesbrough. 10 May 1947. (vg) £8 - £10

▲ Manchester City v Manchester Utd. 27 Sep 1958. (g-vg) £3 - £5

▲ Stranraer v Alloa Athletic. 3 Dec 1955. (f) £4 - £6

▲ Blackburn v Sheffield Wed. 5 Sep 1959. (vg-ex) £2 - £3

▲ Millwall v Stockport County. 26 Dec 1959. (g) £1 - £2

▲ Arsenal v Leeds Utd. 4 Mar 1950. (f) £4 - £6

▲ England v Poland. 24 Sep 1958. (g) £2 - £4

▲ Arsenal v Blackpool. 19 Apr 1957. (g) £2 - £4

▲ Chelsea v Arsenal. 21 Nov 1959. (f-g) £2 - £4

▲ England v Holland. 15 Nov 1952. (f-g) £6 - £8

▲ Manchester Utd v Bolton W. 23 Jan 1954. (f-g) £10 - £12

▲ Leyton Orient v Queen's Park Rangers. 3 Mar 1956. (g) £3 - £5

▲ TSV Munchen 1860 v West Ham Utd. 19 May 1965. (g) £1 - £2

▲ Huddersfield v Manchester Utd. 31 Mar 1956. (f) £8 - £10

▲ Tottenham v Newcastle Utd. 15 Jan 1966. (vg-ex) £1 - £2

▲ Charlton Athletic v Sunderland. 19 Aug 1953. (f) £6 - £8

▲ Sheffield Wed v Burnley. 24 Sep 1960. (g-vg) £2 - £3

▲ West Ham Utd v Chelsea. 6 Oct 1945. (g) £18 - £22

▲ Bristol Rovers v Chelsea. 28 Jan 1961. (g-vg) £2 - £3

▲ Oxford Utd v Stockport. 3 Oct 1962. (vg-ex) £1 - £2

▲ Hitchin Town v Leyton Reserves. 23 Apr 1955. (g-vg) £3 - £4

▲ Blackpool v Manchester Utd. 30 Aug 1958. (g-vg) £7 - £9

▲ Fulham v Brighton & Hove Albion. 26 Dec 1958. (vg) £3 - £5

▲ Darlington v Chesterfield. 19 Oct 1964. (f-g) £1 - £2

▲ Oxford v St Albans City. 3 Sep 1958. (g) £1 - £2

▲ Barnsley v Falkirk. 5 May 1951. (vg) £1 - £2

▲ England v Spain. 3 Apr 1968. (g) £1 - £2

▲ Birmingham v Manchester Utd. 29 Nov 1958. (g-vg) £3 - £4

▲ England XI v Combined Services XI. 29 Apr 1944. (g) £14 - £16

FOOTBALL PROGRAMMES
(With tickets)

The majority of football programmes being sold today do not have the relevant original ticket stub.

Why so many football fans saved their programmes but failed to keep the tickets, is quite puzzling. Perhaps it's because the programme was purchased as an 'extra', whereas the ticket was simply perceived as the means of getting into the ground and therefore not worth keeping.

Anyway, because the ticket stubs are far less common, they can significantly boost the value of a programme.

It would appear that in the last 15 years or so, more tickets are being saved. The trouble is, these newer programmes, are generally yet to acquire much value.

Most pre-1960 programmes with their ticket stubs are seriously collectable, particularly FA Cup. The better the condition, the higher the value.

A good tip is to buy an old ticket through an internet auction (as long as you are confident that you are buying an original and not a fake), then buy the relevant programme. Marrying the two together, can, with a bit of luck, be a 'nice little earner'.

The message to all football fans is to keep every ticket and if you see others disposing of their tickets after the match, grab them and store them safely. In many years to come they may have a decent value.

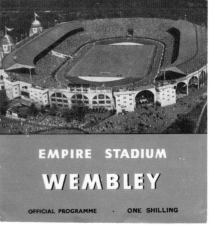

▲ Bolton Wanderers v Manchester United. FA Cup final. 3 May 1958. Prog (vg), ticket (vg) £60 - £70

▲ Arsenal v Manchester United. FA Cup final. 12 May 1979. Prog (vg), ticket (vg) £18 - £22

▲ England v Spain. 26 Oct 1960. Prog (g), ticket (vg) £16 - £18

▲ England v Italy. 14 Nov 1973. Prog (vg), ticket (vg) £12 - £14

▲ England v Hungary. 27 Apr 1983. Prog (g), ticket (vg) £10 - £12

▲ Aston Villa v Southampton. 8 Jan 2000. Prog (vg), ticket (vg) £4 - £5

FOOTBALL - Match tickets

This is a collecting area with investment potential. Knowing what to pay in the first place is crucial if you are to have any chance of making a success of it. Getting a good grasp of current values shouldn't take too long as there's a buoyant internet market.

Match tickets do not take up much space and postal costs are minimal. This collecting area has a lot going for it.

◄ World Cup. 13 Jul 1966. (f) £25 - £30

▲ England v Czechoslovakia. 2 Nov 1966. (vg) £8 - £10

▲ England v Hungary. 5 May 1965. (vg) £6 - £8

▲ England v Scotland. 6 Apr 1963. (vg) £10 - £12

▲ England v Spain. 26 Oct 1960. (vg) £8 - £12

▲ England v Scotland. 9 Apr 1949. (vg) £20 - £25

▲ England v Rumania. 15 Jan 1969. (vg) £8 - £10

▲ England v West Germany. 12 Mar 1975. (g) £5 - £7

▲ England v Denmark. 12 Sep 1979. (g) £4 - £7

▲ England v Scotland. 22 May 1971. (g-vg) £5 - £8

▲ England v Bulgaria. 11 Dec 1968. (vg) £7 - £9

▲ England v Mexico. 10 May 1961. (vg) £10 - £12

▲ England v Portugal. 10 Dec 1969. (g) £8 - £10

▲ England v USSR. 6 Dec 1967. (f-g) £6 - £8

▲ League Cup final. 13 Mar 1982. (g-vg) £5 - £7

▲ England v Scotland. 10 Apr 1965. (g-vg) £8 - £10

▲ Wales v West Germany. 31 May 1989. (vg) £2 - £4

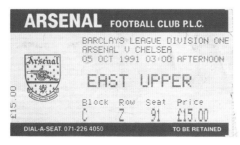

▲ Arsenal v Chelsea. 5 Oct 1991. (f-g) £1 - £2

▲ Norwich City v Portsmouth. 24 Oct 2000. (g-vg) £1 - £2

FOOTBALL - Songs

Collectors of 45rpm singles are not normally considered to be prime candidates for football songs. The music and lyrics are often classed as cheesy. However, for fans of the relevant football teams, these can be 'valuable' pieces of their Club history.

▲ Here We Go - Everton. 1985. Columbia, DB 9106. Vinyl (g) £6 - £8

▲ Good Old Arsenal - Arsenal. 1971. PYE Records, 7N 45067. Vinyl (p) £2 - £4

▲ Glory, Glory, Man. United - Manchester United. 1983. EMI Records, EMI 5390. Vinyl (g-vg) £2 - £4

▲ This Time (We'll Get It Right) - England World Cup Squad. 1982. England Records, ER 1. Vinyl (g) £3 - £5

▲ We Will Stand Together - Manchester United. 1990. Big Wave, BWR 37. Vinyl (g-vg) £4 - £6

▲ Boys In Blue - Manchester City. 1972. RCA Records, RCA 2200. Vinyl (g) £2 - £4

▲ The Red Brigade - Aberdeen. 1983. JY Records, JYR 0020. Vinyl (vg) £2 - £4

▲ Ossie's Dream... - Tottenham Hotspur FA Cup Final Squad. 1981. Shelf, SHELF 1. Vinyl (vg) £4 - £6

▲ Hot Shot Tottenham - Tottenham Hotspur FA Cup Final Squad with Chas & Dave. 1987. Rainbow Records, RBR 16. Vinyl (g-vg) £4 - £6

▲ Blue Is The Colour - Chelsea. 1972. Penny Farthing, PEN 782. Vinyl dinked (f) £2 - £3

▲ Glory, Glory, Leeds United - Leeds United. 1968. Columbia, DB 8506. Vinyl (f) £2 - £4

▲ Here We Are - England. 1975. Inline Records, ENS 1. Vinyl (g) £4 - £6

▲ Onward Sexton's Soldiers - Manchester United. 1979. RCA Records, MAN 1. Vinyl (vg) £5 - £7

▲ We'll Be With You - Stoke City. 1972. Trent, JT 100. Vinyl (f-g) £2 - £4

▲ Liverpool, We Love You - Liverpool. 1973. Bradleys, BRAD 317. Vinyl (p-f) £2 - £3

▲ We Got The Whole World In Our Hands - Nottingham Forest. 1978. Warner Bros, K 17110. Vinyl (f) £2 - £3

▲ Back Home - England World Cup Squad. 1970. PYE Records, 7N 17920. Vinyl (g) £2 - £3

▲ Tottenham, Tottenham - Tottenham Hotspur. 1982. Shelf, SHELF 2. Vinyl (g-vg) £5 - £7

▲ World Cup 1982 - The Keegaroos. 1982. TW Records, HIT 104. Vinyl (vg) £4 - £6

FOOTBALL POOLS

The history of The Pools dates back to 1923 when Littlewoods began trading. Their first sales outlet was outside Manchester United's Old Trafford football ground.

Sherman's Pools was founded in the mid-1930's by Harry Sherman, a Cardiff bookmaker. The business thrived until being taken over by the giant Littlewoods Pools in July 1961. Sadly, Harry died just a matter of weeks after the deal was brokered.

Sherman's issued four sets of (large sized) trade cards between 1937 and 1940.

(Front) (Reverse)

▲ Famous Film Stars. Full set of 8 trade cards. 1940. Each card measures 96 x 133mm. (Card shown: Mickey Rooney). (ex) £8 - £10

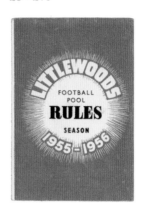

◄ Littlewoods Pools. Rules booklet. 1955. (ex) £3 - £4

◄ Littlewoods advertisement on the reverse of a 2d Brighton Hove & District bus ticket. (1950). (vg) 20p - 30p

► Littlewoods advertisement on the reverse of a Llandudno railway ticket. (1940). (vg) 20p - 30p

◄ Zetters rules booklet. 2002. (g) 1p - 5p

▲ Vernons Bulletin. 1938. 240 x 155mm. (vg) £4 - £6

◄ Littlewoods Pools Advice booklet. 1955. 95 x 90mm. (g-vg) £2 - £3

GADGET STICKS

Gadget sticks are canes that were often designed more as novelties rather than wholesome walking canes. They are so called, because they contained an array of objects from swords to telescopes.

▲ ▶ This gadget stick is dated circa 1910 and is in very good condition for its age. The slightly loose but intact ferrule (cap at the end of the stick) does not detract hugely from its value. The stick is in three parts and reveals a pen. Ink was stored in the ferrule. (vg) £120 - £140

GAMES

◄ 'Knitting Nancy' boxed game. Spear's first produced the game in 1929 and it is still manufactured today. The game pictured opposite, dates from circa 1950 and includes the original instruction leaflet. (g) £3 - £4

There are so many game related collectables, a good collecting tip is to specialise in a particular theme.

Many people nostalgically purchase games they used to play with as children, hence there's a thriving collectables market for old games. Those relating to old TV shows are particularly collectable.

Some really nice examples can be found from time to time at car boot sales, at give-away prices. Collectors Fairs are a good source for quality items.

Merit produced many boxed games in the 1950's and 1960's. It was a British toy manufacturer, owned by J& L Randall of Potters Bar.

▲ Daily Mirror Double Words. 1930. Boxed game (complete) jointly produced by The Daily Mirror and Chad Valley. A well devised word puzzle game. (vg)   £13 - £16

▲ Kan-U-Go. (1950). Boxed crossword card game. Jarvis Porter Ltd., Leeds. Far from rare. (vg) £4 - £5

▲ Winkle's Wedding. (1950). Boxed card game. Chad Valley. (g) £5 - £7

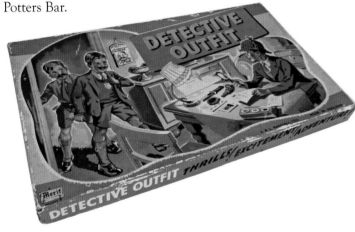

▲ Detective Outfit. Merit game. (1960) Box (355 x 240 x 25mm) in fair to good condition but some contents missing. £5 -£6

▲ Who, What, Where? Fun In A Box. 2007. A Parker product. (ex) £4 - £6

Parker Toys was founded by George S. Parker, Salem Massachusetts in 1883. The company changed its name to Parker Brothers in 1888 when George's brothers Charles and Edward joined. In 1970, Parker Bros. became part of the Palitoy empire. In 1991 Parker Brothers was bought by Hasbro and from 2013 onwards, they began phasing out the reference to 'Parker' on its games.

▲ Spot-A-Lott. 1969. Motoring board game. Magnetic game. Lotts Toys of Barnstaple, Devon. (vg) £12 - £14

GAMES

▲ Colour Dominoes. Spear's Games. (1965). Dominoes (ex), box (f-g) £4 - £6

▲ Photocrime. Pepys. 1952. (vg) £6 - £8

◄ Metal Puzzles. J & L Randall Ltd. (1965). (vg) £3 - £4

▲ Easy Chair. Party Game Publishers. (1950). (g-vg) £3 - £4

▲ Mr Bean Noughts & Crosses. Tiger Aspect Productions Ltd. (2007). (vg) £1 - £2

▲ Mr Bean Bean Football. Tiger Aspect Productions Ltd. (2007). (vg) £1 - £2

▲ Mr Bean Bean Ludo. Tiger Aspect Productions Ltd. (2007). (vg) £1 - £2

▲ Mikado Pick-Up Sticks. Spear's Games. (1975). (vg) £3 - £5

▲ What Do You Know? Pepys. 1960. (vg) £5 - £7

▲ Mouse Game. Merit. (1970). (vg) £3 - £4

▲ The Quickway Key For Crosswords. 1931. 256 pages, 153 x 105mm. (g) £4 - £6

GARFIELD

The lasagne-loving cat with a weight problem and an allergy to Mondays, who is the brainchild of cartoonist Jim Davis, made his comic strip debut in June 1978. At that time he bore only a fleeting resemblance to the character we know today; he was hugely obese, with flabby cheeks and tiny, beady eyes. However, over time he became a much more loveable fellow, with huge, comical eyes that allowed for greater use of emotive expressions. He also lost a lot of weight, although the paunch is ever-evident.

As Garfield's popularity grew, it was only a matter of time before he transferred to television. His first small-screen appearance was in 1982, in Here Comes Garfield, where his thoughts were voiced by the talented Lorenzo Music. The success of the special show resulted in several more being produced, as well as a long-running television series entitled Garfield and Friends, which aired from 1988 to 1995 and included stories based around a collection of farm animals.

Despite his worldwide appeal and continued success, it was not until recently that Hollywood set its sights on turning Garfield into a feature film, and in 2004 Garfield: The Movie was released in cinemas. Rather than being completely animated, or completely live-action, the producers decided to make a movie in which everything would be live-action except for Garfield, who would be brought to life with computer-generated graphics. This resulted in all the actors in the film playing their scenes with an "invisible" Garfield who was added into every shot in post-production. Fans were smitten by the high-energy humour and accurate portrayal of the much-loved characters, and a sequel went into production. Garfield: A Tail of Two Kitties was released in cinemas in June 2006.

Two films, 12 animated specials, one television series, a comic strip that has a place in the Guinness Book of World Records for most syndicated comic strip, and more official merchandise than any one collector could possibly hope to acquire. What's next for Garfield? Who knows, other than Jim Davis, and perhaps Garfield's long-suffering owner, Jon Arbuckle? It looks like Garfield's continuing demands for the limelight of stardom will be keeping us entertained for years to come; surely a good thing for cat-lovers everywhere.

▲ Garfield alarm clock. (1985). Working order. (vg) £4 - £6

▲ Garfield book. Guide To Behaving Badly. 1996. 68 Pages. (ex) £1 - £2

◄ Garfield pin badge. "Have a Nice Day". (1980). 55mm. 50p - 70p

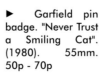

► Garfield pin badge. "Never Trust a Smiling Cat". (1980). 55mm. 50p - 70p

GILES

Ronald "Carl" Giles was born 29 September 1916, in Islington. Although he had no formal art training, by the mid-1930s he was working in animation and was even one of the principal animators on The Fox Hunt, which is one of the first ever British full-length colour cartoons with sound.

In 1937, Giles started working as a cartoonist for Reynolds News. His work came to the attention of the editor of the Sunday Express, and in 1943 he was offered a job on the Daily Express and Sunday Express. His first cartoon for his new employers appeared in the Sunday Express on 3 October 1943. The Giles family, for which he is most famous, first appeared on 5 August 1945.

Giles became so successful that he was in a strong enough position to be quite a difficult employee. He insisted on only providing three illustrations per week and he never went to work in London, relying on the newspaper to despatch taxis (or even a helicopter in bad weather) to collect work from his country home in Ipswich.

Giles' work was popular with the Royal Family, and he was awarded an OBE in 1959. He passed away in a hospital, in Ipswich, on 27 August 1995.

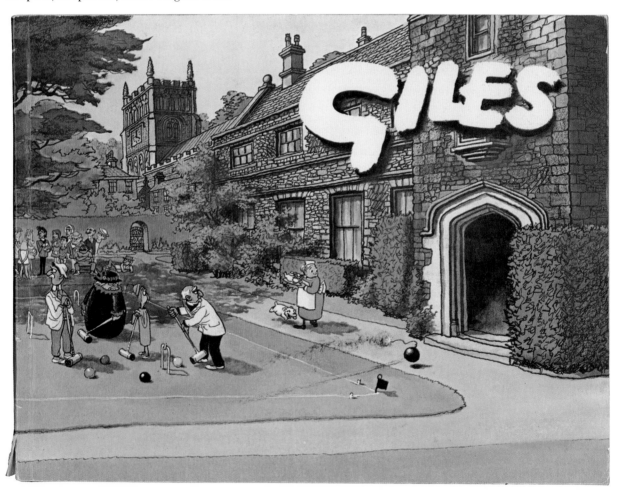

▲ Giles annual (number 21). 1968. Price marked 5/-. Introduction by David Frost. (vg) £5 - £7

There's just one annual that you really need to remember. It's the all important number 1. It was published in 1946 and a copy in very good condition can command a price tag of around £200. Issues 2 – 5 can also attract sums from £40 if in very good condition. Issues 6 – 10 can make around £20. Issues 11 – 15 are priced around £10.

GLOVE STRETCHERS

In Victorian times, particularly, fashionable ladies desired tight fitting gloves, but the materials used were not naturally stretchy, hence the need for a 'glove stretcher'.

The device was spring loaded and when the large ends were squeezed, the smaller ends enabled the fingers of the glove to stretch.

They were typically made of wood, ivory or bone. The more valuable examples are those that are elaborately decorated or carved.

◄ Glove Stretcher. (1900). Ebony. Unknown maker. £8 - £12

GOLF

The game of golf dates back to the 15th century. Like many other major sports, there's plenty of memorabilia for enthusiasts to collect.

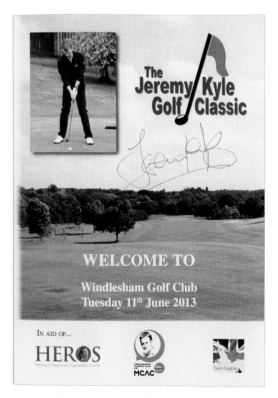

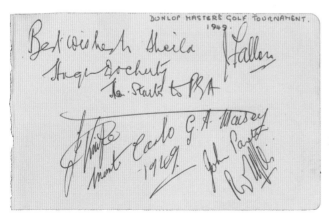

▲ Dunlop Master Autograph page. Clear, blue ink, 155 x 100mm. No dedication. £8 - £10

▲ Jeremy Kyle Golf Classic programme. Signed by Jeremy Kyle. 2013. Clear, blue ink. No dedication. £7 - £9

GRAMOPHONE NEEDLES

For a 78rpm record to be played on a gramophone, a needle had to be placed in the sound box. Most of these needles were only designed to be played once (for each side of a record) and therefore people bought the needles by the hundred.

There was no volume control on the old gramophone players but some degree of sound level could be achieved by using a different thickness of needle. The thicker the needle, the louder the volume.

Most manufacturers packaged the needles in small tins (average size of approximately 45mm x 32mm x 8mm for standard tins). The tins are now the subject of a buoyant collectors' market. They can make a most attractive collection and are easy to store.

The most common tins are Songster, His Master's Voice, Embassy and Edison Bell, although even these have rarer variants.

It's the rarer names that collectors are paying the higher sums for and particularly if the image on the tin is attractive.

As well as tins, gramophone needles were also sold in packets and boxes.

There's a strong collecting area crossover with old tin, advertising and packaging in general. Collectors of old gramophones will also look for tins of the era of the model.

Take great care if you attempt to clean a gramophone needle tin. The best tip is to leave it in the state you have found it. Tins should be stored in individual wrappers to help avoid them touching each other and thereby causing scratches to the lid images.

Modern needles for record players were not generally sold in attractive packaging and are therefore generally of little interest.

▲ Golden Pyramid. Hard to find, tin in the shape of a pyramid. Contained 200 (medium) needles. Some contents remaining. (f-g) £22 - £26

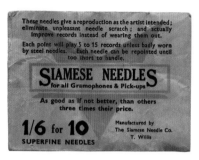

▲ Siamese Needles. Packet. Empty. (g-vg) £8 - £10

◄ Edison Bell. Cinderella stamp. 300 guineas competition. (g - vg) £4 - £6

► Embassy. Tin with some contents. (g) £12 - £14

▲ Concertone. Tin with some contents remaining. (g) £10 - £12

▲ Columbia Duragold. Tin with some contents. (vg) £12 - £14

▲ Gallotone. Almost full tin. (ex) £14 - £16

▲ HMV Loud Tone. Empty box. Originally held approx 200 needles. (g) £7 - £9

▲ Songster Golden. Almost full tin. (vg) £14 - £16

▲ Zonophone. Almost full tin. (f-g) £7 - £9

▲ Crown. Almost full tin. (vg) £10 - £12

▲ Columbia Miniature Thorn. Unopened packet. (vg) £10 - £12

GRAMOPHONE NEEDLES

▲ Songster Trailer. Almost full tin. (vg-ex) £12 - £14

▲ Songster Bronze. Half full tin. (g-vg) £10 - £12

▲ BCN Medium Tone. Promotional card disc that held 12 medium tone needles that could be sharpened. The disc could be used to test the 78rpm turntable speed. (f-g) £14 - £16

▲ Edison Bell Electric. Half full tin. (g-vg) £10 - £12

▲ Edison Bell. Half full tin. (g-vg) £10 - £12

▲ BCN Sharpener. (vg) With original box (g). This needle sharpening device (114mm long) is a hard to find item. £28 - £34

▲ Nita. Some contents remain. (g) £14 - £18

▲ Bestestone. Almost full tin. (vg) £16 - £18

▲ Chicken. Half full tin. (g-vg) £16 - £20

▲ Columbia Ideal. Empty tin. (f) £5 - £7

▲ Songster Sound Box. Empty box only. 65 x 40mm. (f-g) £10 - £14

▲ Trek. Half full tin. (f-g) £8 - £10

▲ Burchard's. Almost full tin. German. (f) £8 - £12

▲ The Tungstyle. Some contents remain. (f) £15 - £18

▲ Gallotone De Luxe Gold. Full contents. (vg) £14 - £16

▲ Waltz. Almost full tin. (vg) £14 - £17

▲ HMV Half Tone. Almost full tin. (f-g) £7 - £9

▲ Decca Loud. Half full tin. (g) £10 - £12

GREETINGS CARDS

Boxes of old greetings cards can turn up at boot sales or be sold as collections on internet auctions. An entire box can often be purchased for next to nothing and you just may find a real gem or two within.

Collecting greetings cards can be a social history study, with the images reflecting fashion and lifestyle. Early valentine cards (pre-1900) can command decent sums. The subject is so wide that collectors often concentrate on a specific topic such as wedding day cards or Easter cards.

There's lots of information available on the subject via internet search engines, and it doesn't take long to acquire enough knowledge to become quite an expert.

Look out for specially printed cards for serving members of the armed forces. Messages can be interesting and value is added when there's a regimental badge or other image (for example a Royal Navy ship).

From 1900 to 1939 greetings cards in the form of postcards were extremely popular, while children's pop-up cards from the 40s and 50s often have charming artwork and are not overly expensive.

Celebrated artists, such as Mabel Lucy Attwell, are also desirable.

▲ Wedding Anniversary. (1930). Message in ink. (g) £2 - £4

▲ House of Commons Christmas Card. 1967. Unwritten. (vg) £3 - £5

▲ Birthday Card. (1950). Message in ink. (g) £1 - £2

▲ Birthday Wishes. Postcard. Postmarked Stratford 1934. Message in ink. (vg) £1 - £2

GREETINGS CARDS

▲ Fond Birthday Wishes. Unknown maker. Written. (1935). (g-vg) £2 - £3

▲ You Are 4. Sharpe's Classic. Written. (1950). (g) £1 - £2

▲ Smilestone. Hills of London. Written and dated 1940. (g-vg) £2 - £3

THE GREETINGS OF THE SEASON

◄ Greetings of the Season. Happy Christmas and New Year. Unknown maker. Corporate card signed by one of the Bucher family and two others. A superbly designed card featuring a coach driver in the Bucher livery. (1935). (vg) £4 - £6

R.Bucher & Co., began their international travel business in 1932 (based in Lucerne, Switzerland) and rapidly expanded. They are still in business today.

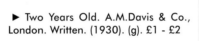

► Two Years Old. A.M.Davis & Co., London. Written. (1930). (g). £1 - £2

▲ Friend With Birthday Greetings. H.B. Series, Postcard. Halfpenny stamp with clear postmark, Bridgend - 1915. (g-vg) £1 - £2

◄ The Story of Mother's Day. Unknown maker. 8 page greetings card. Unwritten. 1983. (vg-ex) £1 - £2

Celebrated around the same time of year across many countries of the world.

Traditionally, Mother's Day is celebrated the second Sunday of May.

Nowadays, it is very much a commercially driven celebration and complements Father's Day (third Sunday in June).

GREETINGS CARDS - Valentines

Saint Valentine's Day was established by Pope Gelasius I in 496AD. Interestingly, the original festivities had nothing at all to do with romantic love. The first recorded association of Valentine's Day with romantic love can be found in Geoffrey Chaucer's Parlement of Foules, written in 1382. Chaucer's poem was written to honour the first anniversary of the engagement of King Richard II to Anne of Bohemia, and the day for celebrating love in the poem was entirely of Chaucer's invention.

The first written Valentines (the forerunner of the modern cards sold each year) are generally attributed to Charles, Duke of Orleans, who was imprisoned in the Tower of London after the Battle of Agincourt in 1415. He spent his time writing romantic verses for his wife in France. By the 17th Century it had become commonplace in many countries for gifts and cards to be exchanged on the 14 February each year.

There are now many collectors of Valentines, and very old cards are in demand. Other popular collectables include novelty cards which have ribbons, moving parts, or other unusual elements.

▲ To My Valentine. (1935). Unwritten. (f-g) £1 - £2

▲ I've Painted A Picture. (1965). Unwritten. (g) £1 - £3

▲ A Valentine For Mummy. (1955). Unwritten. (g) £2 - £3

▲ Be My Valentine. (1960). Message in ink. (g-vg) £1 - £2

◄ The One I Love. Postcard. (1910). Postally unused. Message in ink. (g) £3 - £4

► My Valentine. (1950). Unwritten. (g-vg) £2 - £3

GREYHOUND RACING

▲ Totalisator. Greyhound racing game. (1935). 310 x 260 x 40mm. (g-vg) £22 - £26

Despite not being as popular as horseracing, 'the dogs' still have a sizable following and therefore a market exists for collectables. Look out for old programmes and race cards, betting tickets, badges, official documents, and postcards (particularly those for stadiums that no longer exist).

Items relating to the most famous greyhounds command a premium. Arguably, the most famous greyhound of all time is Mick the Miller (born 1926) although supporters of Ballyregan Bob (born 1986) may disagree.

The best searching ground for items is the internet. The larger stadiums may attract the odd memorabilia stall holder; however, the large horseracing course regular vendors of books and other items will quite often include greyhound items on their stalls.

▲ Monmore racecard. 23 April 1975. (g) £2 - £4

▲ Greyhound Owner newspaper. 12 August 1965. Folded. (g-vg) £3 - £4

Mick The Miller

Mick the Miller was born June 1926 in Killeigh, Ireland. Even though he only raced for three years, his many achievements were greatly publicised and helped to boost the popularity of greyhound racing.

In just those three years (1929-1931), Mick the Miller won five classic races and broke four records. He won the English Greyhound Derby in 1929 and 1930, making him the first dog to win this prestigious race twice. He actually won the race again in 1931, but the race was eventually rerun and history records the real winner as Seldom Led.

Mick the Miller passed away in 1939. He was stuffed and is now displayed at the Natural History Museum at Tring.

Ballyregan Bob

Ballyregan Bob was born in 1983. His career got off to a less than impressive start, as he lost on his first four outings; however, he then went on to win 41 of his next 43 races, including a world record 32-race winning streak. He broke 15 track records, and never raced at odds greater than 4-9.

He set three speed records at Hackney and two at Wimbledon.

After his death, he was stuffed, and he now stands on display just a few feet away from Mick the Miller at the Natural History Museum at Tring. Many greyhound enthusiasts consider him to be the best dog there has ever been, and many believe there will never be another like him.

GUIDES

The Girl Guides was the creation of Robert Baden-Powell, following his very successful scout movement for boys. Baden-Powell met Olave St. Clair Soames aboard the ocean liner Arcadian. She was aged 23 years and he was aged 55. In 1918 Olave Baden-Powell became Chief Guide.

▲ The Girl Guide Annual. 1967. (g-vg) £3 - £4

▲   Olave Baden-Powell autograph. Clear, black ink, 175 x 120mm. No dedication. £80 - £100

▲ Girl Guides Gazette. September 1917. (g) £12 - £16

▲ The Brownie Annual. 1975. (g) £2 - £3

GUINNESS

The story of Guinness started way back in 1725 with the birth of Arthur Guinness. Arthur first set up a brewer's business in 1755 in County Kildare, Ireland. After an encouraging start, he decided to expand the business and purchased a disused brewery at St. James's Gate, Dublin in 1759 (which is still home to Guinness today). Arthur experimented with a few different types of beer before his death in 1803 when his son, also called Arthur, took over. During the 19th century, Guinness began to be exported overseas (by 1870, 10% of Guinness sales were overseas).

The beer continued to become more and more successful all the way throughout the 20th century, and it is now considered one of the most popular beers in the world. During 2001, almost 2 billion pints of Guinness were sold around the world (over 1 million pints a day in Britain alone).

▲ Guinness advertising postcard. Postmarked Baile Atha Cliath (the Gaelic name for Dublin) 1966. Message in ink. (g-vg) £18 - £10

▲ Guinness beer mat. (1955). (g) £4 - £6

▲ Guinness beer mat. (1950). (g) £5 - £7

GYROSCOPES

Mechanical measuring devices based on angular momentum. Essentially, the gyroscope is best known as an educational toy although the physics and mathematics surrounding the device is largely ignored and it was used as a glorified spinning top.

◀▲ Gyroscope. Unknown British maker. (1965). Original box plus instructions leaflet. (g) £4 - £6

HORSERACING

With over 200 years of history, the sport of horseracing has a phenomenal amount of memorabilia for collectors to collect and traders to trade.

Some specialist auction houses have sold amazing items related to the world of horseracing, including the original gates from Ascot Racecourse.

Amongst the most popular items at affordable prices are, racecourse badges, racecards, books, autographs, postcards, games, magazines, cigarette cards, trophies and much more.

▲ The Handicap Race Game. (1950). Tinplate. 220mm diameter. Spinning arrow stops on the winning horse. In full working order. Unknown maker. Game (g). Original box (f) £18 - £22

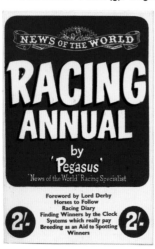

◄ Racing Annual 1951. News of the World paperback book. 164 pages. Includes some superb advertisements from pools companies, bookmakers and tipsters. (vg) £6 - £8

The Derby

The first running of the Epsom Derby was in 1870. It is now Britain's most valuable horserace. The race is watched on television by millions across the world. This ensures plenty of interest with collectors of memorabilia. Racecards, particularly pre-1935 are in demand. Items from any year, signed by the winning jockey, are also of interest.

◄ Derby Day racecard from 1979. Signed by winning jockey Willie Carson (Troy). Also signed by Pat Eddery. Clear, blue ink. No dedication. (g-vg) £12 - £16

▲ Derby Sweepstake ticket. Top Ten Promotions. 1966. (g) £1 - £2

▲ Galtee More. Derby winner 1897. Wrench Series postcard. Postmarked Manchester 1906. (f-g) £12 - £14

▲ Huntley and Palmers empty biscuit tin. Derby Day. 260 x 195 x 80mm. (1935) £16 - £20

HORSERACING

◀ ▲ Newmarket. Card Game. Universal Publications. Original box and instructions. (1935). (vg) £6 - £8

▶ Goff's Racehorse Auction Catalogue. 1937. (vg) £8 - £10

Robert J. Goff was a racehorse auctioneer, appointed by the Turf Club in 1866 as official auctioneer. The business has thrived ever since. Amongst the star racehorses to have been auctioned by Goffs, include; Golden Miller, Red Rum, Hatton's Grace and the mighty Arkle.

Catalogue
OF
Thoroughbred Racehorses and Racing Ponies
TO BE SOLD BY AUCTION
AT
Northolt Park Racecourse
ON
Saturday, May 29th, 1937
at 11.30 a.m. sharp

ROBERT J. GOFF & CO., LTD., Auctioneers,
60-61, Lower Mount Street, Dublin
and
3, St. James's Square, London, S.W.1
TELEPHONE - WHITEHALL 1861/2

▲ Her Majesty's Racing & Breeding Studs. 1971. Imitation leather cover. 100 pages. 150 x 120mm (vg). £6 - £8.

▲ Stable razor blade. (1950). (vg) £2 - £4

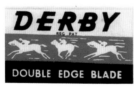

▲ Derby razor blade. (1950). (vg) £2 - £4

▲ Race Fixtures booklet. 1969. Captain Alan Carfax (racing tipster). (vg) £2 - £3

▲ Racing Fixtures. Booklet.100 x 65mm. Daily Herald. 1936. (g) £5 - £8

The Grand National

The Grand National is the world's most famous steeplechase. It was first held at Aintree (a racecourse near Liverpool) in 1839.

There's an abundance of memorabilia associated with the race. Very old race cards are much sought after.

◀ Shot glass. Commemorating Oxo's win in 1959. Circa 1970. (vg) £4 - £6

▶ Jockey model. Plastic. John Smith (race sponsor). (1990). (ex) £3 - £5

◀ Race card. 1969. Highland Wedding was the winner. (g) £2 - £4

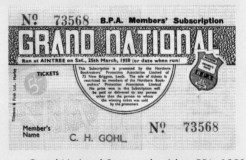

▲ Grand National Sweepstake ticket. BPA. 1950. (vg) £1 - £2

▲ Champion Red Rum - Len Marten. 45rpm single. 1975. Jet Records, JET 753. Vinyl (g) £4 - £6

Red Rum won the Grand National in 1973, 1974 and 1977. He died, aged 30, in 1995 and is buried next to the Aintree winning post.

HORSERACING

Enamel badges

▲ Hurst Park 1958. (vg) £20 - £24

▲ Ascot (Stand) 1989. (vg-ex) £6 - £8

▲ Kempton Park 1957. (vg-ex) £14 - £18

▲ Sandown Park 1986. (ex) £6 - £8

▲ Goodwood 1980. (vg) £6 - £8

▲ Newmarket 1993. (vg-ex) £5 - £7

▲ Ludlow 2001. (ex) £7 - £9

▲ Ascot (Stand) 1995. (vg) £4 - £6

▲ Fontwell 1992. (vg) £7 - £9

▲ Ripon 1987. (vg) £10 - £12

▲ Newbury 2008. (mnt) £4 - £6

▲ York (County Stand) 1980. (g-vg) £6 - £8

▲ Great Yarmouth 1977. (vg) £12 - £14

▲ Ascot (Stand) 1996. (ex) £5 - £7

Card badges

▲ Ludlow 19 Nov 1938. (f-g) £14 - £16

▲ Cheltenham 19 Oct 1988. (vg) £1 - £2

▲ Ascot 25 Jul 1998. (g-vg) £1 - £2

▲ Kempton Park 14 Jun 1989. (vg) £1 - £3

▲ Hereford. 14 Dec 1990. (vg) £1 - £3

▲ Haydock Park 2 Dec 1939. (Gent). (g) £15 - £20

▲ Newbury 11 Nov 1987. (f-g) £1 - £2

▲ Cheltenham 20 Oct 1993. (g) £1 - £2

▲ Wolverhampton 25 Jan 1985. (g-vg) £1 -£2

▲ Worcester 14 Nov 1990. (g-vg) £1 - £2

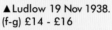

HORSERACING - Racecards

▲ Kempton Park. 5 Apr 1958. (vg) £2 - £4

▲ Goodwood. 31 Jul 1968. (vg) £3 - £4

▲Brighton. 17 Jun 1968. (f-g) £1 - £3

▲North Herefordshire. 6 Apr 1935. (f) £5 - £7

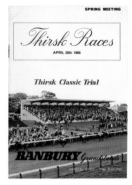

▲Thirsk. 20 Apr 1968. (vg) £2 - £4

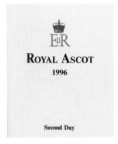

▲ Royal Ascot. 19 Jun 1996. (g) £2 - £4

▲ Ascot. 26 Sept 1957. (g) £3 - £4

▲Fakenham. 12 Oct 1968. (g-vg) £2 - £4

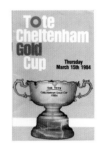

▲Cheltenham Gold Cup. 15 Mar 1984. (g) £2 - £4

▲Beverley. 27 Apr 1968. (g) £1 - £3

▲ Folkestone. 10 Jun 1968. (g) £2 - £3

▲ Towcester. 26 May 1947. (vg) £3 - £5

▲Ayr. 22 Sept 1967. (vg) £2 - £4

▲Wynn's Hunt. 6 Apr 1949. (f-g) £2 - £3

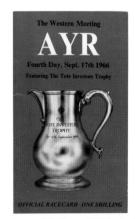

▲Newbury. 12 Feb 1972. (g) £2 - £3

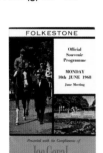

▲ Wolverhampton. 3 Aug 1964. (g) £2 - £3

▲ York. 20 Jul 1963. (g) £2 - £4

▲Cheltenham Gold Cup. 15 Mar 1979. (vg) £2 - £4

▲Ascot. 12 Apr 1969. (vg) £3 - £4

▲ Redcar. 8 Aug 1953. (vg) £5 - £7

▲ Beverley. 15 May 1954. (vg) £4 - £6

▲Leicester. 23 Jul 1968. (vg) £2 - £4

▲ Lingfield Park. 23 Aug 1958. (vg) £3 - £5

▲Ayr . 17 Sept 1966. (vg) £2 - £4

HORSERACING -
Racecards from closed racecourses

When a racecourse permanently closes, the value of associated memorabilia is likely to rise.

Racecards from racecourses that have been shut down years ago are sought after by collectors. They make an interesting collection and need not cost the earth.

► Alexandra Park. 26 Jun 1965. (g) £3 - £5

Front Cover   **Page 4**

Alexandra Park was located in London. It opened in 1868 and closed in 1970. Informally referred to as 'The Frying Pan' because of its shape.

◄ Birmingham. 11 May 1953. (g-vg) £6 - £8

► Hurst Park. 5 Oct 1946. (vg) £10 - £12

Front Cover   **Page 6**

Front Cover   **Page 2**

Birmingham Racecourse was also known as Bromford Bridge. It opened in 1895 and closed in 1965. It was requisitioned during World War II and used as an anti-aircraft station.

Hurst Park Racecourse was situated at West Molesey, Surrey. It opened in 1890 and closed in 1960. Upon closure, one of the grandstands was dismantled and sold to Mansfield Town FC.

◄ Manchester. 5 Apr 1958. (f) £4 - £6

► Stockton. 23 Apr 1932. Some staple rusting (g-vg) £12 - £14

Front Cover   **Page 4**

Front Cover   **Page 2**

Manchester Racecourse was located in Salford and first opened in 1902. On the day it closed in 1963, the last race was won by Lester Piggott.

Stockton Racecourse opened in 1855 and was later more commonly known as Teeside Park. It closed in 1981.

◄ Lincoln. 18 Mar 1950. (g) £4 - £6

► Wye. 12 May 1969. (vg) £4 - £6

Front Cover   **Page 7**

Front Cover   **Page 9**

Lincoln Racecourse origins date back to 1773. The grandstand was built in 1897. The course was finally closed in 1965.

Wye Racecourse was situated in East Kent, near Canterbury. Racing dates back to 1849 but in 1975 when the racecourse failed to meet Jockey Club specifications, it closed.

HOUSEHOLD

This is another classic collecting area to spark social history interest. Many of the everyday items that could be found in homes, decades ago, have survived and are now being collected.

Advertisements in old magazines and newspapers tell a wonderful story. Magazines such as 'Practical Householder' captured images of living accommodation and can be purchased relatively cheaply.

◀ Flying Ducks. Three wall plaques (135mm, 165mm and 185mm). Made of plaster and dating from the 1950's. (vg) £15 - £20

▲ Practicical Householder magazine. March 1958. (g-vg) £2 - £3

Betterwear

The Betterwear Brush Company sold their brushes, mops, and polishes door-to-door in the 1950s and 1960s. Many of their products featured the easily recognisable company logo.

▲ Betterwear lavender wax polish. Sample tin. (1960). Empty. 30mm diam. (g) £6 - £8

▲ Betterwear silicone wax polish. Sample tin. (1960). Empty. 30mm diam. (g-vg) £7 - £9

HOUSEHOLD

▲Anvil Tacks box. (1925). Partial contents remain. (g) £2 - £4

▲ Elastic Woolworths product. (1955). (vg) £2 - £3

▲ Goblin Vacuum Cleaner advertising leaflet. 1935. (vg) £7 - £9

URBAN DISTRICT OF WOODFORD.

HOUSEHOLD FUEL and LIGHTING ORDER, 1918.

Local Fuel Overseer :
JOHN A. SIMPSON, LL B.,
Barrister-at-Law

TELEPHONE WOODFORD 8.

COUNCIL OFFICES,

WOODFORD GREEN

14th May, 1920.

Dear Mr. Barnes,

Many thanks for your letter of the 11th inst.

It is only with reluctance that I am able to sanction a transfer of registration for coal, but I know that there have been, in a number of cases, special difficulties in obtaining a supply from Messrs. Booth Bros., and I have granted the application of some of their customers. If you will complete the enclosed form and get it signed by a coal merchant who is able to supply you, the matter will be arranged.

Yours faithfully,

John A Simpson

F.Barnes Esq.,
Loen,
Grange Avenue.

▲ Household fuel. A letter from the Local Fuel Overseer for the Urban District of Woodford. 1920. (vg) £2 - £3

I-SPY

The I-Spy books were originally self-published by Charles Warrell but were soon taken over by the News Chronicle (which ceased publication in 1960). I-Spy books have recently been published by Michelin Travel Publications.

The books were designed to encourage children to find various items, which they would tick off, and perhaps write a brief note about where they saw the items and what they were used for. Once the children had found everything in the book, it could be sent to Big Chief I-Spy and the children would be awarded with an I-Spy Order of Merit.

Many of the I-Spy books you are likely to find at car boot sales and collectors' fairs will have writing on some of the pages (if not all of them). Unused, clean examples will demand a premium among collectors.

The "tribe" was very successful; especially at its peak in the 1950s and early '60s (print runs regularly ran into six figures).

▲ At The Seaside. No.1. 1954. (f-g) £6 - £8

▲ On The Farm. No.2. (1952). (g) £12 - £14

▲ On The Farm. No.2. (1960). (g) £2 - £4

▲ On The Farm. No.2. 1962. (f-g) £2 - £3

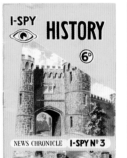

▲ History. No.3. (1958). (vg) £6 - £8

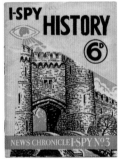

▲ History. No.3. 1953. (g) £8 - £10

▲ On A Train Journey. No.4. 1953. (g) £12 - £14

▲ On A Train Journey. No.4. 1962. (p-f) £3 - £4

▲ Dogs. No.5. 1953. (g) £12 - £14

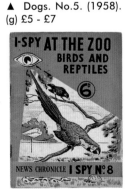

▲ Dogs. No.5. (1958). (g) £5 - £7

▲ In The Country. No.6. (1958). (g) £5 - £7

▲ At The Zoo Animals. No.7. 1955. (g) £6 -£8

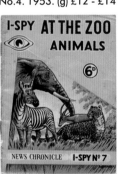

▲ At The Zoo Birds and Reptiles. No.8. (1954). (g) £7 -£9

▲ At The Zoo Birds and Reptiles. No.8. 1955. (g) £7 -£9

▲ In The Street. No.9. 1955. (g) £7 - £9

I - Spy publishing dates:

1948 - 1949
Warrell Way

1949 - 1951
Daily Mail

1951 - 1960
News Chronicle

1960 - 1973
Dickens Press

I-SPY

▲ On The Road. No.10. 1955. (f-g) £6 - £7

▲ The Sights Of London. No.11. (1961). (g) £3 - £4

▲ The Sights Of London. No.11. 1962. (g-vg) £4 - £5

▲ Horses and Ponies. No.12. 1954. (g) £8 - £10

▲Ships & Harbours. No.13. 1954. (f-g) £7 - £9

▲ Boats & Waterways. No.14. 1954. (g) £7 - £9

▲ Aircraft. No.15. 1954. (g) £10 - £12

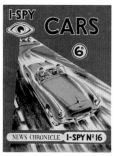

▲ Cars. No.16. 1954. (g-vg) £14 - £16

▲ The Army. No.17. 1954. (f-g) £8 - £10

▲ The Wheel. No.18. 1954. (g) £10 - £12

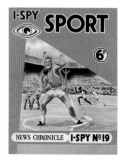

▲ Sport. No.19. 1954. (g-vg) £10 - £12

▲ Sport. No.19. 1956. (g-vg) £14 - £18

▲ People and Places. No.20. 1954. (g) £8 - £10

▲ Musical Instruments. No.21. 1954. (g) £8 - £10

▲ Men At Work - Building. No.22. 1954. (f-g) £6 - £8

▲ Antique Furniture. No.23. 1954. (g) £14 - £18

▲ The Unusual. No.24. 1954. (g-vg) £14 - £18

▲ Town Crafts. No.26. 1955. (g-vg) £12 - £14

▲ Country Crafts. No.27. 1955. (g-vg) £12 - £14

▲ The Sky. No.28. 1955. (g) £8 - £10

▲ The Sky. No.28. 1963. (vg). £6 - £8

▲ People In Uniform. No.29. 1955. (g) £6 - £8

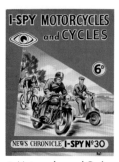

▲Motorcycles and Cycles. No.30. 1956. (g) £5 - £6

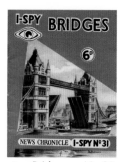

▲ Bridges. No.31. (1957). (g) £4 - £6

▲ Roadmaking. No.33. (1958). (f-g) £5 - £7

ICE CREAM

Prior to the days of refrigerators, ice was taken from mountains and other natural sources and taken to 'ice houses' where insulated walls kept the ice frozen. Consumers purchased the ice and used it to make ice cream etc....

Around the turn of the 20th century, pewter ice cream moulds were all the rage. The moulds came in all shapes and sizes.

◄ Pewter ice cream mould. Novelty shape (tangerine segments). 50mm diameter. (1920). (vg) £13 - £15

► Ice cream dispenser. 116mm high. (1930) £28 - £32

Walls ice cream was the brainchild of Thomas Wall. The company was bought out by Lever Brothers in 1922. Collectables include trade cards and space related items.

(front)   (reverse)

▲ Walls Supersonic Flasher. Morse code flasher card. 65mm x 92mm. Hard to find item. (1965). (vg) £15 - £20

◄ Walls Sky Ray Moon Fleet button badge. (1965). (vg) £5 - £6

In the 1930's, ice cream was sold on the streets by uniformed salesmen on tricycles. The cycles had large refrigerated boxes and famously carried the sign "stop me and buy one".

The popularity of motorised ice cream vans was at its height in the 1960's. The vans' chimes could be heard regularly on Britain's streets, however, to some, the jingles were too loud and irritating. The Government stepped in and created regulations to limit the use of the chimes. They were limited to 80 decibels and could not be sounded more than once every two hours in the same street. Other restrictions included a ban on playing the chimes after 7pm.

Lyons Maid brand was created in 1925 by the J.Lyons & Co., organisation. Give-aways included trade cards. Look out for the collectable lolly sticks from the Goal Lolly. The sticks were printed with a series of famous footballers. Original iced lolly wrappers from the 60's and 70's, in excellent condition, command high sums.

► Lyons Maid ice cream van. Matchbox toys. No.47B. Unboxed. 1967. (g-vg) £5 - £7

◄ Lyons Ice Cream, matchbook. (1965). (vg) £2 - £3

(front)   (inside back cover)

▲ The Space Album. Lyons Maid trade card album with full set of 40 cards affixed. 1963. (f) £12 - £14

These Space albums are becoming increasingly hard to find. It is complemented by the superb advertisement for Zoom iced lollies. 'Zoom' was an example of Lyons Maid cashing in on the 'space age' phenomenon.

JACK-IN-THE-BOX

Believed to have originated in the thirteenth century and associated with a model of a devil in a shoe. The French call a jack-in-the-box "diable en boite" (boxed devil).

▲ Jack-in-the-box. (1985). Ceramic, hand-painted head. (ex) £13 - £16

JAMES BOND

▲ Dr. No. Pan Paperback. 1960. (vg) £4 - £6

James Bond was created by novelist Ian Fleming in 1952 and made his first appearance in the book Casino Royale. The character struck a chord, and became a sensation, appearing in many more novels and short stories, and even in comic strip form (illustrated by John McLusky and first published in the Daily Express newspaper in 1957). However, it was not until 1962, ten years after first donning his iconic tuxedo to match wits with Le Chiffre, that he graduated to the big screen.

Since Dr No, with all of its thrills, spills, and excitement, the franchise has gone from strength to strength. Ian Fleming wrote 14 books (two of which were compilations of short stories), but there have been 24 (official) movies, several unofficial movies (including the David Niven satire, Casino Royale), dozens of novels by other authors such as Kingsley Amis and John Gardner, radio shows, a cartoon series (James Bond Jr), comic strips, and much more.

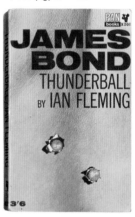

▲ Thunderball. Pan Paperback. 1964. (g) £3 - £4

As can be imagined, there has been a huge amount of merchandise to accompany such a huge franchise, and the collector is really spoiled for choice when deciding what to focus a collection on.

It is worth remembering that lots of James Bond collectors like to keep it "official". That means the books by Ian Fleming, and the films produced by EON Productions. The mocking release of Casino Royale, with David Niven and Peter Sellers, would not appear on many serious collectors' wish lists. Even Sean Connery, reprising his role of the super-spy for Never Say Never Again is not that likely to make the cut as the movie was released by Warner Brothers rather than EON Productions and is therefore not considered an official Bond movie.

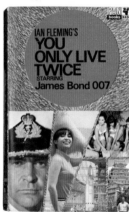

▲ You Only Live Twice. Pan Paperback. 1966. (f-g) £2 - £3

A lot of Bond merchandise is produced in huge quantities, and this means there is not the scarcity required for prices to rise, but investment potential is not the only concern for many collectors, and this is an area in which you can have lots of fun building a collection that becomes a real talking point when visitors call round. If nothing else, your collection is likely to spark the age-old debate of who was the best Bond. If you really must look for items that have serious investment potential, then you can't go wrong with old theatre posters. You will need deep pockets, as some can realise prices upwards of £6,000, but they make for fascinating collectables that should continue to appreciate over the years if they are cared for well.

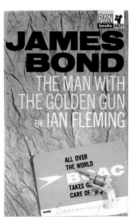

▲ The Man With The Golden Gun. Pan Paperback. 1968. (g) £2 - £4

▲ From Russia With Love. Pan Paperback. 1962. (f-g) £3 - £4

JAZZ

This is one of those subjects that has a niche following and therefore has a niche market. Buying interesting jazz items is relatively simple. The secret is to sell to the right audience and therefore you could consider specialist jazz magazines or enthusiast websites.

Dealing with instruments that may have been owned by famous jazz musicians is tricky. Strong and reliable provenance is essential. You really do need solid documentary and photographic evidence.

Old jazz magazines are tremendous (look for pre-1950). Legendary musicians are often featured with photographs, increasing the value. Jazz records can also have value, although this is dangerous ground unless you have done your homework properly.

Original sheet music is quite collectable. As well as the obvious musical score, a photograph of the artist on the front cover adds to the interest. Jazz sheet music is generally not as desirable as 60s pop.

Books are also worth considering. Autobiographies of the legends are in demand, particularly pre-1960.

Autographs, especially ones on publicity photographs without a dedication, are in demand. Concert programmes and tickets are also highly sought after. Add autographs to concert programmes and you could have some serious items on your hands.

Fats Waller

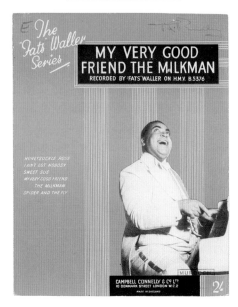

▲ Fats Waller sheet music. My Very Good Friend The Milkman. (1950). (g) £1 - £2

Fats Waller (born 1904) was the son of a preacher and learned to play the organ in church with his mother. In 1934, Fats attended a party given by George Gershwin, where he delighted the crowd with his piano playing and singing. An executive of Victor Records, also attending the party, was so impressed that he arranged for Fats to record with the company. This arrangement continued until Waller's death in 1943, when he died of pneumonia whilst on board a train in Missouri. Fats' most famous hits include "Ain't Misbehavin'" and "Hot Chocolates".

Count Basie

William James "Count" Basie was born in Red Bank, New Jersey, on 21 August 1904. He wasn't much of a scholar, but learned to play the piano by ear while doing small jobs at the Palace Theatre in Red Bank, thus taking the first steps to becoming a celebrated jazz pianist, organist, bandleader, and composer. Some of his most well-known songs are One O'Clock Jump and April in Paris.

Sadly, Basie died of pancreatic cancer, in Hollywood, on 26 April 1984. He was 79 years old. The Count Basie Theatre and Count Basie Field in Red Bank are named in his honour, and Mechanic Street (where he lived) is known as Count Basie Way.

▲ Basie/Jazz - Count Basie EP Record. (1960). Columbia, SEB 10000. Vinyl (vg), sleeve (g) £4 - £6

KALEIDOSCOPES

The word 'kaleidoscope' was conceived by Sir David Brewster in 1817. Derived from the Greek meaning of 'to look at beautiful coloured shapes'.

Mirrors are joined together at 60 degree angles in a tube, and then by rotating the tube, coloured objects create pleasing patterns.

Whilst there are finely crafted handmade pieces, the majority of manufactured kaleidoscopes are mass-produced as children's toys.

Chad Valley was one of the big producers in the sixties and seventies.

▲ Acme Toys Kaleidoscope. (1965). (vg) £10 -£12

KEY FOBS

A key fob is an ornament or electronic device that is attached to a key ring. Most new vehicles these days have an electronic key fob device that activates door lock devices.

Collectors concentrate on the ornamental side. Popular areas include automobilia and tobacciana.

▲ Dunhill. Leather and enamel. (1965). (vg) £4 - £5

▲ Rolls Royce. Leather and enamel. (1970). (g-vg) £8 - £10

▲ Consul. Leather and enamel. (1965). (g) £3 - £5

▲ Bluebell Railway. Leather. (1990). (vg - ex) £1 - £2

▲ American Automobile Association. (1935). (g-vg) £6 - £8

▲ Tribune Lager. Plastic. (1975). (vg) 10p - 20p

KNITTING & SEWING

Knitting needles

▲ Aero. Abel Morrall. (1950). Pack with one needle. (vg) £1 - £2

▲ Quaker Girl. Critchley Brothers, Stroud. (1935). Pack with two needles. (g) £1 - £2

▲ Phantom. Milwards. Aluminium Alloy. Pack with four pins. (g) £1 - £2

Even though the bulk of knitting and sewing collectables are likely to be lower end value, there are some exceptions, such as vintage sewing machines. Singer Sewing advertising postcards produced between 1904 and 1910 are sought after. Old knitting patterns are also collectable for their social history value (wonderful images of clothing and hair styles of the relevant era) and can be picked up very cheaply.

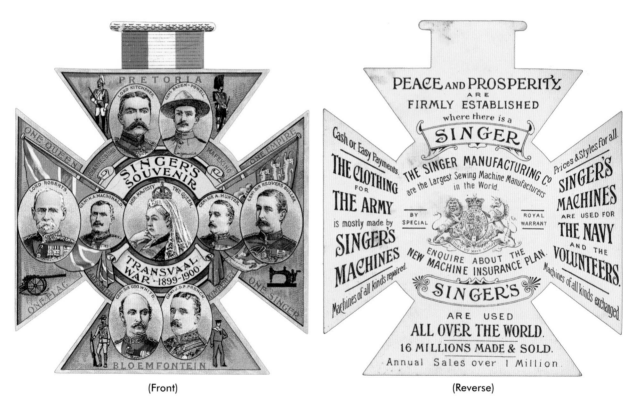

(Front)   (Reverse)

▲ Singer Sewing Machines war souvenir. 1900. Die cut. 100 x 100mm. (vg) £15 - £20

I.M. Singer & Co was established by Isaac Merrit Singer in 1851. The company was renamed as Singer Manufacturing Company in 1865, and became The Singer Company in 1963. It is now known as Singer Corporation.

During World War II the company ceased production of sewing machines and began producing weapons instead. Interestingly, the Singer factories in America supplied Allied troops with weapons while the factories in Germany produced weapons for the Nazis. The company produced 500 M1911 pistols which are now incredibly collectable.

KNOW THE GAME

This is a series of limpback books, first published in the early 50s by Educational Productions and usually in collaboration with a relevant organisation connected to the subject matter.

For example, Know the Game – TRAMPOLINING is in collaboration with The British Trampoline Federation.

The books have attractive covers and appear as if they should be highly collectable. However, this is not necessarily so. In fact, it's a timely reminder that not everything is an ideal subject for money making, even if it's over 50 years old.

However, these books do have some value and they are collectable, particularly for the more obscure sports and games. First editions are even more desirable.

▲ The Laws of Association Football. 1957. (vg) £3 - £5

▲ Squash. 1963. (vg) £2 - £4

▲ Skating. 1968. (g) £2 - £3

▲ Men's Hockey. 1970. (vg) £1 - £2

▲ Athletics. 1955. (vg) £2 - £4

▲ Golf. 1975. (g) £1 - £2

▲ Association Football. 1967. (g-vg) £2 - £3

▲ Netball. 1968. (g-vg) £1 - £2

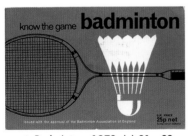

▲ Badminton. 1972. (g) £1 - £2

▲ Bowls. 1987. (vg) 50p - £1

▲ Wind Surfing. 1983. (g-vg) 50p - £1

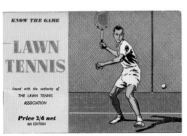

▲ Lawn Tennis. 1958. (g-vg) £2 - £4

▲ Rounders. 1970. (vg) £1 - £3

▲ Game Fishing. 1978. (g) 50p - £1

LADYBIRD BOOKS

Over the years, Ladybird first editions have carried several different logos, and these can be used to help date any of the books you have in your collection. Up until 1961, the logo was an open-winged ladybird. This design was then changed to a ladybird with closed wings. In 1965 the design was changed again; the ladybird still had closed wings, but was now in colour, surrounded by a black box, and was usually found in the top right or bottom right corner of the front cover. Other designs were introduced in the 1970s and 1980s, but it is the 1965 logo that is most commonly recognised.

▲ Things We Like. 1964. (g) £2 - £3

▲ A First Book of Saints. (1973) (g) £2 - £3

▲ Royal Wedding. 1981. (vg) £3 - £4

▲ The Story of Flight. 1970. (vg) £4 - £5

▲ Bunny's First Birthday. (1980). (g) £1 - £2

▲ The Police Force. 1982. (vg) £2 - £3

▲ Stamp Collecting. 1969. (g) £2 - £3

▲ Happy Holiday. 1964. (g-vg) £2 - £4

▲ Our Friends. 1964. (vg) £3 - £4

▲ The Airman. 1967. (g) £2 - £4

▲ Kings and Queens of England. 1968. (g) £2 - £4

▲ Aircraft. 1968. (vg) £3 - £4

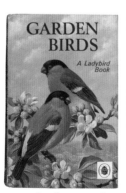

▲ Garden Birds. (1975). (vg) £2 - £4

▲ Superman. 1989. (vg) £4 - £6

▲ Adventure on the Island. (1975). (g-vg) £2 - £4

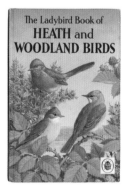

▲ Heath and Woodland Birds. 1968. (vg) £4 - £5

LEGO

Lego was created by a carpenter from Denmark, Ole Kirk Christiansen. He began creating wooden toys in 1932, before calling his company "Lego" in 1934. It wasn't until 1947 that they began producing plastic toys and 1949 when they began producing the now-famous interlocking bricks. The name Lego is derived from the Danish phrase "Leg godt", which means "play well." Interestingly, in Latin, the word "lego" means "I put together", but this is a happy coincidence, and the alternative meaning was not known when the company picked its name.

Lego is becoming increasingly popular among collectors, especially vintage sets from the 70s and 80s. Complete kits with instructions and boxes will obviously raise the most money, but because of the nature of Lego, there is also a strong market for loose blocks and spare pieces, which would invariably get lost when the kits were in use. It is worth knowing that since 1958, all Lego blocks are compatible; so brand new blocks being made today can be used to complete much older sets.

▲ Lego box containing five bricks. (1965). 85 x 65mm. (g) £3 - £5

LETTER OPENERS

Victorian ladies and gentlemen treated the receipt of letters in the post as a major part of daily life. The well-heeled often considered a letter opener to be an essential device and the manufacture of them flourished. They were made from wood, ivory, bronze, silver etc... Designers imagination went into overdrive and the handles became wilder and wilder. The goat's horn handle (circa 1900) with brass knife is a good example.

Between approximately 1950 and 1980, letter openers were used to promote company products and services.

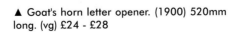

▲ Goat's horn letter opener. (1900) 520mm long. (vg) £24 - £28

▲ Canadian Packers (UK), London advertising letter opener. (1960). 180mm long. (g-vg) £2 - £3

LETTERHEADS AND BILLHEADS

Around 1900, many companies began using ornate images to promote their business names and activities on their stationery. The more ornate the image, the greater the prestige.

These images were used to head invoices, delivery notes and the like, as well as letterheads.

Collectors are now particularly interested in the late 19th century and early 20th century examples. These little pieces of our social history make fine collections.

▲ Ravenhead Sanitary Pipe and Brick Company Limited. Letter. 1928. 260 x 210mm. (g-vg) £3 - £4

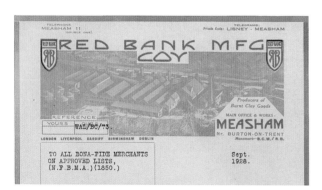

▲ Red Bank MFG COY. Money quotation. 1928. 255 x 200mm. (vg) £2 - £3

▲ FC Thacker slip. 1913. 205 x 120mm. (g-vg) £2 - £4

▲ R. Affleck & Son Ironmongers. Receipted invoice. 1914. 205 x 175mm. (g-vg) £2 - £3

▲ Amelit Works, Belgium. Letter. 1929. 275 x 215mm. (g) £1 - £2

LETTERHEADS AND BILLHEADS

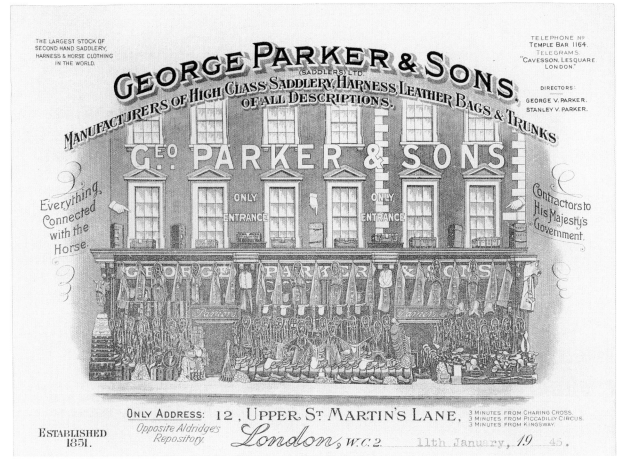

▲ George Parker & Sons. Letter. 1945. 260 x 210mm. (vg) £2 - £3

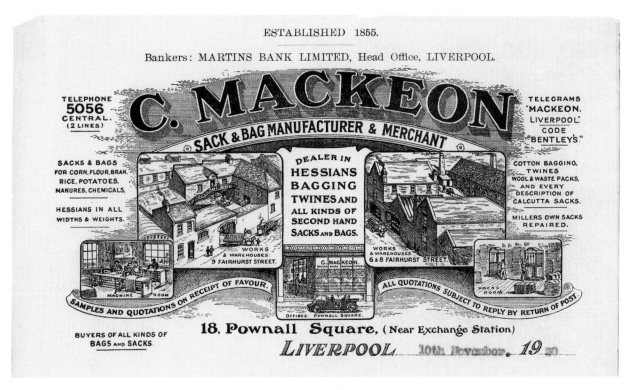

▲ C. Mackeon. Letter. 1930. 325 x 230mm. (g) £2 - £3

LETTERHEADS AND BILLHEADS

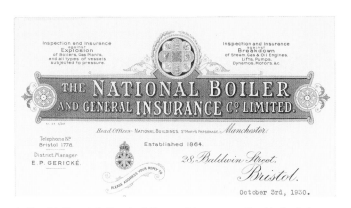

▲ The National Boiler And General Insurance Co. Limited. Letter. 1930. 260 x 205mm. (g-vg) £1 - £2

▲ Fox & Sons' Dinner Ale & Standard Stout. Blank invoice. (1905). 215 x 140mm. (g-vg) £2 - £3

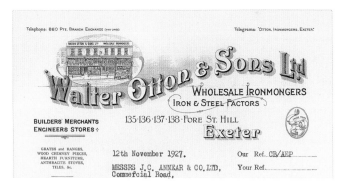

▲ Walter Otton & Sons Ltd. Letter. 1927. 260 x 205mm. (g) £2 - £3

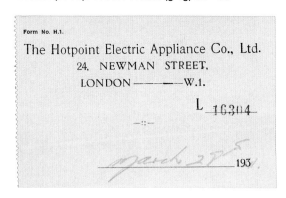

▲ The Hotpoint Electric Appliance Co. Ltd. Receipt. 1939. 195 x 110mm. (g) £1 - £2

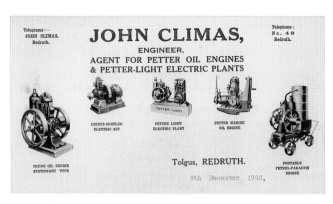

▲ John Climas Engineer. Payment notice. 1928. 260 x 205mm. (f-g) £1 - £2

▲ The Bridge Stationery Depot. Invoice. 1932. 205 x 135mm. (vg) £1 - £2

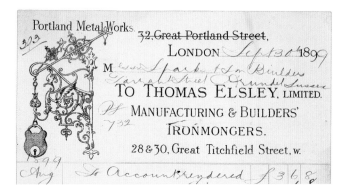

▲Thomas Elsley Limited. Ironmongers. Invoice. 1899. 205 x 130mm. (g) £2 - £3

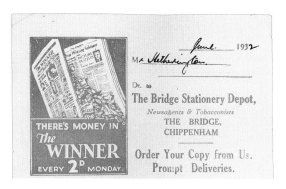

▲ RAC. Letter. 1963. 205 x 125mm. (g) 50p - £1

LIGHTERS

There's plenty of interest in collecting lighters. They have been around for over 100 years, so the scope is wide. However, beware, you really do need to do your homework before investing any substantial sum in a collection of vintage lighters.

The first pocket lighter was produced by Ronson in 1913. It was called the 'Wonderliter'.

Ronson was founded in 1896, in New York by Louis V. Aronson.

▲ Pall Mall lighter. (1960). Not tested. (vg) £12 - £14

▲ Arsenal novelty lighter. (2000). Not tested. (ex) £1 - £2

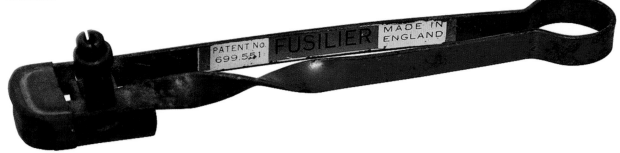

▲ Flint spark lighter. Fusilier (Made in England). In working order. Squeeze action releases a stream of sparks. (1960) (g) £4 - £6

LONE STAR

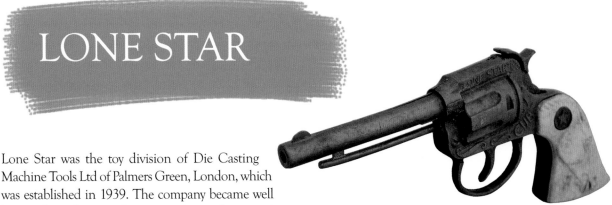

Lone Star was the toy division of Die Casting Machine Tools Ltd of Palmers Green, London, which was established in 1939. The company became well known for making cap-firing guns, but it also started producing a range of diecast cars in 1956.

▲ Lone Star plastic gun. (1960). 150mm long. (f) £4 - £6

The first thirteen Tuf-Tots were introduced in 1969. Five more were added to the series in 1970, and the rest of the range were in production by the end of 1972.

Most of the range was available in numerous colours and were originally sold boxed or in bubble packs. Later on, the models were sold from open counter-top trays. The series was discontinued in the early 1980s. Models in mint, boxed condition can now be expected to sell for around £10.

▲ Lone Star button badge. (1970). (g-vg) £6 - £8

LOOK-in

Look-in was a hit children's magazine/comic based on ITV's television programmes.

It was first published on 9 January 1971 and ran until 1994. The magazine was sometimes known as "The Junior TV Times" and it included many comic strips featuring popular TV programmes including The Six Million Dollar Man, Knight Rider, and The A-Team.

The magazines also featured lots of interviews, posters and competitions, based around the latest TV and music stars. As well as the magazine, television annuals were released yearly between 1971 and 1991.

▲ Marc Bolan cover. 23 Sep 1972. (vg) £8 - £10

▲ Olympics cover. 24 Jul 1976. (vg) £4 - £5

▲ Steve McQueen cover. 21 Oct 1972. (vg) £5 - £6

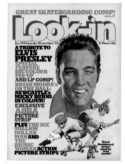

▲ Elvis cover. 5 Nov 1977. (vg) £5 - £7

▲ Paul Nicholas cover. 15 Jan 1977. (vg) £3 - £5

▲ Space 1999 cover. 22 Jan 1977. (vg) £3 - £5

▲ King Kong cover. 29 Jan 1977. (vg) £3 - £5

▲ ABBA cover. 8 Jan 1977. (vg) £3 - £5

▲ The Famous Five cover. 22 Jul 1978. (vg) £3 - £5

▲ Charlie's Angels cover. 19 Jul 1980. (vg) £3 - £5

▲ Swiss Family Robinson 3 Aug 1974. (vg) £3 - £5

▲ David Soul cover. 5 Feb 1977. (vg) £3 - £5

▲ Elephant Boy cover. 28 Oct 1972. (vg) £3 - £5

▲ The Muppets cover. 12 Feb 1977. (vg) £3 - £5

▲ Pardon My Genie cover. 20 May 1972. (vg) £3 - £5

▲ David Essex cover. 1 Dec 1973. (vg) £3 - £5

▲ Six Million Dollar Man 17 Sep 1977. (vg) £3 - £5

▲ ShowaddyWaddy cover. 27 Aug 1977. (vg) £3 - £5

▲ Tri-Star cover. 24 Nov 1973. (vg) £3 - £5

LOTOLOGY

Lotology is the collecting and study of anything relating to a lottery.

As well as lottery tickets, collectors build huge collections of used scratch cards. The attraction here is that they are normally colourful and like many collecting subjects, the whole thing can become rather compulsive.

It's certainly an inexpensive hobby, assuming you only collect the used tickets and scratch cards that you would have purchased anyway for the purpose for which they were intended.

One of the interesting GB collectable lottery tickets is the first day of issue. This was for the National Lottery draw number 1, held on 19 November 1994. Tickets in good condition+ are now fetching around £2 - £3 each. You are probably kicking yourself now. Had you purchased 1000 first day of issue tickets at £1, you may have won a decent sum and then doubled your money on all the losing tickets.

▲ National Lottery, first day of issue, losing ticket. 1994. (vg) £2 - £3

▲ National Lottery umbrella. 2005. Unused. (ex) £10 - £12

▲ National lottery cap. 2005. Unused. (ex) £4 - £5

▶ National Lottery T-shirt. 2005. Unused. (ex) £3 - £4

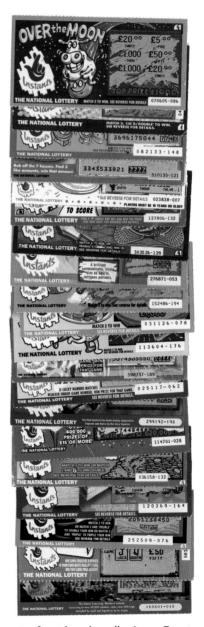

▲ Scratchcard collection. Twenty different used National Lottery scratch cards. (vg) £1 - £2

LUGGAGE LABELS

The main collecting area is pre-1960 and there's plenty of investment potential but you do need to study the market and concentrate on labels in good condition+.

▲ Tajmahal Hotel, Bombay. (1935). (g) £10 - £12

(Front)

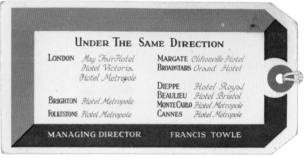
(Reverse)

▲ Grosvenor Hotel, London. Luggage label. (1920). (g-vg) £12 - £14

LURPAK

The Lurpak brand is owned by the Danish Dairy Board. Lurpak butter is sold in its distinctive silver packs in 80 countries around the world.

An advertising campaign in 1985 featured a trombonist named Douglas, who was made of butter. The animation was produced by Aardman and Penelope Keith was the voice behind the UK television campaign.

Lurpak produced ceramic butter dishes, toast racks and egg cups, all with the Douglas figure included. There was also a soft toy version of Douglas.

◄ Lurpak butter dish. Ceramic. (1990). (vg) £5 - £7

► Lurpak toast rack. Ceramic. (1990). (vg) £5 - £7

MAGAZINES

Thousands of different magazines have been sold from newsagent shops for over a century. This means that there's plenty of choice for today's collectors.

There will be relatively few collectors who collect nothing but magazines, for the simple reason that it's not easy to store and display them.

However, many collectors of specialist subjects will be keen to add a relevant magazine to complement a collecting theme.

▲ Life. 6 November 1950. (g) £2 - £4

▲ Woman. 9 July 1955. (g) £2 - £4

▲ Health And Strength. 15 July 1939. (g) £3 - £5

▲ Red Dwarf. Issue 1. March 1992. (vg-ex) £6 - £8

▲ Look. 30 December 1941. Back cover missing. (g) £1 - £3

▲ The Illustrated London News. 13 July 1957. (g) £2 - £4

▲ Sunday Times Magazine. 11 July 1982. (g-vg) £2 - £3

▲ Amateur Wireless. 1 December 1934. (g) £2 - £3

▲ National Enquirer. 16 September 1997. (g-vg) £1 - £2

▲ My Home. August 1958. (g) £1 - £2

▲ Treasure. 12 Dec 1970. (g-vg) £1 - £2

▲ The Tatler. 25 February 1948. (vg) £3 - £5

▲ News Review. 18 August 1949. (g-vg) £2 - £4

▲ The War Illustrated. 11 June 1943. (g) £2 - £3

▲ Practical Mechanics. December 1959. (g-vg) £2 - £3

▲ Red Letter. 25 June 1932. (f) £4 - £6

MAGAZINES

▲ National Geographic. April 1968. (g-vg) £1 - £2

▲ Small Trader. June 1933. (g-vg) £1 - £2

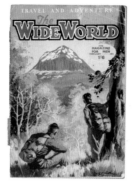

▲ The Wide World. February 1953. (g) £1 - £3

▲ The Leisure Hour. 13 April 1854. (g-vg) £3 - £5

▲ Practical Wireless. 7 January 1933. (g) £3 - £5

▲ Leader Magazine. 14 December 1946. (g) £2 - £4

▲ The Gramophone. August 1961. (g-vg) £2 - £4

▲ Woman's Realm. 11 July 1964. (g-vg) £1 - £2

▲ World Sports Aug 1950. (g-vg) £1 - £3

▲ British Legion Journal. Aug 1955. (g) £1 - £3

▲ The Dittybox. March 1945. (f-g) £2 - £3

▲ Aero Modeller. October 1953. (g) £1 - £2

▲ The Model Engineer. 14 March 1929. (f) £1 - £3

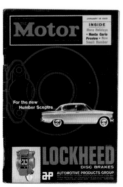

▲ The Motor. 16 January 1963. (g) £2 - £3

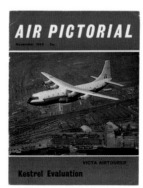

▲ Air Pictorial. November 1965. (g) £2 - £3

▲ Woman's Weekly. 23 July 1955. (g) £1 - £2

MATCHBOX LABELS

This is generally not an expensive collecting area. There are thousands of variations to the theme. An extensive collection displayed in well presented folders can offer much pleasure. Some very old labels will command higher sums. Like many collectable subjects, homework is needed.

▲ Fire Engine. (f) 20p-40p

▲ Monkey Brand. (vg) 40p-60p

▲ VP. (vg) 40p-60p

▲ Double Horse. (vg) 40p-60p

▲ Taj Mahal. (vg) 40p-60p

▲ The Old Hearth. (g) 30p-50p

▲ Swastika Brand. (vg) 40p-60p

▲ SVS. (vg) 40p-60p

▲ Cupid. (vg) 40p-60p

▲ Butterfly. (g) 30p-50p

▲ Condor. (vg) 40p-60p

▲ Silver Bells. (f) 20p-40p

▲ Flight. (vg) 40p-60p

▲ Hibiscus. (f) 20p-40p

▲ Liberty. (vg) 40p-60p

▲ Anchor. (f) 20p-40p

▲ Four Aces. (g) 30p-50p

▲ Two Elephants. (g) 30p-50p

▲ Bargate (f) 20p-40p

▲ Colgood's. (g) 30p-50p

▲ Gloso. (f) 20p-40p

▲ Bronco Brand. (f) 20p-40p

▲ Burma Lion. (vg) 40p-60p

▲ The Press. (f) 20p-40p

▲ Flare Path. (f) 20p-40p

▲ Collier. (f) 20p-40p

▲ Rose of Peckham. (g) 30p-50p

▲ The Top. (vg) 40p-60p

▲ Commonwealth. (g) 30p-50p

▲ Pageant. (vg) 40p-60p

▲ Test Match. (f) 20p-40p

▲ Brittania. (f) 20p-40p

▲ The Favorite Yacht. (vg) 40p-60p

▲ Cactus. (f) 20p-40p

MATCHBOX TOYS

Leslie Smith, who was born March 6, 1918, and died May 26, 2005, was one third of the team responsible for the incredibly popular Matchbox line of model vehicles, made by Lesney Products.

The firm started business in 1947, when Leslie and an old friend from school, Rodney Smith, pooled their resources and bought a metal press for £600. They combined their names to create the company name, and started working out of an abandoned pub called the Rifleman, making industrial parts out of zinc.

It was not long before the firm prospered, and they took on a third partner, Jack Odell. Jack was a keen model-maker, and was the driving force behind Lesney making die-cast children's toys like scale-model steamrollers and milk wagons, which were sold in toy shops and sweet shops.

Lesney's best-selling range of toys was created after Jack Odell's daughter said she could only take a toy into school if it could fit in a matchbox. Jack immediately set out to design a toy that would fit in such a small box, and in 1953 Lesney produced the first of its Matchbox vehicles.

The firm was declared insolvent in 1982, and the Matchbox brand was sold to Universal Toys before being sold on again to previous competitors Mattel.

▲ Bedford coach. London - Glasgow. 1960. 21A. Unboxed. (vg-ex) £20 - £24

▲ British European Airways coach. 1958. 58A. Unboxed. (g-vg) £14 - £16

▲ ERF petrol tanker (Shell). 1959. 11B. Unboxed. (vg-ex) £20 - £24

▲ Mighty Antar tank transporter & Centurion tank. Major Pack No.3. Models (ex), original box (g) £60 - £70

MATCHBOX TOYS

► Chevrolet Impala model. 1961. 576. Black base with black wheels. Unboxed (ex) £16 - £18

◄ Albion Chieftain. 1958. 51a. Unboxed (g-vg) £5 - £7

▲ Bedford Low Loader. 1958. 27b. Grey plastic wheels. (ex) in (vg) original box £120 - £140

► Leyland Tiger Coach. 1961. Silver plastic wheels (g) £3 - £4

◄ London Bus. 1954. 5a. Unboxed (vg) £10 - £12

▲ Scammell Mountaineer Snowplough. No.16. 1963. Black wheels. (vg-ex) in (g-vg) original box £20 - £24

▲ Ford LTS Articulated Tipper. 1973. K-18. Super Kings Diecast model (ex), in original box (f-g) £8 - £10

MECCANO

Invented in 1901 by Frank Hornby, Meccano is a model construction system using metal strips, plates, axles, wheels etc... Various models are constructed by bolting the parts together with nuts and bolts.

Frank originally called his invention 'Mechanics Made Easy'. A few years later the name was changed to 'Meccano'. Demand was so high in the early days, that Frank built a factory in Binns Lane, Liverpool.

▲ Assembled Meccano model. Ambulance. No. AR2. 1972 - 1979. (f) £4 - £6

The first set was manufactured and sold in 1908. Meccano is still manufactured today.

To celebrate the company's first 25 years, 'Meccano in Colours' was introduced, using the now familiar green and red coloured pieces.

Pre-1970 boxed sets are very collectable. If the box is in good condition+ with the original instructions leaflet, the value is enhanced.

A problem exists with boxed Meccano sets, whereby the parts were normally mixed by the user, with other sets and accessory outfits, hence

▲ Meccano Instruction booklet. No.0 Outfit. 1919. Hard to find but sadly this is only in 'fair' condition, although it is complete. £22 - £26

it's difficult to find a Meccano set in very good condition with all the original pieces within the relevant box.

Empty original boxes with their contents listings are relatively valuable items, if in good condition+ as they can be filled with the relevant parts to resurrect a full set.

▲ Meccano Instruction booklet. Outfit no.1. 1960. (g-vg) £14 - £16

MECCANO - Magazines

Obviously not as collectable as Meccano Sets, the Magazines are nevertheless a collectable subject in their own right.

They complemented the construction kits with articles and photographs of models etc...

As well as this, they contained glorious advertisements of Meccano, Hornby and Dinky products. The size changed from A4 to A5 in 1942.

▲ Volume 14, number 9, Sep 1929. (g) £12 - £14

▲ Volume 16, number 3, Mar 1931. (g) £10 - £12

▲ Vol 27, no. 3, Mar 1942. (g-vg) £6 - £8

▲ Vol 28, no. 8, Aug 1943. (g-vg) £6 - £8

▲ Vol 29, no. 3, Mar 1944. (g) £5 - £7

▲ Vol 29, no. 5, May 1944. (g) £5 - £7

▲ Vol 30, no. 8, Aug 1945. (vg) £7 - £9

▲ Vol 32, no. 5, May 1947. (f-g) £6 - £8

▲ Vol 32, no. 8, Aug 1947. (g) £5 - £7

▲ Vol 32, no. 10, Oct 1947. (g) £5 - £7

▲ Vol 33, no. 1, Jan 1948. (g) £5 - £7

▲ Vol 34, no. 7, Jul 1949. (f-g) £5 - £7

▲ Vol 34, no. 11, Nov 1949. (g-vg) £5 - £7

▲ Vol 35, no. 5, May 1950. (g) £4 - £6

▲ Vol, 37, no. 7, Jul 1952. (f) £3 - £4

▲ Vol 38, no. 9, Sep 1953. (f-g) £3 - £4

▲ Vol 39, no. 5, May 1954. (f) £3 - £4

▲ Vol 40, no. 2, Nov 1955. (f) £3 - £4

▲ Vol 41, no. 3, Mar 1956. (f-g) £4 - £6

▲ Vol 42, no. 1, Jan 1957. (f-g) £3 - £4

▲ Vol 42, no. 7, Jul 1957. (g) £2 - £3

▲ Vol 43, no. 1, Jan 1958. (g) £2 - £3

▲ Vol 43, no. 7, Jul 1958. (f) £3 - £4

▲ Vol 44, no. 1, Jan 1959. (f) £2 - £3

▲ Vol 44, no. 3, Mar 1959. (p) £1 - £2

▲ Vol 44, no. 11, Nov 1959. (g-vg) £3 - £4

MILITARIA

Militaria encompasses a variety of collectables relating to the military. The scope of this subject is massive.

Some of the more popular militaria collectables include; antique swords and firearms, uniforms, armour, helmets and buttons.

Military medals are particularly sought after and, if bought correctly, offer investment potential. Other collectables include books, records, art, toys, magazines, postcards and cigarette cards.

▲ German officer (Colonel). Dress cap. Manufactured by Peter Kupper KG. July 1964. (vg-ex) £16 - £20

Formation badges

These badges were first used during WWI but were then discontinued after the war. At the outbreak of WWII they were reintroduced. Their purpose was to provide an easy way to visually identify various units. They were often worn on the upper sleeve of the uniform.

These symbols boosted morale. Each unit became proud of its own symbol.

Formation badges were discontinued after World War II.

▶ H.M. Royal Air Force Band. EP record. 1958. HMV label, 7EG 8462. Conducted by Wing Commander R. P. O'Donnell. Vinyl (vg), sleeve (vg) £6 - £8

◀ Hit Kit. USA song and music booklet. 16 pages. Published by United States Army 1944. Some staple rusting, otherwise in good condition. £6 - £8

▲ Formation badge. 47th London Infantry. (1940). The symbol is that of a bow and two bells (Bow Bells - a sign of London). (vg) £14 - £16

Bed plates

▲ Grenadier Guards bed plate. (1960). Brass. (g-vg) £12 - £16

A bed plate, also known as a bed card, was a brass plate bearing a regimental badge that was issued to each army recruit. The recruit's name and number was stamped on the plate, and then it was placed on the locker or shelf above his bunk. In some regiments, the reverse of the bed plate was stamped "DUTY," and this side would be shown if the recruit was on a duty that required him to sleep somewhere other than his own bunk.

MILITARIA

▲ Admiral Togo postcard. Postmarked London 1906. (g-vg) £4 - £6

Marshal - Admiral Togo. The unparalleled victor of the sea. He was one of Japan's greatest naval heroes and regarded as the equivalent of Britain's admiral Horatio Nelson.

▲ Mikasa postcard. Admiral Togo's flagship. Postally unused, but writing on reverse. (1905). (vg) £4 - £6

▲ Yoshino postcard. Japanese Cruiser. Postally unused, but writing on reverse. (vg) £4 - £6

The Yoshino was built in the United Kingdom in 1892 by Armstrong Whitworth and delivered to the Japanese Navy in 1893. Her first duty was to patrol off the Korean coast due to increasing tension between Japan and China.

▲ HMS Drake postcard. Postally unused, but writing on reverse. (1905). (g-vg) £5 - £7

Prince Louis Alexander of Battenberg was a British naval officer appointed First Sea Lord in 1912. However, because of his German background he was forced to retire at the outset of World War I. He married a granddaughter of Queen Victoria. He was the father of Earl Louis Mountbatten.

RN Barracks - Chatham

▲ RN Barracks Chatham. Parade ground. Postcard. Postally unused, but writing on reverse. (1910). (vg) £4 - £6

▲ RN Barracks Chatham. Guard house. Postcard. Postally unused, but writing on reverse. (1910). (vg) £4 - £6

▲ RN Barracks Chatham. Reading room. Postcard. Postally unused, but writing on reverse. (1910). (vg) £4 - £6

▲ RN Barracks Chatham. Kit inspection. Postcard. Postally unused, but writing on reverse. (1910). (vg) £4 - £6

The barracks were built in 1897 by Holloway Brothers of London. The site was previously a prison. The barracks were named HMS Pembroke (the original base ship between 1873 and 1890).

Discipline was harsh in the barracks. Spotless uniforms were order of the day. Facilities included swimming baths and a bowling alley.

The gates to the barracks were finally closed in 1984. The building is now a university.

MILK BOTTLES

It will be very surprising if any collector ever builds a collection of milk bottles larger than Steve Wheeler from Malvern. He has over 17,500.

Collectors are looking for early milk bottles and also those with advertising from the 1980's and 1990's.

The practice of printing advertisements on the sides of milk bottles ceased in the 1990's for health and safety reasons. The equipment used for hygiene checking was impaired because of the advertisements.

A great place to find collectable milk bottles is the car boot sale.

Anyone with a serious interest in collecting milk bottles, should find the website www.milkbottlenews.org.uk very interesting. There's even details of conventions and swapmeets.

▲'The Mirror'. Unigate. 1986. (vg) £2 - £3

▲ 'Nescafe'. Unigate. (1985). (vg) £2 - £3

▲ 'Macleans'. Unigate. (1985). (vg) £2 - £3

▲'Wonderfuel Gas'. Unigate. (1985). (vg) £2 - £3

▲ 'Marathon'. Unigate. (1985). (vg) £3 - £4

▲ 'Knorr'. Unigate. (1985). (vg) £2 - £3

▲'Polycell'. Unigate. (1985). (vg) £3 - £4

▲ 'Seeboard'. Unigate. (1985). (vg) £2 - £3

▲'Horlicks'. Unknown dairy. (1985). (vg) £2 - £3

▲'Ready Brek'. Unigate. (1985). (vg). £2 - £3

▲'Surrey Police'. Unigate. (1985). (vg) £4 - £5

▲ 'Crusha'. Unigate. (1985). (vg) £3 - £4

▲'Kellogg's'. Unigate. (1985). (vg) £2 - £3

▲ 'Hermesetas'. Unigate. (1985). (vg) £3 - £4

▲ 'St. Ivel Cornish'. Unigate. (1985). (vg) £2 - £4

▲'Brooke Bond'. Unigate. (1985). (vg) £2 - £3

▲ 'Highland Spring'. Unigate. (1985). (vg) £2 - £3

▲ 'Computerised Horoscope' Unigate. (vg) £2 - £3

MISCELLANEOUS

The world of collectables has countless items that have no specific collecting category or are so specialised that they are grouped under the heading 'miscellaneous'. Quite often, such items are intriguing and great fun to research.

Miscellaneous items can often provide a good opportunity to take a punt at a car boot sale or an internet auction. You may just get a feeling that an item is something special and blindly buy it, assuming it's not too expensive, of course.

▲ Dulux dog model. Royal Doulton figurine. 140mm high. Produced in 2011 to celebrate 50 years of the Dulux dog. With original box and insert. (ex) £20 - £24

Dulux paint was an ICI product dating back to 1931. It was originally only available to the decorating trade. Then in the early 1950's it was sold as a retail product. In 1961 an Old English Sheepdog was introduced as a marketing tool for Dulux Paints and has remained so ever since. The association of this breed of dog with Dulux Paints has become so well known, that many people refer to the breed as 'Dulux Dogs'.

Tethering chog

These wooden 'chogs' were used to tether single grazing animals (particularly horses). Used with a loose noosed rope or chain to keep the animal from choking. A heavy wood was normally used, particularly lignum vitae. The standard size was 85 x 85mm.

▲ Tethering chog. (1920). (g) £15 - £20

▲ Deskette. Office aid. (1920). 245 x 100mm. A patented wooden device that despatched paper for note writing. (f-g) £6 - £8

▲ Pension Book Holder. (1975). Real leather. 215 x 95mm. (vg) £2 - £4

MODEL RAILWAY

A very serious collecting area that appeals to all age groups. There's plenty of investment potential but homework is required.

Model railway clubs often hold exhibitions and buy and sell items at the same time. You can learn plenty from them.

▲ Hornby Railways. Modern Signal Box. R145. Circa 1975 model. (ex), original box (f-g) £10 - £12

▲ Hornby-Dublo R080BR. Steam locomotive and tender. OO Gauge. Princess Elizabeth 46201. Unboxed. Working order. (vg) £26 - £30

▲ Hornby-Dublo 4063. Open Corridor Coach. 2nd Class BR. With interior fittings. OO Gauge. (vg-ex), original box (f-g) £12 - £16

▲ Tri-ang Railways Catalogue. 4th Edition. 1958. (g-vg) £22 - £26

▲ Peco Model Railway Catalogue. January 1971. (g-vg) £10 - £12

▲ Hornby Railway Company enamel lapel badge. (1955). (vg) £15 - £18

▲ Lima Model Railways Catalogue. 1979/80. (g) £6 - £8

▲ Trix Twin Catalogue. Circa 1957. (g) £18 - £20

▲ Tri-ang Railways. 45rpm EP record. (1965). Authentic sound recordings of trains. Vinyl (vg), sleeve (vg) £18 - £20

▲ Hornby Railways Catalogue. OO Scale. XXII. 1976. (g) £8 - £12

▲ Mainline Railways Catalogue. OO Gauge. Palitoy. 1976. (g-vg) £5 - £7

▲ Hornby Dublo mini catalogue and price list. April 1963. (f) £6 - £8

MONEY BOXES

Seriously old money boxes are hard to find and expensive, so many collectors concentrate on novelty boxes.

▲ Bloodhound. Ceramic. Unknown maker. 150mm high. (1985). (vg) £3 - £4

▲ Phone Box. Ceramic. Unknown maker. 165 x 85mm. (1995). (vg) £3 - £4

▲ VW Camper. Ceramic. 210 x 130mm. (2005). (vg-ex) £3 - £4

▲ Ceramic ladies (life-size) high heel shoe. Ceramic. Unknown maker. 240 x 115mm. (1995). (ex) £4 - £6

▲ Space Rocket design. Transomnia hand painted. 90 x 85mm. (vg - ex) £4 - £6

▲ Juke Box. Plastic. Made in China. 150 x 115mm. (1980). (vg) £4 - £6

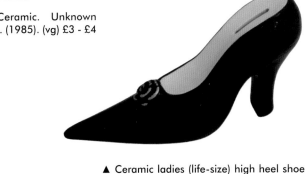

▲ Toadstool. Fine bone china. Unknown maker. 95 x 80mm. (1990). (vg) £3 - £4

◄ Piggy Bank. Ceramic pig. Unknown maker. 125 x 85mm. (1985). (vg) £3 - £4

► Cream Bun. Ceramic. 125 x 93mm. (1990). (vg - ex) £3 - £4

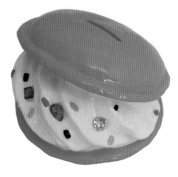

NATIONAL SAVINGS

It was way back in 1861 that the Palmerston Government introduced the Post Office Savings Bank, otherwise known as 'National Savings'. It became the world's first postal savings scheme. It allowed the ordinary person to create a convenient savings device for 'a rainy day'.

Early savings stamps are very collectable, as are the earliest savings books. Other associated collectables include advertising leaflets, badges and medals.

▲ National Savings gift token card. 1953. (g-vg) £3 - £5

▲ Post Office Savings Bank, London. Postmarked Seacombe 1909. Message in ink. (f) £3 - £4

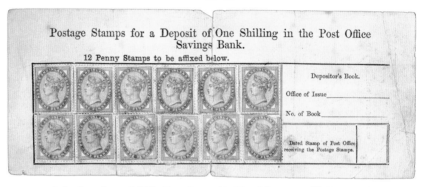

▲ Savings form. 1892. Complete with 12 x 1d stamps. (f) £30 - £36

Front cover   Inside page
▲ National Savings stamp book. 1961. (g) £3 - £4

Front cover   Inside page
▲ National Savings stamp book. (1970). (f-g) £1 - £3

▲ National Savings certificate. 1952. (f) £2 - £3

▲ National Savings button badge. (1940). (vg) £8 - £10

▲ National Savings enamel pin badge. (1980). (ex) £1 - £2

NATWEST PIGS

Wade pottery produced a series of pig moneyboxes for NatWest Bank in 1983 (taking over from Sunshine Ceramics who originally made the pigs in 1982). This was to give youngsters an incentive to save. As a child's balance grew, they were able to increase their collection of pigs.

A child received their first pig (Woody, the baby) when they saved £1 and they received the final pig in the collection (Sir Nathaniel Westminster, the father) when they saved £100. Lady Hillary (the mother), Maxwell (the boy) and Annabel (the girl) were the other pigs in the collection. The offer ended in 1988.

▲ Annabel. Wade backstamp. Original NatWest stopper. (vg) £10 - £12

▲ Maxwell. Wade backstamp. Original NatWest stopper. (vg) £12 - £14

▲ Woody. Wade backstamp. Original Natwest stopper. (vg) £8 - £10

NAUTICALIA

Nauticalia is the collecting of and study of navy and shipping related items.

This is a massive subject with vast amounts of collectables out there in the marketplace.

▲ Queen Elizabeth ship souvenir. 1958. 115mm. (g-vg) £8 - £10

▲ Belgenland. Red Star Line. Original postcard. (1904). Postally unused. (g) £8 - £10

The Red Star Line

The Red Star Line passenger line was founded in 1871 as a joint venture by the International Navigation Company of Philadelphia and the Societe Anonyme de Navigation Belgo-Americaine. The company ceased operation in 1934.

Sir Francis Chichester

Sir Francis was born in Devon in 1901. He emigrated to Australia and set up several businesses at the age of just 19, including an aviation business.

He soon acquired the taste for adventure and in 1929 he moved back to England. From Croydon he flew single handed in a Gypsy Moth aircraft to Sydney, Australia and became the second person to do so.

Many adventures later, in August 1966 he set out from Plymouth on a sea voyage to circumnavigate the world in his yacht named Gipsy Moth IV (different spelling, but the name was linked to his association with the aircraft of the same name). He triumphantly returned to Plymouth in May 1967.

He died in Plymouth in 1972 and was buried at the place of his birth (Sherwell, North Devon).

▲ Sir Francis Chichester first day cover. 24 Jul 1967. Cancelled with Southampton FDI postmark. Typed address. (g-vg) £1 - £2

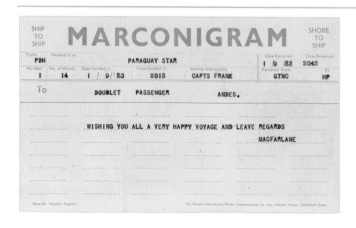

Marconigram

A nautical radiogram service whose origins date back to the great inventor, Marconi.

◄ Marconigram. Ship to ship. Paraguay Star to Andes. 1 September 1953. With original envelope. (g-vg) £12 - £14

NAUTICALIA

White Star Line

This shipping company revolutionised passenger travel. Just about any original piece of White Star Line memorabilia is now much sought after by today's collectors.

The story began in 1845, when Henry Wilson and John Pilkington founded the business in Liverpool. In the early years, White Star concentrated on the Liverpool to New York crossings.

In 1868, White Star went bankrupt and the goodwill, house flag and trade name was purchased by Thomas Ismay. A deal with shipbuilders Harland and Wolff followed.

In 1899 Ismay decided to turn his attention to economy and comfort as opposed to the obsession of his rivals to operate faster ships. He launched Oceanic II. It was an overwhelming success.

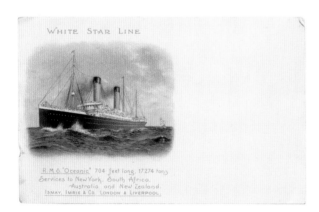

▲ White Star Line, original postcard. (1903). Featuring RMS Oceanic II. Postally unused. (g-vg) £14 - £18

Around 1900, there was a huge demand for ocean travel as thousands of emigrants left the British shores. Between 1901 and 1907 White Star added four more big ships to the fleet, Celtic, Cedric, Baltic and Adriatic. The latter had capacity for 1900 third-class passengers.

▲ RMS Celtic original postcard. (1910). Postally unused. (g) £8 - £10

▲ RMS Cedric original postcard. (1905). Stamp removed, postmark illegible. (g-vg) £8 - £12

▲ RMS Baltic original postcard. Postally unused. (1906). (g) £8 - £12

▲ RMS Adriatic original postcard. (1910). Postally unused. (vg) £10 - £12

Cunard had launched the Mauritania and Lusitania, White Star Line replied to this major competition by launching Olympic and Brittanic II and in 1912, the ill-fated Titanic.

In contrast to the misfortune of the Titanic, the Olympic stayed in service for 24 years.

▲ RMS Olympic original postcard. (1910). Postally unused. (vg) £10 - £14

▲ RMS Olympic, original sepia real photo postcard. Tourist third class lounge. (1920). Postally unused. (vg) £8 - £10

Both Cunard and White Star Line suffered the wrath of the Great Depression in the early thirties. The government bailed both firms out on the condition they merged and so was born Cunard-White Star Ltd.

Eventually, in 1950 Cunard acquired all the interests of the company and the name White Star was dropped.

NAUTICALIA

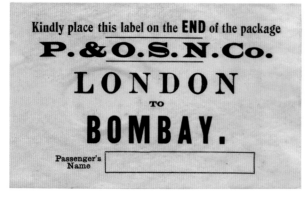

▲ Canadian Pacific. Advertising postcard. (1910). Postally unused. (g-vg) £8 - £12

Canadian Pacific

The Canadian Pacific Railway began in 1881 and entered the transatlantic passenger service in 1903 when taking over the ships of the Beaver Line.

◄ Canadian Pacific. Tourist class programme of events for 26 May 1959. Empress of France. (vg) £2 - £4

► Canadian Pacific. Passenger List (14 pages) booklet. 15 September 1959. Empress of France. (vg) £2 - £4

► Canadian Pacific. Luggage label. 160mm long. 1960. (vg) £2 - £3

P&O (Peninsular And Oriental)

The Peninsular and Oriental Steam Navigation Company (P&O) dates back to 1822. Fifteen years later the company won a contract to deliver mail to the Iberian Peninsula and soon after, the contracts expanded. By the turn of the century P&O had become a major shipping line, which included passenger liners. In 1918 the company took over the British India Steam Navigation Company, adding 131 steamers to the fleet. In the fifties P&O built 15 large passenger liners, including SS Arcadia and SS Iberia.

▲ P & O Matchbook. (1950). In very good condition, save for staple rusting. £2 - £3

▲ P & O luggage label. 178mm x 110mm. (1910). (g-vg) £4 - £6

▲ Two photographs of the Chitral. 1953. (vg) £2 - £3

Two rare photographs of the Chitral passenger liner departing Melbourne on her last voyage in 1953. She was commissioned by P&O in 1923 and made her maiden voyage in 1925. She was requisitioned by the Admiralty for war duties in 1939 and returned to P&O in 1947. Finally sold for scrap in 1953 for £167,500.

NETSUKE

Netsuke date back to 17th Century Japan. Traditional Japanese clothing, such as the kimono, had no pockets, so personal items such as pipes, tobacco, writing equipment, and charms were carried around in sagemono. These small containers were hung from the obi (the sash of the kimono) and were held in place with special toggles called netsuke. Although they had a functional purpose, many netsuke were beautifully sculpted works of art, and many are still manufactured today with style and design taking precedence over function, so they are lovely items for collectors to specialise in and they make fantastic display pieces.

The netsukeshi (netsuke carvers) used whatever materials they had available to make their netsuke, so netsuke are available in box and cherry wood, boar's tusk, amber, narwhal, and bamboo. Ivory was used in the regions of Osaka, Kyoto, and Edo, where it was readily available, but it was not used as exclusively as some people believe, which is good news for those collectors who are delighted by the art of netsuke but cannot stomach the thought of owning anything carved in ivory.

As well as a huge range of materials, there is also a wide range of netsuke designs. The most common form of netsuke is katabori, carved figures like the ones available for sale in this book. Katabori can be on any theme, but the kind seen most regularly are humans and animals from the Japanese zodiac.

Other forms of netsuke include anabori (hollowed out), sashi (thin, stick-like netsuke), manju (flat, round netsuke), mask (miniature masks), and trick (netsuke with moving parts).

With such diversity of design and material, it is no surprise that netsuke are popular among collectors. Some netsuke can be picked up quite inexpensively at online auctions and trade fairs, and they make a fascinating and beautiful collection that is sure to be the talking point of any home.

▲ Netsuke ivory coloured bone swan. (vg) £10 - £12

▲ Netsuke boxwood mouse. (vg) £8 - £10

Netsuke Fakes

Always remember that wherever you find collectables, you will also find people prepared to make poor copies of them to trick unwary collectors into parting with their hard-earned money. Forgeries do exist, and you should take great care when making a purchase to ensure that you are not paying a large sum of money for a fake.

Some netsuke you find will be "Hong Kong" netsuke – modern copies in ivory or plastic that often turn up in souvenir shops to trick tourists looking for a souvenir. There are also much better copies that can defraud a collector for thousands of pounds. Be aware that almost all fakes are ivory, because ivory can be carved easily and quickly, and most people believe that the majority of original netsuke were made of ivory (in fact, only about half were).

NUMISMATICS

The collecting and study of coins. A collector is known as a 'numismatist'.

Technically, the subject of numismatics includes paper money, however, the collecting of banknotes is more commonly known as 'notaphily'.

The collecting of coins can be traced back to over 700 years ago. The first book on the subject was published in 1514.

The Royal Numismatic Society was founded in 1836. Its purpose is to promote interest and research.

The subject of numismatics is truly fascinating and can become thoroughly absorbing, however, a considerable amount of homework is required before deciding to invest heavily.

A good tip for absolute beginners is to concentrate on British Coins minted 1953 - 1969.

The Gold Sovereign

Obverse

Reverse

▲ Queen Victoria. Gold Sovereign. 1894. (ex) £275 - £300

This coin was named after the English gold sovereign (last minted 1604). The name 'sovereign' was revived as part of the Coin Act 1816. The gold content was fixed within this Act and has remained (largely) the same ever since.

The 'reverse' design of the coin depicts Saint George slaying a dragon. This exquisite 'Benedetto Pistrucci' classic design has remained with the coin for almost 200 years.

The Gold Sovereign is, in effect a 'bullion coin'. The value fluctuates in accordance with the market price of gold. These bullion coins normally sell at a premium above market price because of their small size and numismatic interest.

The Cartwheel Penny

The first ever copper penny piece was issued in 1797, during the reign of George III. The coin was a massive 41mm in diameter and 5mm thick, and was the first British coin to feature the image of Britannia on the reverse. It was also the first ever coin to be struck on steam-powered presses.

The coin became known as the Cartwheel Penny because of its large size and raised rim. In Cape Town (which had been captured by Britain in 1795) the coin was known as the Devil's Penny because Britannia was holding a trident, an implement strongly associated with the Devil.

TERMS

Abrasion - A mark or small scratch on the surface of a coin.

Assay - The test to determine weight and purity of a coin.

Beading - The raised dots that border the rim of a coin.

Circulated - Coins that have been worn through circulation.

Die - The engraved metal stamp that is used for stamping out the design of the coin.

Edge - The side of a coin.

Filler - A lower grade or perhaps a damaged coin 'filling' a place in a collection until a better grade coin is found.

Legend - The principal inscription on a coin.

Mint set - A set of uncirculated coins which have been specially packaged and sold by the mint.

Obverse - The front of a coin, often referred to as the 'heads' side.

Reverse - The back of a coin, often called 'tails'.

World coins

You can have some real fun with foreign coins. Researching the history of that country at the time the coin is dated, can take you down many paths.

The coin itself may also have some interesting facts to reveal. An example is the USA coin below.

The Liberty Seated Quarter Dollar coin was issued from 1838 - 1891. The front of the coin (obverse) has the Goddess or Lady Liberty seated. She is holding a small flag (a liberty pole) in her left hand. Her right hand is resting on a shield containing the word 'Liberty'.

Obverse

Reverse

▲ Silver Quarter Dollar. 1855. In generally very good condition but has a small nick which has reduced our valuation by 50%. £8 - £10

NUMISMATICS

Obverse   Reverse

▲ 1836 William IV half crown. (vg) £28 - £32

Obverse   Reverse

▲ 1901 Victoria half crown. (vg) £20 - £24

Obverse   Reverse

▲ 1843 Victoria one and a half pence. (vg) £14 - £16

Obverse   Reverse

▲ 1836 William IV four pence. (ex) £40 - £50

Obverse

Reverse

▲ 1820 George III one shilling. (g-vg) £20 - £24

Obverse

Reverse

▲ 1824 George IV six pence. (g-vg) £28 - £32

Obverse   Reverse

▲ 1696 William II crown. (g) £180 - £200

Obverse

Reverse

▲ 1853 Victoria half penny. (vg) £18 - £22

Obverse   Reverse

▲ 1797 George III two pence. (vg) £42 - £48

Obverse

Reverse

▲ 1826 George IV half crown. (vg) £80 - £100

OBSERVER'S BOOKS

Collecting Observer's books is becoming an increasingly popular pastime, but the vast number of titles, many of which were frequently reprinted or even updated in a new edition, means that the hobby can be a real minefield for the uninitiated.

The first two titles in Frederick Warne & Co's popular series of Observer's books, British Birds and British Wild Flowers, were published in 1937, and their popularity led to the series expanding dramatically. Eventually there were 97 titles in the series, spanning everything from Cathedrals to Football.

The last book was number 98, Opera, published in 1982. That may seem strange, considering there were only 97 books in the series, but number 86, Country Houses, was never published.

For a collector, it is first editions of the 97 titles released between 1937 and 1982 that are of the most interest, and these are the books that have the most investment potential. However, finding and identifying first editions can be quite a chore. The reverse of the title page usually contains relevant information.

There have been two further Observer's Books released since 1982. Book 99, Observer's Books, and book 100, Wayside and Woodland. Although owning the Observer's Book of Observer's Books could be very interesting to collectors, both this title and number 100 were NOT published by Frederick Warne & Co.

As with anything collectable, condition is vitally important. Most Observer's books will be well-used, and you can expect a certain amount of wear and tear, but you should always aim to buy the best quality that you can afford.

Collectors should note that many titles used the word "British" in their original title, but this was later dropped. So, using book number 18 as an example, 'British Birds' Eggs' had its title changed to 'Birds' Eggs'. This is common throughout the series.

Since their introduction, the Observer's books have gone through a number of designs, and anybody interested in starting a collection is advised to spend some time familiarising themselves with how the appearance of the books has changed over time.

▲ Birds. Book 1. 1969. 4th reprint. (vg) £3 - £5

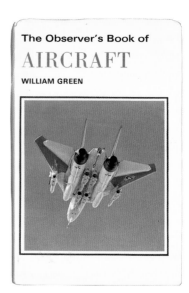

▲ Aircraft. Book 11. 1974. 23rd edition. (g-vg) £3 - £5

▲ Wild Animals. Book 5. 1973. Reprint. (g-vg) £3 - £4

OBSERVER'S BOOKS

1. British Birds
2. British Wild Flowers
3. British Butterflies
4. Trees & Shrubs of the British Isles
5. Wild Animals
6. Freshwater Fishes
7. British Grasses, Sedges & Rushes
8. Dogs
9. Horses and Ponies
10. British Geology
11. Aircraft
12. British Ferns
13. British Architecture
14. The Larger British Moths
15. Ships
16. Music
17. Common British Insects & Spiders
18. British Birds Eggs
19. Common Fungi
20. Mosses & Liverworts
21. Automobiles
22. Weather
23. Railway Locomotives of Britain
24. Pond Life
25. Garden Flowers
26. Painting & Graphic Art
27. Cacti & Other Succulents
28. Sea Fishes
29. Flags
30. Cats
31. Sea & Seashore
32. Astronomy
33. Lichens
34. Modern Art
35. Furniture
36. Old English Churches
37. Sculpture
38. Basic Aircraft - Civil
39. Basic Aircraft - Military
40. Commercial Vehicles
41. Heraldry
42. Postage Stamps
43. Cathedrals
44. Flowering Trees & Shrubs for Gardens
45. Zoo Animals
46. House Plants
47. Association Football
48. Manned Space Flight
49. Cricket
50. London

51. Pottery & Porcelain
52. Unmanned Space Flight
53. Motor Sport
54. European Costume
55. British Awards & Medals
56. Ancient & Roman Britain
57. Sewing
58. Golf
59. Coarse Fishing
60. Show Jumping & Eventing
61. Motorcycles
62. Glass
63. Tourist Atlas of GB & Ireland
64. Small Craft
65. Tropical Fishes
66. Farm Animals
67. Vegetables
68. Fly Fishing
69. Coins
70. Seashells of the British Isles
71. Fossils
72. Pets
73. The Cotswolds & Shakespeare Country
74. The Lake District
75. Firearms
76. Jazz
77. Big Bands
78. Castles
79. Caterpillars
80. Rocks & Minerals
81. Tennis
82. Sea Fishing
83. Devon & Cornwall
84. Roses
85. Herbs
86. Country Houses - NEVER PUBLISHED
87. Folk Songs in Britain
88. Silver
89. Tanks & Other Armoured Vehicles
90. Victoriana
91. World Atlas
92. Vintage Cars & Pre-War Classics
93. Classic Cars After 1945
94. Paris
95. Canals
96. Gardens of England, Scotland & Wales
97. Kitchen Antiques
98. Opera
99. Observer's Book of Observer's Books
100. Wayside and Woodland

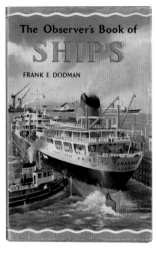

▲ Ships. Book 15. 1966.
Revised edition. (g) £3 - £4

▲ House Plants. Book 46.
1978. 3rd reprint. (g) £3 - £4

▲ Weather. Book 22. 1964.
Revised edition. (f-g) £3 - £5

OLYMPICS

The Olympic Games are natural generators of masses of collectables.

The ultimate collectable has to be a winner's gold medal but these rarely come on the market, so do beware if you are offered one, the chances are that it could be a replica.

Collectables, such as programmes, tickets and souvenirs from Games held over 50 years ago can be found at sensible prices and could prove to be good little investments.

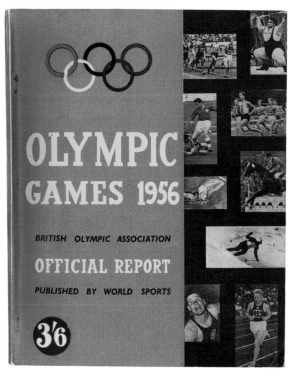

▲ Olympic Games report. Limpback book. 1956. 265 x 210mm. 112 pages. An extensive report of the Melbourne games with many pictures and masses of statistics. Published by World Sports. (vg) £10 - £12

▲ 1972 Winter Olympic Games. First Day Cover. 17 August 1972. Postmarked Washington DC. No address. (vg) £3 - £5

◄ Los Angeles 1984. Souvenir matchbox. Empty. (vg) 30p - 50p

The 1948 Olympics

The 1948 London Olympics football tournament kicked off with two preliminary matches on 26 July 1948.

The first round match between India and France was contested on the Ilford FC ground on 31 July 1948. France beat India, 2-1, but were subsequently knocked out of the tournament in the quarter-finals, where they lost, 1-0, to Great Britain. Great Britain, in turn, were knocked out by Yugoslavia in the semi-finals; and were denied a bronze medal in the play-offs when they were beaten by Denmark.

The gold medallists were Sweden, who beat Denmark in the semi-final round and then beat Yugoslavia, 3-1, in the final.

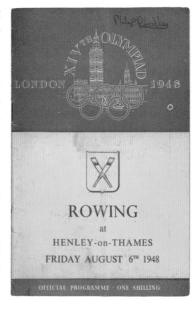

◄ ▲ Rowing official programme. London Olympics 1948. With card 'enclosure' badge. (f-g) £10 - £12

OPERA

Unlike pop memorabilia, because opera has more of a serious and dour air, the demand for memorabilia is less than that of pop and values are generally lower. However, there are exceptions.

◄ ▲ Sadler's Wells opera programme (g) and ticket stub (ex). Friday 6 March 1969. The Flying Dutchman. £2 - £3

▲ Winnie Melville (1895 - 1937). Began her career as a concert singer. In 1929 she joined the D'Oyly Carte Opera Company as principal soprano. Autographed postcard. Postally unused. Clear, black ink. No dedication. (vg)   £5 - £8

Royal Opera

The Royal Opera House is situated in Covent Garden. It is home of The Royal Opera, The Royal Ballet, and the Orchestra of the Royal Opera House.

The current building is the third to have stood on the site, the previous two having been burned down in 1808 and 1857 respectively.

The Royal Opera is the UK's most famed opera company. Its origins date back to 1946, when it was originally called the Covent Garden Opera Company.

It was not until 1968 that the Queen granted permission for the Opera Company to be known as the Royal Opera instead, as a tribute to its immense success and popularity.

The Royal Opera's music is provided by the Orchestra of the Royal Opera House, which also works with the Royal Ballet.

▲ Royal Opera House programme. 1952. (g-vg) £1 - £2

ORNAMENTAL EGGS

Perhaps the attraction of collecting ornamental eggs can be traced back to the Russian link with Faberge.

Peter Carl Faberge (1846 - 1920) a goldsmith and jeweller, was commissioned by the Russian Imperial Court to create exquisite jewels and objects, including the famous Imperial Easter Eggs.

The most valuable ornamental eggs are the originals made by Faberge for Tsar Nicholas II. The romance of these eggs, led to others copying the Faberge model and now the market is awash with collectable ornamental eggs.

Assuming you haven't got a few spare million to acquire a Faberge original, you have plenty more to choose from, via internet auctions at pocket money prices and this is by far the best source.

However, given that many are made from heavy materials, it's quite often better to wait for a bargain or two to turn up at your local car boot, thereby eliminating any postage costs.

▲ Polished stone ornamental egg. (ex) £2 - £3

▲ Wooden ornamental egg. (vg) £1 - £2

―――――― ADVERTISEMENT ――――――

SUBSCRIBE!

COLLECTICUS

THE MONTHLY AUCTION MAGAZINE

December 2015   Issue no. 179

THIS MONTH'S SPECIALIST AUCTION
I-SPY

▲ I-Spy - People In Uniform. No.29. 1955. (g-vg) SP £8.00 (150256)

COLLECTICUS
THE MONTHLY AUCTION MAGAZINE

Collecticus is a fun way for like-minded enthusiasts to broaden their enjoyment of collecting. We provide postal and internet auctions that bring together buyers and sellers from all across the country, creating an incredibly strong market, and arguably one of the best buying and selling communities for collectors.

If you would like to sell your own items and enjoy many other benefits, then join in the action now.

For information on subscription costs, and more, please call us on:

01380 811750

Alterntively, you can visit the Collecticus website at:

www.collecticus.co.uk

Collecticus, P.O.Box 100, Devizes, Wiltshire, SN10 4TE

ORNITHOLOGY

Ornithology is the study of birds. It's a big subject but not with a vast quantity of interesting collectables.

▲ Water Boy postcard. (1925), Postally unused. Valentine's. (g) £3 - £4

▲ Long -Tailed Tits postcard. (1930), Postally unused. Salmon Series. (g-vg) £3 - £4

▲ Bee-Eater postcard. Postmarked 1947. R.S. Art Press. (f) £1 - £2

▲ RSPB First Day Cover. 17 January 1989. Edingburgh FDI postmark. Typed address. (vg) £1 - £2

The Royal Society for the Protection of Birds was founded in 1889.

▲ Listen The Birds. European Phono Club EP record. (1960). Songs of various birds. Vinyl (vg). £3 - £4

▲ Dawn Chorus and Nightingale. Shell EP record. 1969. Songs of various birds. Vinyl (vg) £5 - £7

▲ Songs of British Birds. HMV EP record. (1964). Songs of various birds. Vinyl (vg) £4 - £6

▲ Moor and Heath Birds. Shell EP record. 1967. Songs of various birds. Vinyl (vg) £5 - £7

▲ Garden and Park Birds. Shell EP record. 1966. Songs of various birds. Vinyl (vg) £5 - £7

▲ Estuary Birds. Shell EP record. 1967. Songs of various birds. Vinyl (vg) £5 - £7

OVALTINE

Like other well known products, the history of Ovaltine is over 100 years old and consequently related items are collectable.

Back in 1904, Swiss pharmacist Dr. George Wander had a serious interest in malt. At the time, malt was regarded as nutrient-rich food for children.

He extracted malt from barley, dried it, and mixed it with eggs, milk, and cocoa. He called his concoction 'Ovomaltine.' Five years later, the product hit the UK and it was renamed 'Ovaltine.'

In 1913 the product was manufactured at a factory in Kings Langley, Hertfordshire. By 1929 the business had grown so big that the company bought its own farms to produce milk and eggs.

In 1935 the company devised a brilliant marketing concept, 'The Ovaltine Children's Club.' Members were known as 'Ovaltineys' and today anything relating to 'The League of Ovaltineys' is collectable.

A catchy song called 'We Are The Ovaltineys' became one of the best known music themes in 1935, and even had its own show on Radio Luxembourg. You can hear the song today on the internet.

The popularity of Ovaltineys faded in the late 50s, but ten years later the company attempted a revival, changing 'Ovaltineys' to 'Ovaltiners.' In keeping with the 60s pop era, they created 'The Ovaltiners Beat Group.'

During World War II, British soldiers' ration packs included Ovaltine because of its nourishing benefits.

As with other popular brands, such as Oxo and Bisto, Ovaltine has made use of some iconic images in its advertising. As such, advertising postcards and signs can be rather attractive and will garner interest at auctions.

▲ The Ovaltine Theme. 45rpm record. (1960). Ovaltine promotional record. Eric Delaney and his Music. Vinyl (vg) £2 - £4

▲ League of Ovaltineys. Metal pin badge. (1935). 25mm diameter. Clasp missing, otherwise (vg) £8 - £12

OVER-SEAS LEAGUE

An organisation that described itself as "The strongest non-party brotherhood in the Empire".

They produced a monthly publication, titled 'Over-Seas'.

▶   Over-Seas League certificate. 1940. 200 x 130mm. (g-vg) £8 - £10

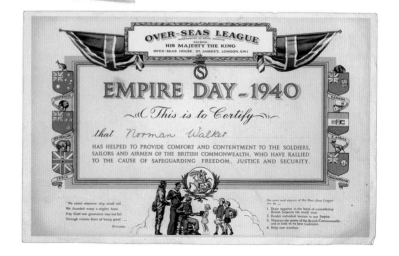

OXO

Concentrated meat extract was invented by Justus von Liebig and began being sold through his company, the Liebig Extract of Meat Company, in 1866. It was not until 1899 that the Oxo trademark was introduced.

Originally, the meat extract was a thick liquid, but in 1910 the first cubes were introduced. Oxo had sponsored the 1908 London Olympic Games, and this level of coverage, combined with the cheaper price of the cubes, ensured the products huge popularity. Oxo has always been well advertised, and one of their best remembered campaigns was the series of "Oxo family" television advertisements that began in 1983 and showed a typical family gathering around the dinner table to enjoy Oxo products. Other advertising and promotional items included information leaflets, recipe books, children's games, and posters.

Some of the most popular collectables to emerge from all the advertising products are the various series of trade cards. These cards were given away free in the same way that tobacco companies were giving away illustrated cards in cigarette packets, and they are now very desirable. Oxo branded tins are also very collectable, and are available in all kinds of shapes and sizes.

▲ Oxo van. Bedford 1950. Days Gone Vanguards model. (1990). (ex) £2 - £4

▲ Coronation souvenir tin. Oxo promotional product. 1953. (vg) £10 - £14

Page 1

Page 2

Page 3

Page 4

▲ Oxo recipe leaflet. Wartime (1940). 83 x 70mm. (g) £3 - £4

PAGE TURNERS

These items are believed to have been common in the Victorian era. They are distinguishable from letter openers in that they do not normally have sharp edges. As the name suggests, they were used to turn the pages of a book.

▲ Wooden page turner. 1896. Promotional item of The Eastern Telegraph Company, Broad Street, London. (f) £30 - £40

PAINT BOXES

One of the best known makers of children's tinplate water colour paint boxes was Page of London.

Rather surprisingly, perhaps, these paint boxes command a fair amount of interest. They are generally colourful and stir many memories of childhood hours spent indoors whilst the rain lashes down outside.

Condition of the tinplate box is more important than the state of the paint blocks inside. The Shipyard tin shown here is in good condition and has a price estimate between £8 and £12 but could be more than double this figure if in excellent condition.

▲ Shipyard. Page of London. 1965. 360 x 245mm. Most paint blocks have been used. (g) £8 - £12

PANTOMIME

The pantomime has its roots in the Middle Ages and has slowly evolved into the traditional events that we know today.

Look out for old programmes with star names in the cast.

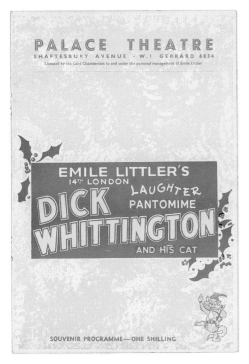

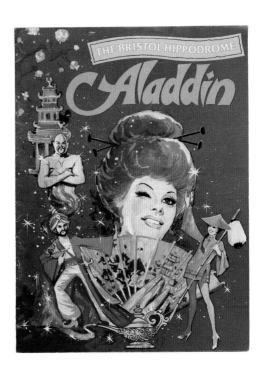

► Aladdin. Bristol Hippodrome prog. 1980. Starring Danny La Rue. (vg) £2 - £4

◄ Dick Whittington. Pal. Theatre, Shaftesbury Ave, London prog. 1956. The star was the legendary George Formby. (f-g) £3 - £4

◄ Cinderella. Winter Garden Theatre, Drury Lane, London. 1944. Stars included Binnie Hale, Hermione Baddeley and Kathleen Moody. This is a war-time four page programme, and it includes information on what to do if an air-raid warning is sounded. (f) £2 - £3

► Robinson Crusoe. New Palace Theatre, Plymouth programme. 1979. The stars were Norman Wisdom and Alvin Stardust. (g) £1 - £3

PAPER BAGS

It wasn't until the turn of the twentieth century that the concept of printing an advertising message on a paper bag became popular. These bags are now collectable, particularly where they relate to popular collectable themes, such as obsolete shipping lines.

Not surprisingly, there's no reference guide to the value of old paper bags, so it's a case of using commonsense. A visit to auction websites may surprise you. There are often examples of quite high prices being asked for classic bags.

The trouble with paper bag collecting is the difficulty in finding examples in very good condition. Most bags were used to hold products and this generally meant that the condition instantly deteriorated at the point of acquisition.

Bags from local outlets are generally of greater interest (and therefore have a potentially higher value) to people in the relevant area. So a 1960's bag from a local store in Carlisle is likely to fetch far more if being offered to potential buyers in Cumbria, than in Devon.

From time to time, quantities of unused bags are found and these are instantly collectable. Values depend on the advertising as well as condition.

Some bags were printed with messages relating to events, for example, the 1953 Coronation of Queen Elizabeth II.

Carrier bags generally use much stronger paper than a standard paper bag but still fall under the heading of 'paper bag collecting'. Another to fall under this classification is the paper coin bag used by a bank, to hold coins of a specific denomination.

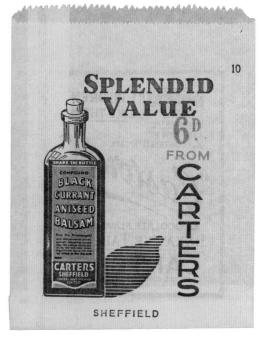

▲ Carters Balsam. (1920). Unused. (vg) £2 - £3

◄ Bristol Wireless. To hold 7" record. (1960). Used. (f-g) £1 - £2

▲ Silver Jubilee. 1977. Used. (g) £1 - £2

PENCIL SHARPENERS

◄ Lead policeman sharpener. (1930). (p-f) £3 - £4

Your first reaction to this area of collecting could be that of amazement. It may be surprising, but some people really do collect pencil sharpeners.

The more you study this subject, the more you will be amazed. Manufacturers seem to have invested quite large sums of money producing an array of items.

The two on this page are the tip of the iceberg. You'll find many more on the internet. They also crop up all the time at car boot sales, often heavily disguised and being sold by people who don't necessarily know what they are selling. However, it would be fair to say that value-wise we are not talking bank-breaking sums.

▲ Diecast car novelty sharpener. (1980). (vg) £1 - £2

PENDELFIN

Based in Burnley, the company produced Stoneware figurines and was formed in the early 1950's by Jeanie Heap and Jean Walmsley Heap. Early pieces are much sought after, particularly the Pendle Witch.

◄ The Pooch. Pendelfin model. (1970). 55mm high. Boxed. (g-vg) £8 - £12

PETROLIANA

A classification not too far removed from 'Automobilia' but worthy of its own category and indeed the subject of many specialist collections. As the collective name suggests, it relates to petrol and oil. Examples include petrol and oil cans, old petrol pumps and their 'globes', advertising signs, badges etc...

On March 19, 1899, Charles Wakefield set up an oil company in England called CC Wakefield and Co. Ltd. In 1909, he produced a new lubricant that would revolutionise transport. He called the new oil Castrol, and eventually adopted the name for his company.

▲ Castrol Oil can. (1960). 210mm high. (g) £10 - £12

Put a tiger in your tank

SELF-STICK EMBLEMS

PUT A TIGER IN YOUR TANK!

·TO REMOVE:
BEND N' PEEL DIE CUT EDGE.
--- REMOVE EMBLEM BEFORE WASHING

▲ Self-Stick Emblems. Unused. (1965). 167 x 108mm. (vg) £2 - £4

"Put a tiger in your tank" was a very famous Esso advertising campaign that began in 1964 and quickly caught on as one of the best known slogans of the era. Esso subsequently produced a wide variety of associated merchandise.

You could buy badges, stuffed toys and even fluffy tiger tails that countless motorists hung from their rear-view mirrors.

These items have now become collectable and you may find them at car boot sales and collectors' fairs.

PETROLIANA

▲ Esso map. London. 1959. No.1. (g-vg) £3 - £4

▲ Esso map. South and East England. 1960. No.2. (g-vg) £3 - £4

▲ Esso map. South and West England. (1960). No.3. (f-g) £3 - £4

▲ Esso map. Southern Scotland. 1959. No.6. (g-vg) £3 - £4

▲ Esso map. Northern Scotland. 1960. No.7 . (g) £3 - £4

Petrol can caps

Slightly obscure but nevertheless serious enough to attract collectors.

The majority of the caps date between 1900 and 1940 and were mainly made of brass with screw thread. They were made so well, that the majority of those that have survived are in good condition or better.

Like most collecting areas there are rarities and these can be established from much research on the internet.

Autojumbles are a good source for these caps. Alternatively, try internet auction sites.

▲ Redline. (g-vg) £15 - £20

▲ Pratts XX Spirit. (vg) £12 - £14

▲ BP L'Alliance Anvers. Belgian. (vg) £14 - £16

▲ Shell Mex. (vg) £13 - £15

▲ Shell. (g-vg) £10 - £12

PETROLIANA - Badges

Badges are so easy to store and are therefore ideal for collecting. Add the fact that there is a big demand for the rarer petroliana related items and you have a formula for investment potential.

▲ Globe button badge. 1960. 25mm. (vg) £8 - £10

▲ Super Shell button badge. (1960). 25mm. (vg) £6 - £8

▲ Bluecol button badge. (1960). 25mm. (g-vg) £6 - £8

▲ Esso Man pin badge. (1960). 40mm. (g-vg) £6 - £8

▲ Shell Anti-Freeze button badge. (1970). 30mm. (g) £4 - £6

▲ Mobil button badge. (1960). 30mm. (f) £2 - £3

▲ Regent button badge. (1965). 30mm. (vg) £4 - £6

▲ Esso Extra pin badge. (1960). 35mm. (vg) £7 - £9

▲ Amoco button badge. (1965). 30mm. (vg) £4 - £6

▲ Cleveland Discol button badge. (1960). 30mm. (vg) £6 - £8

▲ BP Super-Plus button badge. (1965). 30mm. (f-g) £4 - £6

▲ Jet button badge. (1960). 25mm. (vg) £8 - £10

▲ Shell button badge. (1960). 25mm. (f) £2 - £3

▲ Esso Drive Generously button badge. 30mm. (f) £4 - £6

▲ Redex Motor Oil button badge. (1960). 30mm. (vg) £6 - £8

▲ Gold Cross Motor Oil button badge. (1975). 30mm. (f-g) £7 - £9

▲ Fina button badge. (1960). 25mm. (f-g) £4 - £6

▲ Redex button badge. (1965). 30mm. (g-vg) £4 - £6

▲ NBC Motor Oils metal lapel badge. (1955). 35mm. (f-g) £20 - £25

▲ Redex button badge. (1965). 30mm. (vg) £6 - £8

▲ Globe button badge. (1960). 25mm. (f-g) £4 - £6

PETROLIANA - Model vehicles

Whilst the Day's Gone series of model vehicles are not generally in huge demand with serious collectors, related models certainly complement petroliana collections and are generally easy to find in excellent condition, often mint boxed.

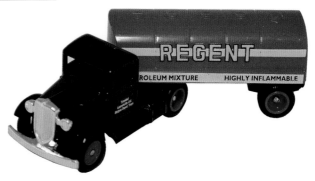

▲ 1935 Ford Articulated Tanker. Regent Petrol. No. 62000. Days Gone Premier Collection. Model (mnt), box (vg) £4 - £6

▲ 1934 Mack Tanker. Penzoil. No. 42007. Days Gone. Model (mnt), box (g) £3 - £4

▲ 1939 Dodge Streamliner. Mobiloil. No. 78000. Days Gone. Model (mnt), box (vg) £4 - £5

▲ 1939 Ford Tanker. Gulf Gasoline. No.57004. Days Gone. Model (mnt), box (g-vg) £3 - £4

▲ 1934 Mack Tanker. National Benzole. No. 42000. Days Gone. Model (mnt), box (g) £3 - £4

▲ 1920 Model 'T' Ford Tanker. Pratts Motor Oil. No.8018. Days Gone. Model (mnt), box (vg) £3 - £4

▲ 1920 Model 'T' Ford Tanker. Texaco. No.8016. Days Gone. Model (mnt), box (vg) £3 - £4

PHILATELY

Quite simply one of the most fascinating collectable subjects. With countless variations to countless themes, this can be as expensive as you like. Our tip is to begin with low value examples and progress as you learn.

The Penny Black

Penny Blacks can sometimes be over-rated. You really do need to know what you are doing with this famous (the first) (adhesive) postage stamp. When stamps were first produced, there was no such thing as perforations and each stamp had to be cut out of a sheet with scissors or a knife. Consequently many stamps were poorly cut or damaged. One factor that affects the value of a Penny Black is the quantity of (and depth of) clear margins. The margin between each stamp on the sheet was only 1mm. Some of the poor examples can be valued at around £10. Another factor is the (printing) plate number. Some are rarer than others. The record price paid for a single Penny Black stamp is $345,131 (around £266,000) (from the Penny Black's first-ever registration sheet, from before the stamp was hardened). Because of the huge variation in values, it should therefore be readily obvious that expert advice is needed when thinking about investing in this fascinating postage stamp. There are plenty of reputable dealers to assist.

▲ Penny Black stamp. 1840. Three margins.(f) £40 - £50

The postal cancellation was originally in black ink but later changed to red ink to make it more visible. Eventually the colour of the penny stamp was changed to red (the Penny Red) and the cancellation reverted to black ink. Penny Reds are generally much easier to find but consequently have much less value, a fair example (one good margin and generally reasonable) can be bought for around £1.

How to remove stamps from envelopes

Stamps are usually affixed to envelopes or cards and need to be removed for storage and display, particularly for mounting in albums. A simple tip is to partially fill a small dish with cold water (definitely not hot). Cut the stamps away from the envelope, leaving a small margin but taking great care not to damage any of the perforations around the stamp. Float the stamps facing upwards and within a matter of minutes the backing should start to loosen. If the backing does not peel away freely and easily, then carry on soaking for a while longer. Using tweezers, carefully remove the stamps from the dish and remove the backing from the stamp (not the other way round). Then place the stamps on a plain white sheet of kitchen roll (if you use coloured kitchen roll, the dye may run into the stamps and spoil them). Let the stamps dry naturally. Never try steaming stamps away from envelopes, using a kettle or similar utensil. Not only can the steam cause injuries, the stamps are likely to curl and damage.

PHILATELY - First day covers

Before beginning a collection, it is important to know exactly what a First Day Cover is, and what elements are of greatest importance to collectors.

A First Day Cover is an envelope or card with newly issued postage stamps that were postmarked (cancelled) on the first day of issue. In order to be worthy of collecting, the cover, the stamps, and the postmarks should all be of a high quality (good condition or better) and they should be related.

The cover is the envelope or card on which the stamps are mounted. There are two categories of cover:

Standard (Commercial) Covers are produced for general sale. They are made available, prior to the release of a new issue of stamps, from philatelist stores and the Post Office. They are generally purchased blank, and it is left for the collector to affix stamps and arrange for them to be cancelled.

Official (Sponsored) Covers are produced by private organisations, who also sponsor a special handstamp (postmark) for use on that cover. These are normally very limited issues.

Postmarks are also commonly referred to as cancellations or franks. It is important that every stamp on a First Day Cover is correctly cancelled in order to validate the authenticity of the cover.

There are five categories of postmark:

Special Handstamps are normally pictorial and are the most popular with collectors.

First Day of Issue (FDI) Postmarks are circular and feature the date, location, and the words "first day of issue".

Counter Date Stamp (CDS) Postmarks are the everyday postmarks you see used at Post Office counters. They look more authentic than Special Handstamps, and are therefore favoured by some collectors. However, postmarks at Post Office counters may be printed imperfectly, and this can affect value.

Slogan Postmarks have a circular part the same as a CDS and a "tail" that forms a wavy line or slogan.

Meter Marks are applied by companies using their own franking machines. They are not applied by Royal Mail and are not technically postmarks.

There are many types of stamps, but they all fall into one of two main categories.

Commemorative stamps are small works of art that normally celebrate an aspect of history or modern society.

Definitive stamps are the small portraits of the Monarch you see in everyday use.

Occasionally, an Official First Day Cover may also feature an autograph. These covers will be strictly limited, and if the celebrity is related in some way to the event commemorated by the cover, then the value can be significantly increased.

▲ King George VI Coronation Commemoratives. May 1937. Magpie postmark. Written address. (g-vg) £8 - £10

▲ Commemorating the visit of Elizabeth II and Prince Philip. 10 Oct 1957. Ontario, Canada postmark. Written address. (vg) £4 - £6

▲ British Achievements. 2 Apr 1969. London FDI postmark. Typed address. (vg) £1 - £2

▲ Royal Air Force. 29 May 1968. London FDI postmark. Typed address. (g-vg) £1 - £2

▲ 150th Anniversary Isle of Man Steam Packet Company. 6 May 1980. Douglas, IOM FDI postmark. Typed address. (vg) £2 - £4

PHILATELY - PHQ cards

PHQ cards (Postal Headquarters cards) are postcards depicting designs from commemorative postage stamps. The first set of stamps for which a PHQ card was produced was the County Cricket issue in May 1973.

Since July 1976 cards have been released for each commemorative issue, and they are usually made available several weeks before the stamps, so that collectors can obtain them, affix the stamps when they become available, and then have the cards cancelled with relevant First Day of Issue (FDI) postmarks.

▲ D-Day. 1994. Set of five. (ex) £1 - £2

▲ Famous Trains. 1985. Set of five. (ex) £1 - £2

▲ British Fairs. 1983. Set of four. (ex) £1 - £2

▲ British Films. 1985. Set of five. (ex) £1 - £2

▲ Cattle. 1984. Set of five. (ex) £1 - £2

▲ Urban Renewal. 1984. Set of four. (ex) £1 - £2

▲ Europa. 1984. Set of four. (ex) £1 - £2

▲ Arthurian Legend. 1985. Set of four. (ex) £1 - £2

▲ British Composers. 1985. Set of four. (ex) £1 - £2

▲ Safety At Sea. 1985. Set of four. (ex) £1 - £2

▲ Christmas. 1984. Set of five. (vg-ex) £1 - £2

▲ British Council. 1984. Set of four. (ex) £1 - £2

▲ The Royal Mail. 1984. Set of five. (ex) £1 - £2

▲ Victorian Britain. 1987. Set of four. (ex) £1 - £2

▲ The Royal Air Force. 1986. Set of five. (ex) £1 - £2

▲ Christmas. 1986. Set of five. (ex) £1 - £2

▲ Sport. 1986. Set of five. (ex) £1 - £2

▲ Halley's Comet. 1986. Set of four. (ex) £1 - £2

▲ The Sixtieth Birthday of Her Majesty The Queen. 1986. Set of four. (ex) £1 - £2

▲ Industry Year. 1986. Set of four. (ex) £1 - £2

PHILATELY - Stamp booklets

Stamp booklets originally had plain covers. In 1968, the GPO introduced pictorial covers.

Collectors are mainly interested in booklets in very good condition with all stamp panes intact.

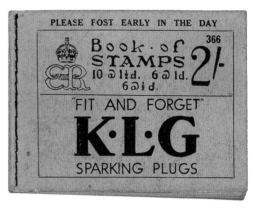

▲ Book of Stamps. Complete. Feb 1937. (vg) £50 - £60

▲ Stamp booklet. 1964. Complete. (vg) £4 - £6

▲ Stamp booklet. Jul 1968. Complete. (vg) £3 - £5

▲ Stamp booklet. Sep 1968. Complete. (vg) £3 - £5

▲ Prime Ministers. 1994. Complete. (vg) £2 - £3

▲ Postal Vehicles. 1993. Complete. (vg) £4 - £6

▲ Great Expectations. 1989. Complete. (vg) £7 - £9

▲ Sherlock Holmes. 1987. Complete. (vg) £3 - £5

▲ British Birds. Dec 1972. Complete. (vg) £5 - £7

▲ British Birds. Apr 1973. Complete. (vg) £4 - £5

▲ British Birds. Jun 1973. Complete. (vg) £5 - £6

▲ British Birds. Aug 1972. Complete. (vg) £5 - £6

▲ Museums. 1981. Complete. (vg) £3 - £4

▲ British Canals. 1978. Complete. (vg) £3 - £5

▲ Military Aircraft. 1980. Complete. (vg) £3 - £4

PHILATELY - Postal slogans

This is an area of philately that is relatively inexpensive but still interesting.

Whilst you are not likely to find a penny black stamp at a car boot sale, you could find some rare postal slogans, simply because the vendor has no idea they are worth money.

Look out for boxes of old postcards at car boot sales. Once you have scoured through for interesting cards, turn them all over and go through again but this time checking for postal slogans.

Clear and whole slogans are the best and, generally, the older they are the better. Perhaps the best known slogan is 'Remember the Postcode' and, as you would expect, it is generally not worth anything. However, if you are collecting you will need a really good example, and maybe you would stretch to 50p to obtain the cleanest, clearest example possible from the 60s.

The first slogan postmark was introduced in 1917, and stated, 'Buy National War Bonds Now.' Since then they have been used to promote all manner of things.

The beauty of postal slogan collecting is that you can get three or four bites of the cherry, as you can have the stamp, the postcard, and the linked collecting themes.

▲   It's Quicker To Telephone. 1932. 30p - 40p

▲   British Goods Are Best. 1925. 10p - 20p

▲   Investiture Day. 1969. 80p - 90p

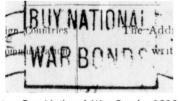

▲   Buy National War Bonds. 1918. 20p - 30p

▲   Long Live The Queen. 1953. 20p - 30p

▲   Blood Donors Are Still Urgently Needed. 1948. 20p - 30p

▲   Mind How You Go On The Road. 1949. 20p - 30p

▲   MGP Races. 1969. 30p - 40p

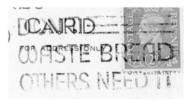

▲   Don't Waste Bread Others Need It. 1946. 40p - 50p

▲   Cheap Recorded Delivery. 1964. 10p - 20p

▲   Post Early For Christmas. 1926. 20p - 30p

▲   Postage On Letters for Europe 4d. 1952. 20p - 30p

PHONECARDS

Collectors of phonecards are known as fusilatelists.

The heyday of the UK phonecard was 1980 - 2000 and then the industry suffered dramatically with the growth in popularity of mobile phones. That downturn eventually gave the interest in collecting a major boost.

Collectors can be found worldwide, and in the USA the hobby is known as telegery.

Standard cards are the same size as credit cards and made from similar material. They come in various denominations and the highest in a particular series is often the most sought after by collectors.

Standard cards began with magnetic stripes to carry the required information. They then moved to an optical structure and finally the chip card was introduced.

▲ Zestril. BT 10 units. Used. (g) £3 - £5

▲ Time For Tea. BT 100 units. Used (g-vg) 40p - 60p

▲ Spring Is In The Air. BT 100 units. Used. (vg) 50p - 70p

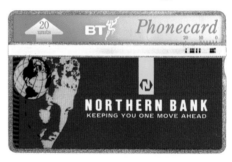

▲ Northern Bank. BT 20 units. Used. (g-vg) £6 - £8

▲ Faces Of Britain. BT £5 unit. Used. (vg) 20p - 30p

▲ Virgin Megastore. BT £2 unit. Used. (vg) 30p - 40p

▲ AUA Sheffield 94. BT 10 units. Used. (vg) £5 - £7

▲ Aladdin. BT 20 units. Used. (g-vg) 50p - 70p

▲ Hercules. BT £2 unit. Used. (vg) £1 - £2

▲ Dream Phone. BT 5 units. Used. (g) £3 - £4

▲ David Platt. BT 20 units. Used. (vg) £2 - £3

▲ Alan Shearer. BT 20 units. Used. (vg) £2 - £3

PHOTOGRAPHICA

The collecting of and study of, photographic equipment and images, is known as 'photographica'.

As a general rule, many old cameras can be purchased at reasonable prices.

Because it's often difficult to determine if a particular model is in good working order, at the point of purchase, many people base their offers on the assumption that each one is not in good working order. In other words many old cameras are purchased for display purposes. In any event, finding the old film for them is often quite a problem, so most vintage models are never used for the purpose for which they were intended.

Where a camera is guaranteed to be in working order, the likelihood is that the vendor is an enthusiast. Some models (particularly modern) command high sums, especially where the lens is considered valuable. Such cameras and lenses require so much knowledge and expertise that they are best left to the experts.

▲ Kodak Autographic Brownie camera. 1926. Ball bearing shutter. (g) Not tested - display only. £15 - £20

▲ Photo Tint Outfit. Johnsons of Hendon. All bottles (vg) intact in original box (p-f). Tints have dried and cannot be used. (1935) £3 - £5

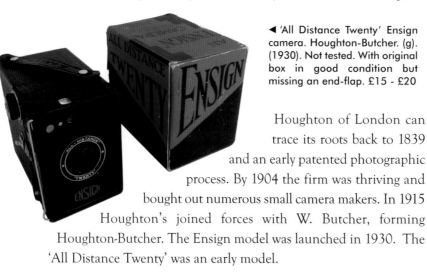

◄ 'All Distance Twenty' Ensign camera. Houghton-Butcher. (g). (1930). Not tested. With original box in good condition but missing an end-flap. £15 - £20

Houghton of London can trace its roots back to 1839 and an early patented photographic process. By 1904 the firm was thriving and bought out numerous small camera makers. In 1915 Houghton's joined forces with W. Butcher, forming Houghton-Butcher. The Ensign model was launched in 1930. The 'All Distance Twenty' was an early model.

Photo tinting

Before the days of colour photography, black and white photographs and postcards were coloured by hand using photo tint paints and inks. Manufacturers of tints included Windsor & Newton and Johnsons of Hendon.

► Kodak Brownie 127 camera. 1960. In very good condition but not tested. Complete with original instruction leaflet. £4 - £6

▲ Ilford photograph wallet. Empty. (1955). (g) £2 - £3

▲ Kodak photograph wallet. Empty. (1965). (f-g) £1 - £2

◄ Lledo model vintage van. Days Gone. Kodak livery. 1986. (g-vg) With box. £2 - £3

The printed paper wallets that contained developed photographic prints and the negatives, offer an interesting and inexpensive collecting theme. They are a small slice of social and photographica history.

PHOTOGRAPHICA

◄ Campro Cine camera-projector. (1935). (g) not tested - display only. (165mm x 125mm) £10 - £15

▶ Baby Cine-Camera. Made in France circa 1925. Not in great condition but an absolute must for the collector who has yet to be lucky enough to discover such an early example. Not tested - display only. (105mm x 88mm) £20 - £30

▲ Movie Projector. 9.5mm. Circa 1925. Unknown maker. An interesting piece of photographica, for display only. £20 - £25

The Kodak Cine Eight Model 20 was introduced in 1932 and was the first cine camera to use 8mm film. It was actually a 16mm reel which was divided in two. When the film had gone through one way, it was then reversed to use the other half.

▲ Cine Kodak Eight, Model 20. (f) not tested - display only. £10 - £12

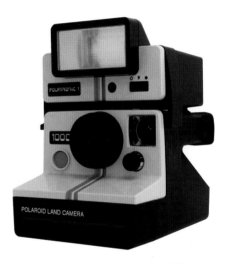

▲ Polaroid Land Camera 1000 and electronic flash unit. 1979. Not tested. With original separate camera and electronic flash unit instruction booklets. (vg) £6 - £8

▶ Prinzmatic 8. Super 8 movie camera. 1967. (g-vg) not tested. £8 - £10

Polaroid cameras are instant cameras whereby the special film develops almost instantly.

Edwin Land (USA) is credited for inventing the first commercial instant camera.

The first version of the Land Camera was manufactured in 1948.

Digital photography made the Polaroid instant cameras virtually redundant. This has made them more collectable as pieces of photographic history.

Prinz was a trademark of Dixons.

PIGGIN'

In 1993, wildlife artist David Corbridge was inspired to create a series of collectable ceramic pigs. He named the series Piggin'. The first one, Piggin' Tired, was released in 1993 by Collectible World Studios, who continued producing the loveable characters until 2006, when Xystos took over the range. There are now more than 250 different models.

Piggin' statues fall into the category of items that are specifically manufactured and marketed with collectors in mind. These items are definitely collectable, you can display them on your mantelpiece, and they look very nice; but they are unlikely to be the best investment.

Given the quantity being offered on the market at any one time, the tip is to be patient and try to restrict your purchases to those with their original boxes (in good condition+). The box will always enhance the value. Piggin' models are also referred to as 'figures' 'ornaments' and 'statues'.

▲ Piggin' Desperate. 1995. Boxed. (vg) £4 - £6

◄ Piggin' Paralytic. 1997. Boxed. (vg) £5 - £7

► Piggin' Gorgeous. 1997. Boxed. (vg) £4 - £6

◄ Piggin' Alarming. 2000. Boxed. (vg) £5 - £7

◄ Piggin' Snoring. 1996. Boxed. (vg) £4 - £6

◄ Piggin' Winter. Wall Plaque. 1999. Unboxed. (vg) £3 - £4

► Piggin' Lovely. Photo Picture Frame. 1997. Boxed. (vg) £6 - £8

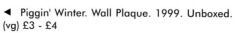

The PINK PANTHER

The Pink Panther is a fictional character, who owes his immense fame to the Peter Sellers film The Pink Panther (1964). Sellers played one of his most memorable roles, as the bumbling Inspector Jacques Clouseau. Other actors who starred in the Pink Panther films were Herbert Lom and Burt Kwouk. The original film theme music was composed by Henry Mancini.

In a spin-off television series, the cartoon character starred in The Pink Panther Show. Shown on BBC TV in Great Britain, the series was hugely popular.

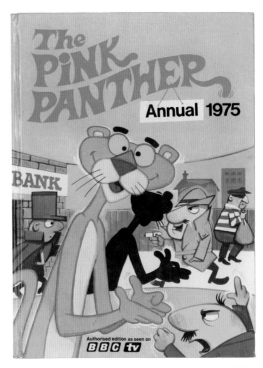

▲ The Pink Panther Annual. 1975. (vg) £5 - £7

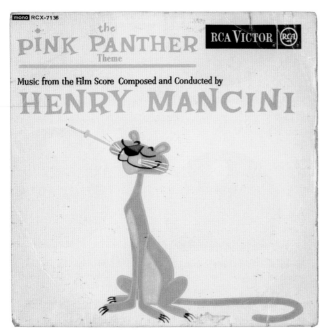

▲ The Pink Panther Theme - Henry Mancini. EP record. 1964. RCA Victor label, (RCX 7136). Vinyl (g), cover (f-g). £6 - £8

(reverse)   (front)

◀ ▲ Pink Panther on empty milk bottle. Unigate Dairies. 1986. (vg) £2 - £4

▲ Peter Sellers autograph. Clear, blue ink. 150 x 100mm. No dedication. £65 - £75

▲ Herbert Lom autographed publicity photograph. Clear, blue ink 140 x 90mm. No dedication. £20 - £25

▲ Burt Kwouk autographed publicity photograph. Clear, black ink. 185 x 135mm. Dedicated. £7 - £9

PIT CHECKS

▲   Daw Mill. (vg)
£10 - £12

Pit Checks (also known as Pit Tallies) played an important role in mining. Before a miner descended into the pit he would be given two tallies (small metal tags usually made of brass). Both tallies had the same embossed number and one would be handed to the Banksman before the miner descended. They provided a method of keeping track of who was down the mine. Nowadays, swipe cards are used.

▲   Grimethorpe Colliery. (g) £6 - £8

▲   Maltby. (g) £6 - £8

▲   Goldthorpe. (vg) £8 - £10

▲   Barrow Colliery. (g) £6 - £8

▲   Old Silkstone. (f) £3 - £4

▲   Silverwood Coliery. (p) £2 - £3

▲   Asfordby Mine. (vg) £10 - £12

▲   Yorkshire Main. (g) £5 - £7

▲   North Notts. Area Colliery. (g) £6 - £8

▲   Wheldale.   (g) £6 - £8

▲   Rossington.   (g) £6 - £8

▲   Hucknall No.2 Colliery. (g) £6 - £8

▲   Cadeby Main. (g) £4 - £5

▲   Highmoor Colliery. (g) £3 - £4

▲   Baddesley.   (p-f) £2 - £3

▲   Annesley.   (vg) £8 - £10

▲   Shirebrook Colliery. (f) £3 - £5

PLACES

There's a rich history associated with most places. For example; Blackpool is probably best known as a northern centre of summer holiday entertainment. The building of the railway (circa 1850) made it accessible to the masses and popularity reached dizzy heights (circa 1880). Blackpool Tower opened in 1894. It was inspired by the Eiffel Tower. It incorporated the famous Tower Circus and Tower Ballroom.

Blackpool

▲ Rocket Tram. Valentine's postcard. (1965). Postally unused. The first Blackpool Illuminations date back to 1879. (g) £1 - £2

▲ Reginald Dixon (1904 - 1985). Autographed postcard. No dedication. He was the famous resident organist at Blackpool Tower Ballroom for 40 years. £14 - £16

▲ Blackpool Pleasure Beach postcard. (1910). Unknown maker. Postally unused. (g) £6 - £8

Blackpool Pleasure Beach was founded in 1896 by William Bean. An additional 30 acres was purchased in 1903.

The Mersey Tunnel

▲ Interior of Mersey Tunnel. Valentine's postcard. Postmarked Southport 1936 on 1d stamp. (g) £3 - £4

The Queensway Tunnel, best known as the Mersey Tunnel, is a road tunnel (under the River Mersey) opened by King George V on 18th July 1934. It connects Liverpool with Birkenhead. It is now owned by Merseytravel along with the Kingsway Tunnel (1971) and the Mersey Railway Tunnel (1886). The tunnels have their own police force, known as The Mersey Tunnels Police. The Mersey Tunnel has been the location for a number of films, including Fast & Furious 6 and Harry Potter and the Deathly Hallows.

▲ Mersey Tunnel afternoon ticket for a private vehicle. 17 July 1937. (vg) £1 - £3

▲ Mersey Tunnel morning ticket. 17 July 1937. (vg) £1 - £3

▲ Dinky no.255. Mersey Tunnel Police Land Rover. (1958). Played with. (g) £12 - £16

PLAYING CARDS

The most common collecting area for playing cards are promotional packs, designed to advertise various products and services.

Frowned upon by some, glamour cards (ladies in erotic poses) from the 50's and 60's are much sought after.

Another area is the collecting of 'joker cards' from a multitude of packs. These can look really attractive when displayed in made-to-measure plastic wallets.

Machines designed to shuffle playing cards were first patented around 1880 and evolved over the years to the sophisticated electronic machines now used in casinos all over the world.

When buying packs of playing cards, always check that all 52 cards are present and none are damaged, otherwise the pack can be seriously devalued. The absence of jokers from a pack does not normally devalue it.

◄   Jet petrol. Full promotional pack. (vg) £4 - £6

►   Wills Woodbine promotional pack. (1950). Box (f), cards (vg) £8 - £12

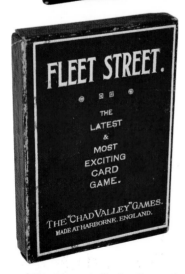

◄ Travel Agent. A card game for five people. De La Rue. (1965). (vg) £8 - £10

▲ Fleet Street. A Chad Valley card game. (vg) £12 - £14

▲ Graleine Card Shuffler. (1955). Mechanical. A robust device in working order. (g) £10 - £15

POETRY

The popularity of poetry dates back many centuries. It employs a complex variety of language aesthetics and is an art form.

Having widespread appeal, there's plenty of scope for building a poetry based collection.

Old, first edition, poetry books can command high sums. Unlikely to turn up at a car boot sale, but you never know your luck!

Edwin Waugh
1817-1890

Edwin Waugh was a poet and author in the Lancashire dialect. His poems exude lyrical charm. The most famous of his works, the poem titled, "Come whoam to thi childer an' me" was penned in 1856 on the page of a diary in the Clarence Hotel, Manchester on Friday 10 June.

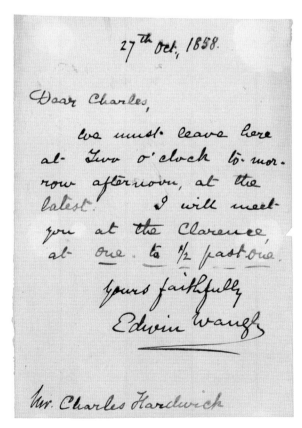

▲ A letter written to Charles Hardwick (English historian and clergyman) and signed by Edwin Waugh, arranging a meeting at the Clarence (Hotel). Dated 27 October 1858. Written and signed clearly in black ink by Edwin Waugh. 157 x 112mm. £35 - £45

▲ Autographed postcard photograph of Alfred Austin. Signed on both the front and back by him in clear, black ink. Rotary Photographic. It carries a clear 1905 postmark, Ashford, Kent, on a halfpenny stamp. £30 - £35

Alfred Austin
Poet Laureate

Upon the advice of the Prime Minister, the Monarch appoints the honorary position of Poet Laureate to a single individual. In 1896 Queen Victoria bestowed the honour upon Alfred Austin, upon the death of Alfred, Lord Tennyson.

It was assumed that his friendship with the British Prime Minister, Lord Salisbury, helped Austin acquire the role of Poet Laureate.

Alfred Austin was born in Headingley, Leeds in 1835. He died in Ashford, Kent in 1913, having retained the title of Poet Laureate for 17 years.

POLICE

There's a buoyant market for UK police collectables. There are plenty of dedicated enthusiasts' websites to browse. Collectors' clubs also exist. Stretch your interest to the USA and you will find an even greater selection of memorabilia.

Vintage items over 75 years old can fetch substantial sums. Collectors without deep pockets can still find reasonably priced, yet still very interesting, collectables from the 50s and 60s. Scour the better Collectors' Fairs for items, although perhaps the best source is the internet. Specialist clubs offer sales and swaps.

A word of warning: It is an offence to use Police items to impersonate a serving police officer. The Police Act (1996) covers the essential points. Basically, collectable items must be lawfully obtained and used for lawful purposes (therefore, collecting memorabilia for display is fine).

Various police forces have their own museums, containing artefacts, documents, and even old police vehicles. These are absolutely fascinating and well worth visiting on fact finding missions.

▲   Northumberland Constabulary cap badge. King's Crown. (vg) £10 - £12

There's a huge range of collectables out there in the general marketplace, for example: helmets, badges, medals, truncheons, postcards, stamps, whistles, diecast toys, books, photographs, manuals, books, autographs, uniforms, and cigarette cards. They can all make strong investments if bought at the right price.

◄   Police Drivers' Manual. 1960. HMSO publication. 78 pages. Limpback. (g-vg) £6 - £8

►   Real photograph postcard of three police officers. Postmarked Durham 1909. Message in ink. (g) £6 - £8

POLICE

Sir Robert Peel

As well as being regarded as one of the founders of the modern Conservative Party, Robert Peel is credited as the founder of the modern British police force. He established the Metropolitan Police Force in 1829.

The policemen were nicknamed 'bobbies' and 'peelers'. The term 'bobby' has remained to this day.

He was Prime Minister of the United Kingdom from August 1841 to June 1846 and gained a second term between December 1834 and April 1835.

▲ A letter written by and signed by Robert Peel. 4 June 1842. Clear, black ink, 180 x 110mm. (g) £100 - £120

POLITICS

For the past two hundred years or so, a wealth of items associated with politics have been collected. Postcards depicting our political leaders were popular collectables approximately 1904 - 1924. A few were personally signed by the politicians and these are now much sought after. The higher ranking the politician, the higher the value is likely to be.

Political election flyers are also in demand, with well known politicians commanding the most interest from collectors.

(Front)

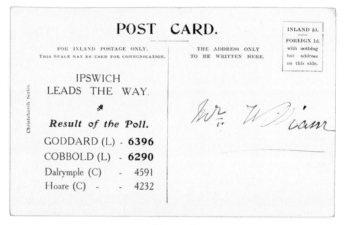

(Reverse)

▲ Result of poll postcard. 1906. Postally unused. (g-vg) £8 - £10

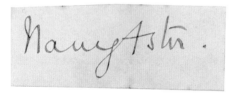

▲ Mary Astor signature. The first woman to sit in British Parliament. Clear, black ink, 60 x 22mm. No dedication. £20 - £30

▲ Betty Boothroyd autographed photograph. The first female speaker. Clear, blue ink, 125 x 90mm. No dedication. £5 - £6

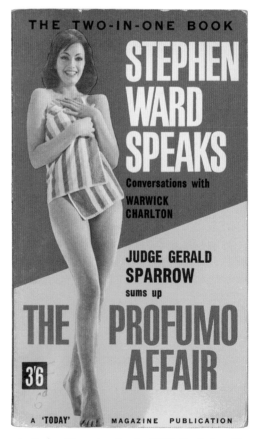

▲ Today Magazine book. 1963. Featuring The Profumo Affair. Limpback. 176 pages. (g) £2 - £3

POLITICS

THE LOCAL GOVERNMENT ACT, 1888.

COUNTY OF LEICESTER.

THE BALLOT ACT, 1872.
SECTION 4.

(To be read before taking Declaration of Secrecy).

Every Officer, Clerk, and Agent in attendance at a Polling Station shall maintain and aid in maintaining the secrecy of the Voting in such Station, and shall not communicate, except for some purpose authorized by law, before the poll is closed, to any person, any information as to the name or number on the Register of Voters of any Elector who has or has not applied for a Ballot Paper or Voted at that Station, or as to the official mark, and no such Officer, Clerk, or Agent, and no person whosoever, shall interfere with or attempt to interfere with a Voter when marking his Vote, or otherwise attempt to obtain in the Polling Station information as to the Candidate for whom any Voter in such Station is about to Vote, or has Voted, or communicate at any time to any person any information obtained in a Polling Station as to the Candidate for whom any Voter in such Station is about to Vote, or has Voted, or as to the number on the back of the Ballot Paper given to any Voter at such Station. Every Officer, Clerk and Agent in attendance at the counting of the Votes shall maintain and aid in maintaining the secrecy of the Voting, and shall not attempt to ascertain at such counting the number on the back of any Ballot Paper, or communicate any information obtained at such counting as to the Candidate for whom any Vote is given in any particular Ballot Paper. No person shall directly or indirectly induce any Voter to display his Ballot Paper after he shall have marked the same, so as to make known to any person the name of the Candidate for or against whom he has so marked his vote.

Every person who acts in contravention of the provisions of this Section shall be liable, on summary conviction before two Justices of the Peace, to imprisonment for any term not exceeding six months, with or without hard labour.

STATUTORY DECLARATION OF SECRECY.

I solemnly promise and declare, that I will not at this Election for a County Councillor for the Blaby Electoral Division of the County of Leicester, do anything forbidden by Section Four of " The Ballot Act, 1872," which has been read to me.

Taken before me this 10th day of April 1895.

Geo Rowlatt
Returning Officer (or) Justice of the Peace for the County of Leicester.

J M Gamble
Declarant,

▲ Declaration of Secrecy by T.M. Gamble in accordance with The Ballot Act. Signed and dated 10 April 1895. (g-vg) £20 - £25

POP MEMORABILIA (1950s)

This era laid the foundation for the fab sixties. Skiffle was a big influence, with particular credit to Lonnie Donegan. For example, John Lennon began his music career by forming a skiffle group called The Quarrymen, in 1956.

The Rock & Roll influences of Elvis inspired Cliff Richard, Billy Fury and many others. Whilst Bill Haley & The Comets caused a sensation wherever they appeared.

▲ Jimmy Young programme. 14 July 1956. 215 x 140mm. 12 pages. (g) £6 - £8

Joan Regan

▲ Disc Stars card no.19. Kane Confectionery. (vg) £1 - £2

Her career began when she made a demo record, which was then taken up by impresario Bernard Delfont. She was signed to Decca Records in 1953. Her rehearsal pianist was Russ Conway.

Amongst her many TV show credits was an appearance on Six Five Special.

In 1958 she left Decca and moved to HMV. Her career dwindled through the sixties.

In 1984 she slipped in the shower and suffered a brain haemorrhage. With the help of old friends, including Russ Conway, she fought her way back to a stage career.

Joan died in 2013 at the age of 85.

▲ Joan Regan autograph. Clear, blue ink, 115 x 100mm. No dedication. £20 - £25

Tommy Steele

▲ Tommy Steele tour programme. Autumn 1958. 242 x 185mm. 8 pages. (f-g) £12 - £14

Tommy Steele was born Thomas Hicks in London in 1936. Tommy started his musical career by playing in a skiffle group, "The Cavemen". Along with other famous recording artists of the 1950s and '60s such as Cliff Richard, Hank Marvin and Gary Glitter, Steele was discovered in London's famous 2 'I's coffee bar and became one of Britain's first manufactured pop stars. He was spotted by impresario Larry Parnes who convinced Hicks to change his name to Tommy Steele and attempted to turn him into a British version of Elvis Presley.

Tommy's most famous hits include Rock with the Cavemen, Give! Give! Give!, and Little White Bull.

Tommy's career followed a varied and ever-developing course, embracing almost all areas of the entertainment world. He made his film debut in 1956 and his films include The Tommy Steele Story and Finian's Rainbow, in which he played a leprechaun attempting to retrieve a pot of gold. His autobiography was published in 2006.

POP MEMORABILIA (1950s)

Gene Vincent

Born Vincent Eugene Craddock in 1935, Norfolk, Virginia, USA. He was an exponent of rockabilly (early 1950's music that began the rock and roll era) and therefore Gene Vincent can be classed as a major rock and roll artist.

In 1956 he wrote and recorded 'Be-Bop-A-Lula' which rocketed him to international stardom. In April 1960 he toured the UK with Eddie Cochran. Whilst driving through the town of Chippenham, Wiltshire, the car was involved in a serious road accident, in which Eddie Cochran died whilst Gene Vincent escaped with relatively minor injuries.

Gene Vincent died from a ruptured stomach ulcer in 1971. He has a star on the Hollywood Walk of Fame and was the first inductee of the Rockabilly Hall of Fame.

▲ Granada Theatre Programme. January 1960. In good condition save for two minor tears but essentially contains an undamaged Gene Vincent autograph in clear blue ink. No dedication. £250 - £300

◄ Record Date Part 1 - Gene Vincent. EP record. 1959. Capitol, EAP1 1059. Vinyl (vg), sleeve (f). A rare record. £40 - £50

► Lotta Lovin' - Gene Vincent. 45rpm single record. 1957. Capitol, 45-CL 14763. Vinyl (g) £10 - £12

Johnny And The Hurricanes

Their big success was in 1959 and from there it was downhill all the way.

The group's leader was saxophonist Johnny Paris (real name John Pocisk). He died in 2006, aged 66, from an infection following an operation.

The group will be best remembered for their biggest hit; Red River Rock (reached no.3 in the charts in 1959).

► Stormsville - Johnny & The Hurricanes. LP record. 1960. London, HA-I 2269. Vinyl (vg), sleeve (f-g) £15 - £20

POP MEMORABILIA (1960s)

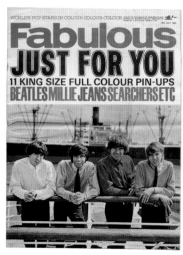

▲ Fabulous magazine. 25th July 1964. (g-vg) £13 - £15

The sixties was a period of revolution. The youth of the day were rebelling. Pop songs conveyed messages to the establishment.

Pop groups were colourful and loud. Skirt lengths shortened and hair lengthened. Above all, the music was creative and melodic. With the rock & roll and skiffle influence of the late 50's, it was the base of a music revolution. The world had never known anything like it.

Known as the 'fab (fabulous) sixties', it was the decade that introduced The Beatles, The Rolling Stones, Cliff Richard & The Shadows, Gerry & The Pacemakers, The Who, Bob Dylan and many others.

Collectors are hungry for quality 60's pop memorabilia and values reflect the importance of the decade.

Examples of top-notch memorabilia are concert tickets, programmes, posters, flyers, autographs and stage-wear.

Items relating to The Beatles are in a league of their own, however, there are plenty more items relating to iconic groups and individual artists that collectors are eager to acquire.

Fabulous magazine was launched in January 1964 by Fleetway Publications. The name was changed in 1966 to Fabulous 208.

Early copies of the magazine only had 28 pages but the format was large (345mm x 260mm) and it was in full colour.

There were full page pictures of the top stars and consequently many copies were cut up. Finding intact copies in very good condition is difficult, hence why they command high sums now.

1963 tour programme

▲ 1963 tour programme. (g) £15 - £17

The programme for the Arthur Howes production in 1963. Sixteen pages of pure nostalgia (including some photographs).

The line-up for this fab concert was Gerry & The Pacemakers, Del Shannon, Jet Harris & Tony Meehan, Cilla Black, Duffy Power and The Bachelors. The compere was Bryan Burdon.

Donovan

Born Donovan Philips Leitch in 1946, he was one of the most influential pop artists of the 1960's.

His career began with an appearance on the TV show 'Ready Steady Go' and it was there that he met his future wife, Linda Lawrence (a former girlfriend of Brian Jones of the Rolling Stones).

In 1966 Donovan was at the centre of 'flower power'. Indeed, it was believed that his songs Mellow Yellow and Sunshine Superman influenced songs written by Lennon & McCartney on the Sergeant Pepper album.

Bob Dylan introduced Donovan to The Beatles and a long friendship began with the Fab 4, which was well documented in the music press and in television clips.

Donovan's signing to producer Mickie Most is thought by many to have been a key factor to his huge success.

By the end of the sixties, Donovan's fame had peaked and he gradually became disillusioned with the music industry. His career revived in 2000.

▲ Catch The Wind. Donovan sheet music. 1965. (f-g) £10 - £12

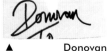

▲ Donovan concert ticket. 1969. Royal Festival Hall. (f) £4 - £5

▲ Donovan autograph. Clear, black ink, 114 x 45mm. £6 - £8

▲ Universal Soldier sheet music. Plus EP record (vinyl vg). 1965. £16 - £20

POP MEMORABILIA (1960s)

Billy Fury

Ronald Wycherley was born in 1940, he became one of the biggest pop stars of the 1960's. His career began in 1955 when he bought his first guitar and started his own group. This was more of a hobby as he began working on a tugboat and then at the docks.

In 1958 he entered a talent competition run by the impresario Larry Parnes. Ronald won the competition, Larry signed him up and changed his name to Billy Fury. A fabulous career followed with a number of hit records. Sadly his life was cut short at the age of 42.

▲ Billy Fury Monthly. No.5. July 1963. 240 x 192mm. A quality 16 page magazine published by Albert Hand. (vg) £14 - £18

▲ Record Mirror. 19 Feb.1966. Complete. Minor foxing. (g) £7 - £9

▲ Billy Fury and the Tornados. EP record. 1963. Decca, DFE 8525. Sleeve and vinyl (f) £10 - £14

Johnny Kidd And The Pirates

Johnny Kidd (real name Fred Heath) started his musical career in skiffle. In the early sixties he and his band 'The Nutters' were given a contract by HMV. Insisting the name of the group was changed, HMV came up with Johnny Kidd and the Pirates. Their biggest hit was 'I'll Never Get Over You'. Their stage act involved them dressing up as pirates.

▲ Johnny Kidd. EP record. 1963. HMV, 7EG 8834. Vinyl (vg), sleeve (f-g) £35 - £45

Disaster struck in 1966 when Johnny Kidd died (aged 30) in a car accident in Radcliffe, Manchester. Fellow group member, Nick Simper, escaped uninjured and later went on to fame and fortune with Deep Purple.

▲ I'll Never Get Over You. Sheet music. 1963. (g) £12 - £14

Little Eva

Eva Narcissus Boyd was born in North Carolina, USA, in 1943. Her family called her 'Little Eva' and the name stuck when her musical career was launched. Her biggest hit was 'The Locomotion', which reached no.1 in the USA in 1962 and no.2, in the UK the same year and no.11 in the UK when re-released in 1972. Her only other UK top twenty hit was with 'Let's Turkey Trot' which reached no.13 in 1963.

The backing singers on 'The Locomotion' were the all-girl group 'The Cookies' who also had a successful recording career.

With no further major success in the recording industry, Eva decided to call it a day in 1971 and stopped touring. However, in 1988, Kylie Minogue released a cover version of The Locomotion and this resulted in renewed interest in Little Eva, so much so that she came out of retirement and began touring again.

Eva died of cancer in 2003. She is buried in a Belhaven, USA, cemetery. Originally her grave merely had a small white cross but some years later was replaced with an elegant headstone with an image of a steam locomotive on it. The epitaph reads "Singing with the Angels".

▲ Let's Turkey Trot. Original sheet music. 1963. (g-vg) £8 - £12

▲ Concert ticket. Granada, Tooting. Brian Hyland and Little Eva. Sunday 24 February 1963. (g-vg) £7 - £10

POP MEMORABILIA (1960s)

Crazy Elephant

A classic 'bubble gum' pop group, which was actually a studio creation made up of session musicians under the direction of Jerry Kasenetz and Jeff Katz. Their biggest hit was Gimme, Gimme Good Lovin'.

▲ Gimme, Gimme Good Lovin'. Sheet music. 1968. (g) £5 - £8

BUBBLEGUM MUSIC - Originated in the USA in the late 1960's, this is a genre of pop that was manufactured for the teeny bopper market. A classic example is Sugar, Sugar by The Archies. Other exponents were Ohio Express, 1910 Fruitgum Company and Crazy Elephant.

The Mindbenders

The group was founded in 1963 by Wayne Fontana and became known as Wayne Fontana and the Mindbenders. A number of hits followed (including, The Game of Love, Pamela Pamela and Um Um Um Um Um Um) but Fontana left the band in the middle of a USA tour in 1965. The group retained the Mindbenders name and Eric Stewart became the new lead singer. They had one major hit (A Groovy Kind of Love). Bob Lang was replaced by Graham Gouldman two years later. After the group finally split in 1968, Stewart and Gouldman went on to huge success as 10cc.

▲ Record Mirror. Pop newspaper. 26 Feb 1966. Complete, no markings, some foxing. (g-vg) £12 - £14

◄ Mindbenders concert ticket. 11 March 1967. (g) £3 - £5

◄ A Groovy Kind Of Love. 45rpm single record. 1965. Fontana, TF 644. Vinyl (vg) £2 - £4

The Migil 5

This is a great example of a lesser well-known group from the sixties, commanding much interest from pop memorabilia collectors. Their EP record released in 1964 is particularly hard to find and examples in very good condition command sums of around £25. Interestingly, although this was the only EP record they released, it didn't contain their one and only top 10 hit, Mockin' Bird Hill.

They had one other minor hit with 'Near You' which achieved a best chart position of no.31.

The group got their name from the two founder members, Mike Felix and Gil Lucas.

At one point in their early career, Rolling Stones drummer Charlie Watts, stood in for Mike Felix.

Their contract with Pye Records, expired in 1966 and after that, little more was heard of them.

Mike Felix tried his luck as a stand-up comedian with some success. He later turned to acting and appeared in The Bill, TV series.

▲ Meet The Migil 5. EP record. 1964. PYE records, NEP 24191. Vinyl (vg), sleeve (g-vg) £20 - £30

▲ Near You - The Migil 5. Single record. 1964. PYE records, 7N 15645. Vinyl (g-vg) £3 - £4

▲ Mockin' Bird Hill - The Migil 5. Single record. 1964. PYE records, 7N 15597. Vinyl (g). With original sheet music. 1964. (g-vg) £10 - £12

▲ The Migil 5. Publicity photograph (centre fold). Signed by four members of the group. 138 x 88mm. One clear, red ink, two clear, blue ink, one slightly faded, blue ink. No dedication £35 - £45

POP MEMORABILIA (1960s)

Peter And Gordon

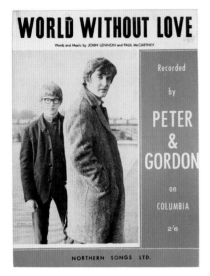

▲ World Without Love - Peter and Gordon.
Sheet music. 1964. (g-vg) £8 - £10

Peter and Gordon were friends at the private Westminster School. They played pubs and clubs. Their unique folk sound quickly developed.

Their big break came in a rather odd way. Peter Asher's sister (Jane) started dating Paul McCartney, and the duo picked up some of The Beatles' material.

They secured a record deal with Columbia and their first release in 1964, A World Without Love (written by Lennon and McCartney), became a number one hit. Other hits included True Love Ways (number two in 1965).

The pair split up in 1968 following arguments. Gordon Waller stayed in showbiz, becoming an agent for James Taylor, while Peter retired from the business.

Look out for original Peter and Gordon EP and LP records, generally worth between £15 and £20 in excellent condition. Their hit singles (45rpm records) are worth just a few pounds in good condition.

Freddie And The Dreamers

A bundle of energy, a born entertainer, a talented pop singer. That sums up Freddie Garrity, lead singer of sixties pop group Freddie & the Dreamers.

Freddie left school in 1952 to become an apprentice engineer but his main love was always entertaining and making music. He eventually gave up engineering and took a variety of other jobs, while he concentrated on a showbiz career. He tried his hand at being a brush salesman and a milkman.

The milk round was perfect. He would finish work late morning and have the afternoon to rehearse his new skiffle group, which he called The Dreamers Rhythm Group.

The group had plenty of work in the Manchester area and began supporting established artists in concert. In 1961 they made their first broadcast for the BBC Light Programme and it just started getting better and better.

In 1961 Freddie and the lads - Derek Quinn (lead guitar), Roy Crewsdon (rhythm guitar), Pete Birrell (bass guitar) and Bernie Dwyer (drums) - changed their name to Freddie & The Dreamers. They signed to the Columbia label and released their first record, If You Gotta Make a Fool of Somebody, in 1963. The song was a huge success, reaching number 3 in the charts. A few months later the follow-up, I'm Telling You Now, went one place higher.

▲ Turn Around - Freddie and the Dreamers. Sheet music. 1966. (g) £6 - £8

They had a string of hits but by 1966 their popularity was waning. Turn Around failed to change their good fortune and there were to be no more hits. The band disbanded in 1969 but reformed (with new personnel) in 1976 - their fame and Freddie's stage presence kept them busy until 2001. Then, sadly, Freddie was taken ill on a flight from New York and emphysema was diagnosed. Freddie Garrity died on 19 May 2006, aged 69.

POP MEMORABILIA (1960s)

The Pretty Things

Dick Taylor quit The Rolling Stones to go to the London Central School of Art. While he was there he met Phil May, and together they formed The Pretty Things. Taylor played guitar and May sang and played harmonica, and they also brought in Brian Pendleton (rhythm guitar), John Stax (bass), and Pete Kitson (drums).

The band's first single was Rosalyn, which reached number 41 in the UK singles chart, and this was followed by the hits Don't Bring Me Down (peaking at number 10) and Honey I Need (which reached number 13). During the following years, the band's line-up would change many times.

Following a string of commercial failures, the band finally split up in 1970. However, in 1971, Skip Alan (who had become the drummer in 1965) was driving with manager Bill Shepherd and he put on a tape of The Pretty Things. Shepherd loved it, and within three months the band was back together. The current lineup are still touring today.

▲ The Pretty Things - The Pretty Things. LP record. 1965. TL 5239, Fontana. Vinyl (f), cover (g-vg) £30 - £40

▲ New Musical Express. 14 Sep 1962. Eden Kane on the front page. (f) £8 - £10

▲ Eden Kane autograph. Clear, black ink, 130 x 90mm. No dedication. £4 - £6

Eden Kane

Richard Sarstedt was born in Delhi in 1942. His father managed a tea plantation in Calcutta until his untimely death. The family then moved to England, although their small flat in Croydon was a far cry from the luxury in India.

In 1960 he entered a talent competition at the Classic Cinema, Chelsea, which he went on to win. He was spotted by producer Phillip Waddilove, which was the break he needed. He gave up his job in a gent's outfitters and changed his name to Eden Kane. His first singing job was to record a Cadbury's chocolate jingle for Radio Luxembourg. This led to a record release, Hot Chocolate Crazy, on the Pye label which failed to chart (the record is now worth £20+). A switch to the Decca label brought instant success in 1961 with a number one hit, Well I Ask You. Other hits followed, including Boys Cry which reached number 8 (Fontana label, 1964). He had five top ten hits in total and toured extensively with his backing band The Downbeats.

Eden has worked ever since, including in Las Vegas. He moved to Los Angeles, where he lived next door to Peter Falk (Columbo). He tried his luck in films (Eden's sister-in-law is actress Stefanie Powers). Among other things, he has played the part of pilot of the Starship Enterprise in the TV series Star Trek.

Eden's brothers Peter and Robin Sarstedt both enjoyed individual successes in the pop charts.

POP MEMORABILIA (1960s)

New Musical Express

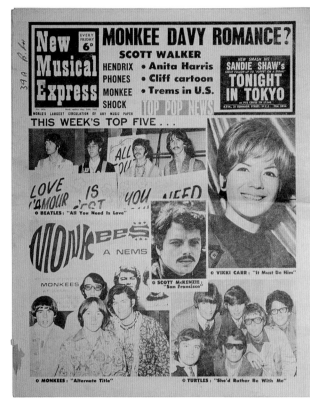

▲ NME. 29 July 1967. (g) £13 - £16

▲ NME. 29 July 1960. (vg) £15 - £18

▲ NME. 5 November 1965. (g) £12 - £14

▲ NME. 9 April 1965. (g) £12 - £14

POP MEMORABILIA
(1970s)

The magic of the 1960's had, arguably, begun to wane from 1968 onwards. Pop music had evolved again in the 1970's, notwithstanding that the influence of the sixties was not only evident in this period but from thereon.

From a collecting point of view, results at auction demonstrate that the interest in and values of, seventies related items (generally) do not match the sixties.

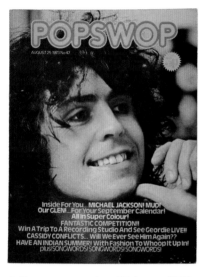

▲ Popswop magazine. 25 August 1973. (vg) £4 - £6

▲ Popswop magazine. 11 August 1973. (g) £3 - £4

▲ Popswop magazine. 18 August 1973. (vg) £4 - £6

▲ Top Of The Pops magazine. October 1975. (vg) £4 - £5

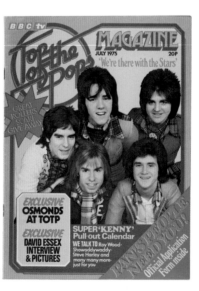

▲ Top Of The Pops magazine. July 1975. (vg) £4 - £6

▲ Top Of The Pops magazine. September 1975. (vg) £4 - £5

POSTAL ORDERS

Postal Orders were issued in fixed denominations until April 2006, after which they were available in any amount, similar to a personal cheque.

A postal order from the first year of issue (1881) was found by a lucky person at a car boot sale. It was found inside an old cookery book. It sold at auction for £3450.

From a collecting perspective, postal orders have long term investment potential. Generally, the key factors are age, condition and rarity of denomination. For example a 7 shillings order can be worth more than a 10 shillings order because fewer were likely to have been issued.

▲ One shilling postal order. 1895. Only in fair condition but very rare. £70 - £80

◀ 35p postal order. 1975. With counterfoil. (g-vg) £8 - £10

▶ One shilling Irish postal order. 1969. (g-vg) £8 - £10

POSTAL ORDERS

▲ Two shillings and 10p postal order. 1971. (vg) £4 - £6

▲ Twelve shillings postal order. 1939. Has three small hole punches (f). £10 - £12

▲ Two shillings postal order. 1939. (f-g) £6 - £8

▲ Six pence postal order. 1940. (f) £10 - £12

▲ Ten shillings postal order. 1965. (g-vg) £4 - £6

▲ One shilling and sixpence postal order. 1942. (f) £8 - £10

▲ Five shillings postal order. 1965. (vg) £5 - £7

▲ One pound postal order. 1975. Has small tear otherwise (vg) £3 - £5

POSTCARDS

Before 1902, it was not permissible to write an address and a message on the same side of a postcard. As a result, any pictures on the cards were generally quite small, and there were spaces around the edges for messages to be written. Cards from this period are collectable, but are often devalued by messages hastily scrawled across the picture side.

When the regulation was changed, it ushered in the "golden age" of postcard collecting, which lasted until the beginning of World War I. The cards from this period are particularly desirable for their attractive appearance and their historical significance.

▲ Novelty embossed postcard. (1910). Postally unused. (g-vg) £5 - £7

Leap Year

At the height of the popularity of the postcard era (1903 - 1914), the traditional belief was that the 29 February in a leap year was the only day of the year when a woman could propose marriage to a man. Needless to say, this subject matter was tailor-made for comic postcard artists.

Leap year, as a subject, may not be the most popular areas but for value purposes, it is helped by the lack of supply. This is a classic example of the countless number of subjects encompassed by postcard collecting.

► Inter-Art 'Leap Year'. (1908). Postally unused. (g) £5 - £7

Collecting to a theme

Postcards offer such diversity of subject matter that it is possible to theme a collection around almost anything. It is hard to imagine a subject that has not appeared on at least one postcard, and that variety gives collectors plenty of options. You could pick something very common, such as the comic postcards from a certain artist, or you could choose something slightly more obscure.

POSTCARDS - Comic

Donald McGill (1875 - 1962)

Born in London in 1875, Donald McGill became one of the most famous comic postcard artists.

He produced anti-German comic cards depicting life during the dark days of World War I.

Following the war he concentrated on saucy cards. The trouble was that as time progressed, they became more risqué and in 1954 he was the subject of a major court case for breaking the Obscene Publications Act 1857. He was found guilty and was fined £50. The case led to many postcard manufacturers destroying much of their saucy card stock. In 1957 McGill managed to persuade the Government to amend the 1857 Act. This led to a revival in the saucy card market.

The Donald McGill postcard Museum was opened in 2010 in Ryde, Isle of Wight.

▲ "Poor man..." (1915). Message in ink. (g-vg) £3 - £4

▲ "You can see..." (1915). Message in ink. (g-vg) £2 - £4

▲ "Everybody seems... " Postmarked London 1915. Message in pencil. (g) £3 - £4

▲ "All I need..." Postally unused. (g-vg) £2 - £4

▲ "A protected Cruiser" (1915). Message in ink. (g-vg) £3 - £5

▲ "Mother told..." Pmarked 1918. Message in pencil. (g-vg) £3 - £5

▲ "Kamarade! Kamarade!!" (1925). Message in ink. (vg) £2 - £4

▲ "That reminds me..." Postally unused. (g) £3 - £4

▲ "View of the..." Postmarked Southend-On-Sea 1934. Message in pencil. (f-g) £2 - £3

▲ "Along came..." Postmarked Sutton 1930. Message in ink. (g) £2 - £3

▲ "Peace and plenty!" (1925). Pmarked Shanklin. . (g) £2 - £3

▲ "Food control..." Postmarked 1919. Message in ink. (g) £2 - £4

◄ "I wish Pa hadn't..." (1915). Message in ink. (g) £2 - £4

► "Can't see you..." 1934. Postally unused. (vg) £2 - £4

POSTCARDS - Comic

Fred Spurgin (1882 - 1968)

In 1900 Frederick Spurgin moved from Latvia to Britain, along with his parents and two brothers. His real name was Izydor Spurgin.

Fred's talent as an artist was quickly discovered and before long, several publishing companies (including The Inter Art Company) had commissioned him.

In 1916, Fred's brother, Maurice, created the 'Art & Humour Publishing Company' as a vehicle for Fred's work.

As well as comic, Fred is known for World War I military (patriotic/propaganda), child and glamour subject matter.

▲ Seaside Series. "We're Splashing It". Postmarked 1912. (g) £3 - £4

▲ Unknown maker. "I'd Kiss Her". Postmarked 1919. (g-vg) £3 - £4

▲ Art & Humour. "My Dicky". (1916). (g) £2 - £3

▲ Art & Humour. "If It's Pressing". (1920). (vg) £4 - £5

▲ Unknown maker. "Hi Missus". (1915). (vg) £3 - £4

▲ Art & Humour. "Who Said". (1918). (g-vg) £3 - £4

▲ Art & Humour. "Even The Old". (1916). (g-vg) £3 - £4

▲ W & K. "Ma He'rts". (1914). (g) £2 - £3

▲ Art & Humour. "Oh Sir". Postmarked 1917. (g-vg) £3 - £4

▲ Inter-Art. "Nothing Can". (1912). (vg) £4 - £6

▲ Art & Humour. "Glad You're Here". (1918). (g-vg) £3 - £4

▲ Art & Humour. "If You Don't". Pmarked 1917. (vg) £3 - £4

▲ Art & Humour. "I'll Make". Pmarked 1917. (g-vg) £3 - £4

▲ Inter-Art. "I Feel". (1912). (g-vg) £3 - £4

▲ Inter-Art. "Let Me Whisper". (1910). (g-vg) £3 - £4

▲ Unknown maker. "A Pair". (1910). (vg) £4 - £6

▲ Art & Humour. "Glad You've". Pmarked 1917. (vg) £3 - £4

▲ Art & Humour. "Hi You're Losing". (1918). (vg) £4 - £5

▲ Art & Humour. "I Have Everything". (1918). (f) £1 - £2

▲ Unknown maker. "Do I Look". Unreadable duplex pmark. (1905). (vg) £4 - £6

POSTCARDS - Railway stations

This is a popular area of railwayana with some old postcards commanding sums of £50 or more.

Value generally depends on how rare the card is. A small town railway station that closed long ago, is likely to be in much higher demand than Paddington, London, for example.

▲ Tilehurst. (1908) (vg-ex) £35 - £40

▲ Birmingham, New Street.   (1905) (g-vg) £25 - £30

▲ Templecombe. (1907) (g-vg) £25 - £30

▲   Hayes.   Postmarked   1908.   (g-vg) £25 - £30

▲   Yelverton.   Postmarked   1912.   (f) £15 - £20

▲   Bradford.   Postmarked   1909.   (vg) £20 - £25

▲ Gravelly Hill. (1910) (g) £15 - £20

▲   Malmesbury.   Postmarked   1906.   (vg) £25 - £30

▲ Ambergate. (1955) (vg) £5 - £8

▲ Charing Cross. (1905) (vg) £10 - £14

▲ Crouch End. Postmarked 1911. (f) £15 - £20

▲ Lynton. Postmarked 1908. (f) £10 - £12

▲ Denham. Postmarked 1917. (vg) £15 - £20

▲ Furness. (1905) (g-vg) £12 - £15

▲ Llantwit Major. (1905) (p-f) £15 - £20

POSTCARDS - Railway stations

▲ Tidworth. (1905) (f) £25 - £30

▲ Hullavington. Postmarked 1915. (f-g) £35 - £40

▲ Llandrindod Wells. Postmarked 1907. (f-g) £20 - £25

▲ Reading. (1915) (vg) £20 - £25

▲ Newcastle. (1908) (g-vg) £25 - £30

▲ Derby. Postmarked 1903. (vg) £10 - £12

▲ Lymington Pier. Postmarked 1938. (g-vg) £12 - £15

▲ Swindon. Postmarked 1913. (g-vg) £20 - £25

▲ Stamford. (1910). (p-f) £10 - £12

▲ Folkestone Warren Halt. Postmarked 1911. (g-vg) £15 - £20

▲ Devil's Bridge. Postmarked 1975. (vg) £3 - £5

▲ Wickham Market. Postmarked 1911. (vg) £10 - £12

▲ Nottingham. (1905). (vg) £12 - £15

▲ Maiden Newton. Postmarked 1906. (g-vg) £25 - £30

▲ Penzance. (1910). (vg) £5 - £7

▲ Milverton. Postmarked 1915. (f) £15 - £20

▲ Towyn Wharf. (1975). (vg) £2 - £4

▲ Milton Keynes. 1982. (vg) £6 - £8

POSTCARDS - Topographical

This category relates to cards that depict a particular area of the country. Seaside cards are not generally classed as topographical. They can be wonderful photographic records of our social history.

▲ Dedham. (1905). (vg) £3 - £5

▲ Newmarket. (1950). (vg) £4 - £6

▲ Clifton, Bristol. (1905). (vg) £12 - £14

▲ Harrogate. (1905). (vg) £2 - £3

▲ Halifax. Postmark 1905. (g) £2 - £3

▲ Dipton. (1910). (vg) £8 - £12

▲ Liverpool. (1905). (vg) £8 - £10

▲ Kingston-on-Thames. (1935). (vg) £4 - £6

▲ Bradford. Postmark 1913. (vg) £7 - £9

▲ Colchester. Postmark 1913. (g) £7 - £10

▲ Marlborough. Postmark 1906. (g) £1 - £3

▲ Manchester. (1925). (g-vg) £8 - £12

▲ Dunster. Postmark 1909. (g-vg) £3 - £4

▲ Wantage. (1920). (g-vg) £6 - £8

▲ Minehead. Postmark 1908. (f-g) £2 - £3

▲ Eynsham. Postmark 1964. (vg) £3 - £4

POSTCARDS - Messages

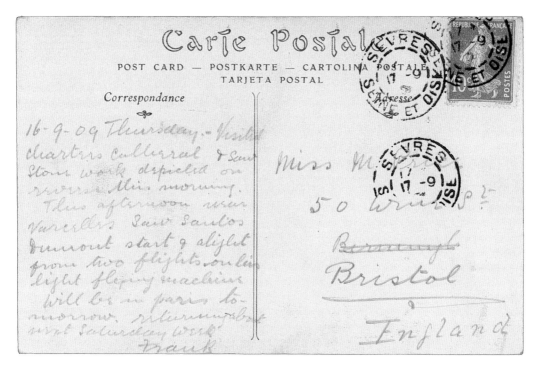

▲ Postcard (Chartres Cathedral). Postmarked Sevres 1909. Message in pencil. (g) £3 - £4

Some social historians search out and collect old postcards for their interesting messages. Whilst it is a great pity that the picture postcard phenomenon didn't start 100 years earlier, we should be grateful for such a vast insight to life 100 years ago.

The postcard featured here depicts a 16th century stone carving in Chartres Cathedral, France, not exactly the most collectable of images. Turn it over and there are three postmarks 'Sevres – Seine et Oise' dated 17th September 1909 with a 10centimes postage stamp – not quite a philatelist's delight but still mildly interesting. Then look at the address of the recipient – Miss M. Price, 50 Wine Street, Bristol, England. This is a prestigious Bristol address. The message is signed by 'Frank'. Imagination can lead to an assumption that here are a couple of sweethearts keeping in touch and probably from wealthy families.

Frank tells Miss Price that he is on holiday in France for a few weeks – that would not have been cheap in 1909. Furthermore, unlike many of the messages written a century ago, the spelling and grammar indicates an educated gent.

However, Frank's holiday greeting is not the interesting part of the message – Frank says that that afternoon he had seen "Santos Dumont start and alight from two flights on his light flying machine". It is this snippet of information that makes this message interesting and (to a limited extent) valuable. Frank is relaying a fragment of aviation history. He had witnessed the flight of one of the world's most famous aviators. Frank's use of the word "on" rather than 'in' is significant. Santos would have been exposed to the elements, virtually strapped to the contraption. Then the term "light flying machine" (rather than 'light aircraft' really makes this message a gem.

POT LIDS

In the mid-nineteenth century, retailers of paste-like products for domestic consumption marketed them in glazed stoneware pots. Such pots were originally covered with greaseproof paper or a plain glazed stoneware lid.

Enterprising manufacturers hit on the idea of using the stoneware lids to advertise the products. By the turn of the century they had reached the height of their popularity.

It is these pot lids that collectors are interested in and the beauty of collecting these lids is that they can be purchased relatively cheaply and can even be dug up in old rubbish dumps at no cost at all.

The majority of examples are black on white but full-colour examples are plentiful.

The easiest and cleanest method of acquiring them is from car boot sales, collectors' fairs, and the internet.

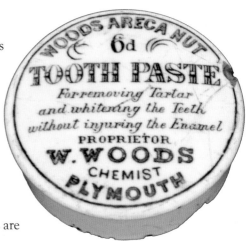

▲ Woods Areca Nut. W. Woods Chemist, Plymouth. (1890). (f) £8 - £10

POUNCE POTS

In Victorian times, 'pouncing' was the act of sprinkling a finely ground, sand, chalk or cuttle-shell on sheets of parchment paper, to prepare them for writing.

In those days, parchment paper was untreated and therefore needed 'pouncing' otherwise the paper would absorb the ink and cause blurring.

Pounce pots came in a variety of shapes and sizes. They are sometimes referred to as 'ponce pots'.

▲ Pounce Pot. Spelter. (1900). 80mm high. (vg) £25 - £30

PREMIUM BONDS

▶ £1 Premium Bond. 1968. (vg) £2 - £3

First introduced in 1956, by the Harold Macmillan Government.

Effectively, they are lottery bonds which are entered into prize draws.

▶ £2 Premium Bond. 1973. (vg) £2 - £3

The draw is made by ERNIE (Electronic Random Number Indicator Equipment).

The bonds are not transferable and have no face value if sold as collectable items. However, the irony is that a £1 bond in very good condition is worth a minimum of £2.

▶ £5 Premium Bond. 1977. (vg) £3 - £4

The PROMS

The Proms (short for Promenade Concerts) were the brainchild of Robert Newman, manager of the Queen's Hall in London. In 1894, Newman met with Henry Wood, a conductor and voice coach, to discuss his idea of nightly concerts that would create a new audience for classical and modern music. His aim was to encourage those people who would not normally attend classical concerts but who would be attracted by low ticket prices and an informal atmosphere.

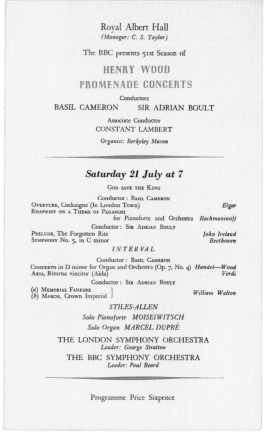

Newman offered conductorship of an orchestra, and the first season of the Proms, to Wood in 1894.

The 50th anniversary of the Proms was in 1944, and this was to be Woods' last season. He bequeathed the Proms to the BBC shortly before his death, at the age of 75, just three weeks after conducting his last performance.

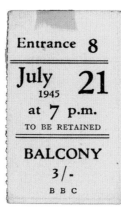

▲ Proms ticket. 21 July 1945. (g) £2 - £3

▲ Promenade Concert programme. 21 July 1945. (vg) £3 - £4

RADIO

The subject includes radio receiving equipment as well as items associated with the countless number of radio shows.

BBC Radio began transmissions in 1922. Old copies of The Radio Times can be classed as associated memorabilia. Records and books are also sought after by collectors and enthusiasts. The collecting of autographs of the radio stars, complements the subject.

In the 1930's particularly, tobacco companies released cigarette card series featuring radio celebrities.

▲ Radio Times. Vol. 160, No. 2073. 1 Aug 1963. (vg) £8 - £10

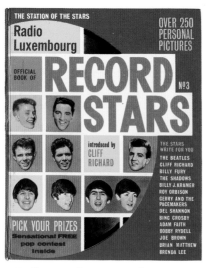

▲ Radio Luxembourg Record Stars. No.3. Hardback book. 1964. 156 pages, 260 x 210mm. (vg) £12 - £14

Radio Luxembourg

Radio Luxembourg (1933 - 1992) was an important forerunner of pirate radio and modern commercial radio in Europe. It was a cheap and effective way to advertise in the UK by circumventing the broadcasting restrictions in place at the time.

For many years complete programmes were pre-recorded in London and flown to the tiny independent grand duchy of Luxembourg on mainland Europe. A powerful transmitter enabled broadcasts to be received throughout Northern Europe.

Radios

Vintage radios in working order are in demand but carry a risk warning. Repairing them requires specialist knowledge. It helps to have an enthusiastic local dealer who also carries out repairs, but, of course, the business will not be around forever.

A much cheaper alternative to collecting radio (wireless) sets is to collect literature relating to them. There's a market in Radio sales catalogues and instruction manuals.

▲ Ferranti VPT4 radio valve. (1935). Not tested. (g) £1 - £2

▲ EKCO Radio sales leaflet. (1955). 16 pages of the latest models. (f-g) £3 - £4

▲ Enamel arm band. BR Look Out. (1960). (g) £6 - £8

The collecting of, and interest in, items relating to the railway, is known as Railwayana.

▲ Salmon Series postcard. (1935). Postally unused. (vg) £4 - £5

The Flying Scotsman. Probably the most famous British locomotive of all time. It was built in 1923 for the London and North Eastern Railway (LNER). Restored in 2016.

Great Western Railway

The GWR (Great Western Railway), sometimes colloquially referred to as God's Wonderful Railway or the Great Way Round, was a British railway company that linked London with the south west of England and most of Wales and was therefore a popular means of travelling to holiday resorts in those locations.

The company was founded in 1833 at a public meeting in Bristol, at the behest of Bristol merchants looking to maintain the city's status as the second most important port in the country (a status that was being threatened by Liverpool). Isambard Kingdom Brunel, who was only 29 years old, was appointed as the engineer.

As a result of World War I, the GWR was taken into government control in 1914. When the war ended, 120 railway companies throughout the country were compulsorily amalgamated, with only the GWR retaining its name.

The GWR was once again taken into government control during World War II before finally becoming the Western Region of British Railways in January 1948. The Great Western Railway Company was formally closed on 23 December 1949.

RAILWAYANA - Books

There are hundreds of books for railway enthusiasts. Some are extremely specialised and, as long as the right person spots your books for sale, you can sell for many times the cost price.

The best place to buy is a car boot sale. Some traders sell books by the van-load and very often they include a sprinkling of railway books. It's worth making the effort to find them.

In particular, look out for books published by Ian Allan. Ian Allan Publishing was established in 1942 and specialises in books and magazines related to the field of transport. Such books are in demand, and good, clean examples can often be expected to sell well. The first book the company ever produced was ABC of Southern Locomotives, and a first edition will be of much interest to a collector.

▲ Holiday Haunts. GWR limpback book. 1947. 686 pages. (f) £8 - £10

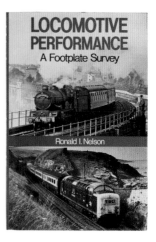

▲ Locomotive Performance. A Footplate Survey. Hardback book. 1979. 234 pages. (g-vg) £6 - £8

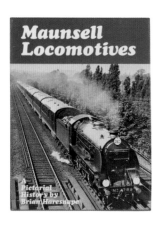

▲ Maunsell Locomotives. Hardback book. 1977. 130 pages. (vg) £4 - £6

▲ The Midland Railway. Hardback book. 1955. 192 pages. (f-g) £8 - £10

▲ LNWR. Hardback book. 1980. 96 pages. (vg-ex) £6 - £8

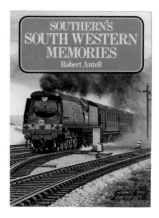

▲ Southern's South Western Memories. Hardback book. 1977. 112 pages. (g-vg) £6 - £8

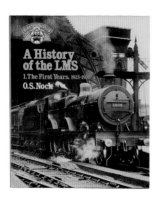

▲ History of the LMS. The First Years, 1923-1930. Hardback book. 1985. 94 pages. (vg-ex) £5 - £7

▲ Stanier Locomotives. Hardback book. 1974. 128 pages. (vg). £4 - £6

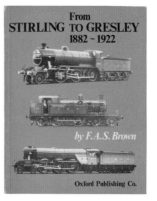

▲ From Stirling To Gresley 1882 - 1922. Limpback book. 1974. 152 pages. (g-vg) £4 - £6

▲ Branch Line Album. Second Series, Hardback book. 1965. 120 pages. (g) £4 - £6

RAMPWALKERS

Also known as 'slant walkers', 'ramp walkers' are toys that 'walk' down slopes. They have been around for 100 years or so and were originally made of metal. The majority are plastic and were often given away as premiums.

Their simple design enables them to 'walk' down an incline without any necessity to be wound up.

Some were given away in cereal packets, while others were sold in toy shops (particularly in the '60s).

They are now most popular with collectors in the USA and the internet can help you locate traders. However, be aware the prices are high. In this country your best bet is likely to be a large (collectors') toy fair.

The best known manufacturer is Marx. They also produced ramps. Subject matter includes Disney characters, Hanna-Barbera, various animals, etc.

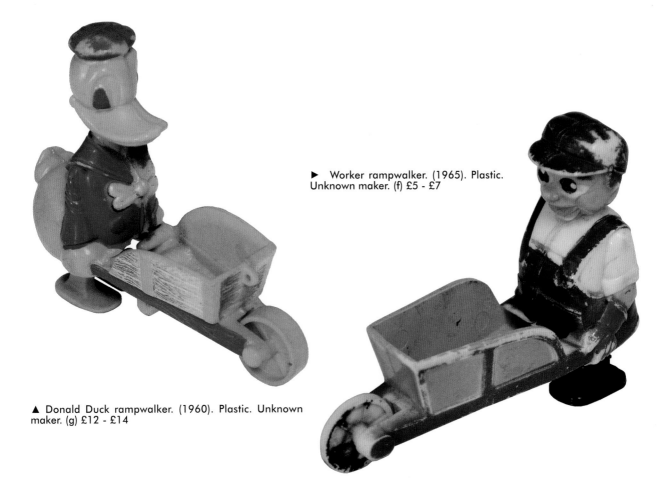

▶ Worker rampwalker. (1965). Plastic. Unknown maker. (f) £5 - £7

▲ Donald Duck rampwalker. (1960). Plastic. Unknown maker. (g) £12 - £14

RAZOR BLADES

Some collectables may seem to be unusual at first glance, but delve deeper into the subject and you may find the items to be fascinating and (potentially) very profitable. When the first person started collecting stamps, people laughed. Stamps are now the most collected item in the world. A similar thing happened with tax discs. Could razor blades be next?

Old razor blades are a perfect low budget collectable, they are extremely easy to store and they are made even more interesting by the wonderfully colourful packets produced by the multitude of companies who traded in them. Razor blades were first used in 1901, and they are still used today, meaning there are literally thousands of different blades that can be collected.

The majority of collectors specialise in razor blade wrappers (RBWs) but some collect full boxes of blades (it is better to specialise in cardboard boxes, rather than the more common plastic boxes).

▲   Nacet.   (vg)
£1.50 - £2.50

▲ Gillette Extra. (g)
£1 - £2

▲   Valet.   (vg)
£1.50 - £2.50

▲   Minx.   (vg)
£1.50 - £2.50

▲ British Ocean. (vg)
£2 - £3

▲   Minora.   (vg-ex)
£1.50 - £2.50

▲ Wardonia. Advertising showcard. (1940). (vg) £16 - £20

RAZOR BLADES

▲ Kleen. (vg) £2 - £3

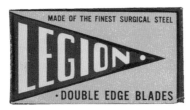
▲ Legion. (vg) £2 - £3

▲ Emerald. (g-vg) £1 - £3

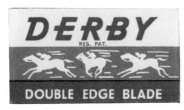
▲ Derby. (vg) £3 - £4

▲ Maro. (vg) £2 - £4

▲ Globusmen. (vg) £2 - £4

▲ Laurel. (vg) £2 - £4

▲ Star. (vg) £1 - £3

▲ Town Talk. (vg) £3 - £4

▲ Radio Gold. (vg) £2 - £4

▲ The Stable. (vg) £3 - £4

▲ Knockout. (vg) £2 - £4

▲ Pal. (g-vg) £2 - £4

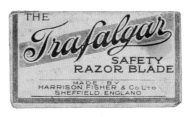
▲ Trafalgar. (f-g) £5 - £7

▲ Cesar Luxus. (vg) £1 - £2

▲ 7 O'Clock. (vg) £1 - £2

▲ Best British. (g-vg) £2 - £4

▲ Wilmar. (g-vg) £3 - £4

RAZOR BLADES - Boxes

The small boxes that generally contained 5 blades are also collectable but because they are not as easy to store as the individually wrapped blades, they are not in so much demand. The boxes are also more likely to be in less good condition. Remember that many of these collectable items are over 50 years old.

Beware if buying from an unknown person via an internet auction. A common ploy is to offer razor blade boxes containing the original five (or so) blades. The trouble is that when you receive the goods the wrappers have all been removed from the blades, so, whilst it is true that the original blades are sold in the original boxes, the blades are virtually worthless without the wrappers.

◄ Scotty. USA. Empty box. (vg) 60p - 80p

► Blue Bell. England. Empty box. (g-vg) 80p - £1

▲ Blue Star. USA. Empty box. (g-vg) 50p - 70p

▲ New Yorker. Sweden. Empty box. (vg) 40p - 60p

▲ Clix. USA. Empty box. (g-vg) 80p - £1

▲ The Barber Blade. USA. Empty box. (vg) 30p - 40p

▲ City. USA. Empty box. (vg) 30p - 40p

▲ Sheer. USA. Empty box. (g-vg) 50p - 70p

▲ Ohio. USA. Empty box. (vg) 60p - 80p

▲ Cooper. USA. Empty box. (vg) 30p - 40p

▲ Rotbart. Germany. Empty box. (vg) 30p - 40p

▲ Astor. Greece. Empty box. (vg) 50p - 70p

▲ Paris. France. Empty box. (vg) 80p - £1

▲ Razorbill. England. Empty box. £1 - £2

RECORDS

▲ **78rpm Shellac record. William Heseltine Orchestra. (1930). The original Ellis & Co., cardboard sleeve (g-vg) is more collectable than the record. £3 - £4**

Emile Berliner invented the 'record' in 1888. It was a flat disc made of vulcanised rubber. He later created the 'shellac' disc which was a brittle and hard wearing material. These played at 78 rpm (revolutions per minute) and were phenomenally popular between 1920 and 1956. Then came the 45rpm vinyl disc, which was hugely popular worldwide until the mid 1980's.

Sadly, today, 78rpm shellac records are not overly popular with collectors. They are so fragile that they are not ideal for posting and therefore are not traded in great quantities over the internet.

The market in old records, rests with vinyl, particularly those from the 1960's. Many collectors/enthusiasts play them on old record players (Dansette etc) and seem to actually enjoy the trademark crackle from scratched record surfaces. There's a kind of magical nostalgia associated with this.

▲ **Musonic (card) stroboscope - designed to help set and adjust record player turntable speeds. (1965). (vg) £1 - £2**

Amazingly, vinyl records are making a comeback and some record pressing plants are working overtime to cope with the new demand.

There's still a strong market for collectable old records but knowing what is 'collectable' is the key. You really do need to do plenty of homework.

▶ Rice Crispies promotional 45rpm vinyl record. Shakin' Stevens. 1981. Kellogg's label. Plain sleeve. Vinyl (vg) £2 - £4

Musonic began supplying record player accessories such as styli and cartridges in 1954 and are still in business today, supplying parts to keep our old record players turning and playing. Web address: www.musonic.co.uk.

Flexi Discs

A flexi disc is a thin sheet of plastic or card with record grooves. Unlike vinyl records, flexi discs are flexible and light, and are therefore cheap to produce in big quantities and cheap to post. It was an ideal advertising/promotional tool.

The demise of the record player sent the flexi disc into the history books. It has now become a classic low-cost collecting area. Our tip is to snap up as many as you can. We forecast a steady increase in value. We imagine they are going to be a lot harder to find in just ten years time.

Already some flexi discs change hands for serious money. The most valuable are those that were given away to members of The Beatles Fan Club in the '60s. At the other end of the scale, among the least desirable are Reader's Digest promotional discs.

As with all collectables, condition affects the value of any flexi disc. They are quite fragile items. Make sure you don't bend them too much, otherwise they may crease/kink and become unplayable and also lose aesthetic appeal.

Two of the big names in the manufacturing of flexi discs were Lyntone and Sound For Industry.

RECORDS - Singles 45rpm

▲ What Am I Living For - Chuck Willis. 1958. London, 45-HL-E 8635. Vinyl dinked (vg) £30 - £40

▲ Johnny Remember Me - John Leyton. 1961. Top Rank, JAR-577. Vinyl (g) £1 - £2

▲ That's My Home - Acker Bilk. 1961. C o l u m b i a , 45-DB 4673. Vinyl (g) £1 - £2

▲ I'm Serious - The Hilltoppers. 1957. London, 45-HL-D 8441. Vinyl dinked (vg) £8 - £10

▲ Angela Jones - Johnny Ferguson. 1959. MGM, 45-MGM-1059. Vinyl (g) £3 - £4

▲ I Will Live My Life For You - Don Neilson. 1963. Piccadilly, 7N 35103. Vinyl dinked (g) £2 - £3

▲ Go Away, Little Girl - Mark Wynter. 1962. Pye, 7N 15492. Vinyl (g-vg) £2 - £3

▲ Loch Lomond Rock - The Ramrods. 1960. London, 45-HLU 9355. Vinyl (g-vg) £8 - £10

▲ Jeannie - Danny Williams. 1962. His Master's Voice, 45-POP 968. Vinyl (g) £2 - £3

▲ The Grass Is Greener - Nancy Wilson. 1965. Capitol, CL 15396. Vinyl (vg) £1 - £2

▲ I Don't Know Why - Eden Kane. 1962. Decca, 45-F 11460. Vinyl (g-vg) £2 - £3

▲ Waterloo - The Mudlarks. 1959. C o l u m b i a , 45-DB 4331. Vinyl (g-vg) £2 - £4

▲ Can't Let You Go - Barry Ryan. 1971. Polydor, 2001-256. Vinyl dinked (g) £1 - £2

▲ Anyone Who Had A Heart - Cilla Black. 1964. Parlophone, R 5101. Vinyl (vg) £2 - £3

▲ Makin' Love - Vince Eager. 1959. Top Rank, 45-JAR 191. Vinyl (vg) £3 -£4

▲ Wind Me Up (Let Me Go) - Cliff Richard. 1965. Columbia, DB 7745. Vinyl (vg) £1 - £2

▲ Palisades Park - Freddy Cannon. 1962. Stateside, 45SS-101. Vinyl (vg) £4 - £6

▲ Can You Please Crawl Out Your Window? - Bob Dylan. 1966. CBS, 201900. Vinyl (g-vg) £6 - £8

▲ Goodness Gracious Me! - Peter Sellers & Sophia Loren. 1960. Parlophone, 45-R 4702. Vinyl (vg) £3 - £4

▲ The Only Man On The Island - Tommy Steele. 1958. Decca, 45-F 11041. Vinyl (g) £2 - £3

▲ I'll Always Be In Love With You - Michael Holliday. 1958. Columbia, 45-DB 4155. Vinyl (vg) £2 - £3

▲ Always On My Mind - The Settlers. 1967. Pye, 7N 17262. Vinyl (vg) £2 - £3

▲ Beans In My Ears - The Serendipity Singers. 1964. Philips, BF 1341. Vinyl dinked (ex) £1 - £2

▲ Sweet Sixteen Bars - Earl Grant. 1962. Brunswick, 45-05877. Vinyl (vg-ex) £2 - £3

▲ Sugar Moon - Pat Boone. 1958. London, 45-HL-D 8640. Vinyl (g-vg) £1 - £2

RECORDS (EP)

Many EP (Extended Play) records are currently considered to be as good as 'money in the bank'. This is particularly the case with the pop groups of the 1960's. A few of the really rare EP's can sell for hundreds of pounds. It's a case of studying the market, buying right and then gambling that the market will not dip.

▲ Cliff's Lucky Lips. Cliff Richard. Columbia SEG 8269. 1963. Vinyl (g-vg) £12 - £16

▲ The Late Great Buddy Holly. Buddy Holly. Coral FEP 2044. 1958. Vinyl (g-vg) £14 - £18

▲ If You Gotta Make A Fool Of Somebody. Freddie & The Dreamers. Columbia. SEG 8275. 1963. Vinyl (vg) £12 - £14

▲ The Hits Of Shirley Bassey. Shirley Bassey. Columbia. SEG 8252. 1962. Vinyl (vg) £4 - £6

▲ Lemon Pipers and the 1910 Fruitgum Company. Pye. NEP 44091. 1968. Vinyl (g) £8 - £10

▲ Ricky - Part 1. Ricky Nelson. London. RE-P 1141. 1958. Vinyl (vg) £24 - £28

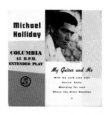
▲ My Guitar And Me. Michael Holliday. Columbia. SEG 7638. 1957. Vinyl (vg) £6 - £8

▲ Scrumpy & Western. Adge Cutler & The Wurzels. Columbia. SEG 8525. 1967. Vinyl (vg) £8 - £10

▲ The Blood Donor. Tony Hancock. Pye. NEP 24175. 1961. Vinyl (g-vg) £6 - £8

▲ The Sounds Of The Tornados. The Tornados. Decca. DFE 8510. 1962. Vinyl (vg -ex) £12 - £14

▲ The Best of Chuck Berry. Chuck Berry. Pye. NEP 44018. 1968. Vinyl (vg) £10 - £12

▲ The Swinging Side of the Four Pennies. The Four Pennies. Philips. BE 12570. 1964. Vinyl (vg-ex) £14 - £16

▲ Another Six. Russ Conway. Columbia. SEG 7905. 1959. Vinyl (vg) £2 - £4

▲ Deck of Cards. Wink Martindale. Dot. DEP 2000. 1965. Vinyl (vg) £5 - £7

▲ Pepe. Duane Eddy. London. RE-W 1287. 1960. Vinyl (vg) £6 - £8

▲ Emile. Emile Ford & The Checkmates. Pye. NEP 24119. 1960. Vinyl (vg) £7 - £9

▲ Ole ala Lee. Peggy Lee. Capitol. EAP1-1475. 1960. Vinyl (vg-ex) £3 - £4

▲ Frank in Films. Frankie Vaughan. Philips. BBE 12317. 1959. Vinyl (g-vg) £3 - £4

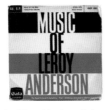
▲ The Music of Leroy Anderson. The Royal Farnsworth Symphony Orchestra. Gala. 45XP1057. 1958. Vinyl (ex) £2 - £3

▲ Ain't Gonna Kiss Ya. The Searchers. Pye. NEP 24177. 1963. Vinyl (g-vg) £10 - £12

▲ Nonsense Songs. Elton Hayes. Parlophone. GEP 8551. Vinyl (vg) £2 - £3

▲ Kwyet Kinks. The Kinks. Pye. NEP 24221. Vinyl (g) £12 - £14

▲ Jolson. Norman Brooks. Gala. 45XP1009. 1958. Vinyl (vg-ex) £1 - £2

▲ Lemon Tree. The Kingston Trio. Capitol. EAP1-20655. 1961. Vinyl (vg) £6 - £8

▲ Sing Something Simple Vol 2. The Adams Singers. Pye. NEP 44006. 1959. Vinyl (vg-ex) £3 - £4

▲ Around The World. Nat King Cole. Capitol. EAP1 813. 1958. Vinyl (g) £3 - £4

▲ Four Hits and a Mister. Acker Bilk. Columbia. SEG 8156. 1961. Vinyl (vg) £3 - £4

RECORDS (LP)

It's safe to say that generally, the bulk of LP records that you will find for sale (by the truck load) at car boot sales, will be of very little value.

However, amongst these, lurks the odd rare record. You really do need to do your homework on this subject. You are looking for original labels, rare issues and vinyl in good condition+.

▲ In Dreams - Roy Orbison. 1963. London, SH-U 8108. Vinyl (vg), sleeve (g) £15 - £20

▲ More Hits By Cliff - Cliff Richard. 1963. Columbia, SCX 3555. Vinyl (vg), sleeve (g) £8 - £10

▲ The Story of The Who - The Who. 1970. Polydor, 2478 091-A. Vinyl (f), sleeve (f) £4 - £6

▲ Scotch Corner - Andy Stewart. 1973. Starline, SRS 5159. Vinyl (g), sleeve (g) £1 - £2

▲ Up Jumped A Swagman - Frank Ifield. 1965. Columbia, SCXO-3559. Vinyl (g), sleeve (f) £2 - £4

▲ Mad Dogs & Englishmen - Joe Cocker. 1970. AM Records, AMLS 6002. Vinyl (vg), sleeve (g) £2 - £4

▲ Dangerous - Michael Jackson. 1991. Epic, EPC 465802 1. Vinyl (vg), sleeve (g) £3 - £4

▲ You Don't Have To Say You Love Me - Dusty Springfield. 1958. Contour, CN 2016. Vinyl (g), sleeve (g) £1 - £2

▲ Freddie and The Dreamers in Disneyland - Freddie and The Dreamers. 1966. Columbia, SX 6069. Vinyl (f), sleeve (g) £5 - £7

▲ Gary Lewis and The Playboys - Gary Lewis and The Playboys. 1966. Liberty, LST-7487. Vinyl (vg), sleeve (g) £8 - £10

▲ The Hit-Making World of Blue Mink - Blue Mink. 1975. Gull, SPA-R 437. Vinyl (vg), sleeve (g) £2 - £4

▲ Your Top TV Themes - Geoff Love and His Orchestra. 1972. MFP, MFP 5272. Vinyl (f), sleeve (g) £1 - £2

▲ The World of Cat Stevens - Cat Stevens. 1970. Decca, SPA 93. Vinyl (vg), sleeve (g) £4 - £6

▲ Dutch Swing College On Tour - Dutch Swing College Band. 1960. Phillips, SBBL. 603. Vinyl (vg), sleeve (vg) £3 - £4

▲ The Orange of Ulster - The Loyal Orangemen. 1967. Allegro, ALL 864. Vinyl (vg), sleeve (vg) £1 - £2

▲ Up In Arms - The Yetties. 1974. Argo, ZDA 100. Vinyl (f), sleeve (g) £3 - £5

▲ Rock Around The Clock - Bill Haley & The Comets. 1968. Hallmark, SHM 668. Vinyl (vg), sleeve (vg) £1 - £2

RECORDS (LP)

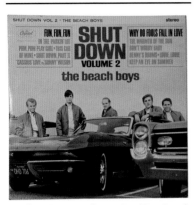

▲ Shut Down Volume 2 - The Beach Boys. 1963. Capitol, ST 2027. Vinyl (vg), sleeve (g-vg) £18 - £20

▲ Standing Room Only! - The Highwaymen. 1962. United Artist, SULP 1002. Vinyl (vg), sleeve (g-vg) £5 - £7

▲ I'll Remember You - Frank Ifield. 1963. Columbia, 33SX 1467. Vinyl (vg), sleeve (vg) £8 - £10

▲ Best of the Troggs - The Troggs. 1967. Page 1 Records, FOR 001. Vinyl (vg), sleeve (vg) £16 - £18

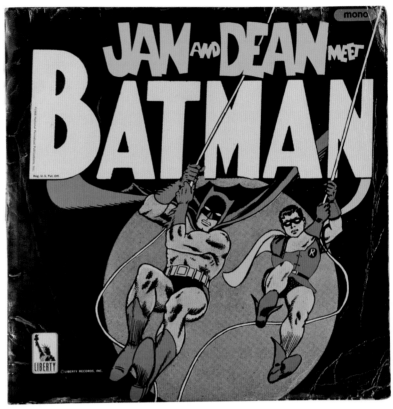

▲ Jan and Dean Meet Batman. 1966. Liberty, LBY 1309. Vinyl (g), sleeve (f-g) £20 - £22

This is a classic example of a dual-collectable item. Jan and Dean are classic sixties pop. The songs are a spoof on Batman & Robin. A superb cover image in good condition. The LP is quite hard to find.

▲ Daydream - The Lovin' Spoonful. 1966. PYE Records, NPL 28078. Vinyl (vg), sleeve (g) £20 - £24

▲ Portrait - The Walker Brothers. 1966. Philips, 843 468 BY. Vinyl (vg), sleeve (g) £22 - £24

▲ The Best of the Lettermen - The Lettermen. 1966. Capitol, T 2554. Vinyl (vg), sleeve (g-vg) £4 - £6

▲ The World of Amen Corner - Amen Corner. 1969. Decca, SPA 33. Vinyl (vg), sleeve (g-vg) £6 - £8

RECORDS - Demo discs

Demo (demonstration) discs are sample records designed to promote a new release.

The most valuable are those 'demos' that were withdrawn and the record never actually released to the public.

Labels were often printed with a large 'A' (Advance copy).

▲ Colour My World - Don Partridge. 1969. Columbia, DB 8583. Vinyl (vg) £6 - £8

▲ Church Bells - Bing Crosby. Brunswick, L 11217. Vinyl (g) £8 - £10

▲ Bridget The Midget (The Queen Of The Blues) - Ray Stevens. 1971. CBS Records, CBS S 7070. Vinyl (g) £4 - £6

▲ (Susquehanna River) Valley Song - Wesley Parker. 1983. President, PT 515. Vinyl (ex) £3 - £5

▲ Bon Doo Wah - The Orlons. Cameo-Parkway, C 287. Vinyl (f) £30 - £35

▲ A Long Way To Go - Emotions. 1977. CBS Records, S CBS 6118. Vinyl (g) £3 - £4

▲ See You Ma - Art Nouveau. 1974. Decca, F 13527. Vinyl (vg) £6 - £8

▲ Now Is The Time - Jimmy James. 1976. Pye Records, 7N 45606. Vinyl (g) £16 - £18

▲ Old Home Movies - Vickie Lawrence. 1974. EMI Records, INT 504. Vinyl (g) £2 - £3

▲ Tears And Roses - Al Martino. Capitol, CL 15349. Vinyl (g-vg) £2 - £3

▲ Witch Doctor Bump - The Chubukos. 1973. Pye Records, MSS 303. Vinyl (g) £12 - £14

▲ Jeanie Marie - Trini Lopez. 1963. London, HL 9808. Vinyl (g) £12 - £14

▲ She's My Lady - Dave Dee, Dozy, Beaky, Mick & Tich. 1974. Antic, K 11510. Vinyl (g) £8 - £12

▲ Backroom Boys (Night After Night) - Flying Squad. 1978. Epic, S EPC 6542. Vinyl (f-g) £2 - £4

▲ Tonight - Ted Heath. Decca, F 11410. Vinyl dinked (f) £2 - £4

▲ Mame - Robert Preston & Corus. 1974. Warner Bros, K 16423. Vinyl (g) £1 - £2

▲ Light Up The Fire - Parchment. 1972. Pye Records, 7N 45178. Vinyl (g-vg) £7 - £9

▲ Don't Say Goodnight and Mean Goodbye - The Shirelles. Stateside, SS 213. Vinyl dinked (f-g) £18 - £20

RECORDS - Picture discs

Record collectors normally refer to 'picture discs' as those that were released from the 1970's onwards as 45rpm (7inch) singles.

However, 'picture discs' date back much further, approximately sixty years earlier when some novelty picture postcards had transparent recordings glued over the picture.

Whilst the modern era 'picture discs' are deemed collectable, the majority are not of any significant value and are often overrated either deliberately or inadvertently by vendors.

As well as singles, some 'picture discs' are the larger 12inch, 33rpm, format long players.

▲ How Can You Love Me - Ambrosia. 1982. Warner Bros, K17933P. Vinyl (vg) £1 - £2

▲ I Just Want To Dance - Robert Marlow. 1984. Reset Records, 7 REST 3. Vinyl (vg) £1 - £2

▲ The Power Of Love - Frankie Goes To Hollywood. 1984. ZTT Records, PZTAS 5. Vinyl (vg) £2 - £3

▲ Like A Virgin - The Lords. 1985. Illegal Records. Vinyl (vg) £1 - £2

▲ Love Potion No.9 - Tygers Of Pan Tang. 1982. MCA, MCAP 769. Vinyl (vg) £1 - £2

▲ Wouldn't It Be Good - Nik Kershaw. 1984. MCA, NIKP 2. Vinyl (vg) £1 - £2

▲ Heart And Soul - Huey Lewis And The News. 1985. Chrysalis. Vinyl (vg) £2 - £3

▲ You'll Come 'Round - Status Quo. 2004. Universal, 9868066. Vinyl (vg) £1 - £2

▲ Who Were You With In The Moonlight - Dollar. 1979. Carrere, CAR 110 P. Vinyl (vg) £1 -£2

▲ How Lucky You Are - Skin. 1996. Parlophone, R 6426. Vinyl (g-vg) £2 - £3

▲ Hollywood - Thin Lizzy. 1981. Phonogram, LIZ PD 10. Vinyl (vg) £2 - £3

▲ Wise Up! Sucker - Pop Will Eat Itself. 1989. RCA, PB 42793. Vinyl (vg) £1 -£2

▲ Self! - Fuzzbox. 1989. WEA Records, YZ408P. Vinyl (g) £1 - £2

Whilst there are plenty of collectables relating to religious matters, it may be fair to say that it's not the most popular of subjects. Imaginative collectors can take advantage of this and build quite an interesting collection at relatively low cost.

◄ Roman Catholic button badge. (1935). 22mm diameter. (g) £10 - £12

▲ Christian Miscellany publication. February 1898. 82 pages. 225 x 175mm. (g) £6 - £8

Randall Davidson - Archbishop Of Canterbury

Randall Thomas Davidson, 1st Baron Davidson of Lambeth, was an Anglican bishop who served as Archbishop of Canterbury from 1903 until 1928.

He was born 7 April 1848, and studied at Harrow and Trinity College, Oxford. Before being enthroned as Archbishop, he was Bishop of Rochester from 1891 until 1895, and Bishop of Winchester from 1895 until 1903.

He was the first Archbishop to ever retire, and as there was no procedure in place for such an event, it was necessary for a commission of three bishops to be hastily appointed to receive the resignation and subsequently convey it to the king.

Randall Davidson passed away 25 May 1930, aged 82.

◄ Randall Davidson postcard. (1905). Halfpenny stamp affixed, but not posted. (f) £6 - £8

► Lambeth Palace card signed by Randall Davidson. 10th April 1905. Clear, black ink, 115 x 90mm. No dedication. £20 - £30

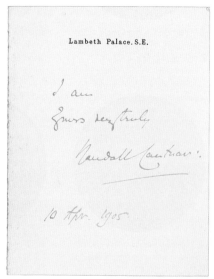

RELIGION

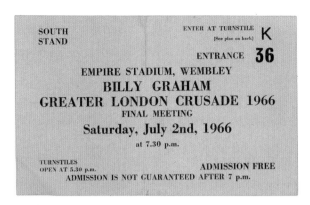

▲ Billy Graham ticket. Wembley. 2 July 1966. (g) £4 - £6

▲ Billy Graham 45rpm record. Greater London - Crusade Choir. (1966). Redemption Records, RRS 2003. Vinyl (vg) £2 - £4

The Boy's Own Paper

The idea for the Boys' Own Paper originated in 1878 when the Religious Tract Society decided to introduce a paper that would encourage young children to read and to instil them with Christian morals. The first issue went on sale 19 January 1879.

The paper ran until 1967, during which time 2511 issues were produced. From 1879 until 1940, each year's issues were bound together and sold as an annual. It was also possible to buy the cover and bind the issues yourself, and this means not all Boys' Own Paper annuals are exactly alike (some may be missing issues, or may be bound in a different order).

▲ 16 Oct 1880. (f) £3 - £5

▲ 2 Jul 1892. (g) £2 - £4

▲ 17 Feb 1894. (g) £2 - £3

▲ 2 Jan 1904. (g) £1 - £2

▲ 6 Feb 1904. (f-g) £1 - £2

▲ Jan 1923. Back page loose. (p-f) £1 - £2

▲ Jun 1923. (f) £1 - £2

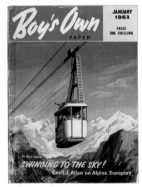

▲ Jan 1963. Cover loose. (f) 50p - £1

REWARD CARDS

In the early 1900s, schools gave Reward Cards as prizes for good attendance. They generally had an educational theme and were published by the local authorities. The most sought after by collectors are those published by commercial organisations.

Companies wanted to be associated with the good work of the education authorities and at the same time they used the cards to promote their products.

While the cards are not postcards, they are sought after by postcard collectors as well as those specialising in this field.

(Front)   (Reverse)

▲ Cadbury's Cocoa reward card. (1920). (g-vg) £5 - £7

ROBERTSON'S GOLLIES

The earlier enamel badges (pre-1960) are the more valuable and most collectable. However, there are plenty of fakes and even official reproductions out there. Therefore, it is important not to buy until you know exactly what you are looking for (there are plenty of websites with specialist information). Pay particular attention to backstamps to identify the age and authenticity.

One enamel badge was exchanged for ten paper golly tokens (one was affixed behind each jar label). These paper gollies were a variety of musicians and sportsmen. The 60s and 70s varieties of these are collectable, but are not fetching anywhere near as much as the enamel versions. However, they are becoming more collectable and now could be the time to start building a collection. As with all collectable items, condition plays an important role in the item's value.

▲ Robertsons jam jar label. (1965). (g-vg) £2 - £3

(Front)   (Reverse)

▲ Paper bag advertising Robertsons. (1980). Unused. (ex) £2 - £4

▲ Robertsons label (opposite side of jar). (1975). (f) £1 - £2

The paper golly was lodged behind these labels.

Ten paper gollies were affixed to the bags and then posted off to Robertsons. They then mailed out an enamel golly badge.

ROBERTSON'S GOLLIES (Enamel badges)

Enamel badges are the most desirable in the Robertson's range. Beware though, they were reproduced over the years and it's easy to be fooled if you haven't done your homework.

Backstamps have maker's names and are a helpful aid to verifying age and authenticity.

There's a very helpful website www.gollycorner.co.uk

▲ Footballer. Gomm. (1965). (vg) £10 - £12

▲ Cricketer. Fattorini. (1980). (vg) £5 - £7

▲ Hockey player. Fattorini. (1965). (vg) £10 - £12

▲ Golfer. Gomm. (1960). (vg) £12 - £14

▲ Tennis player. Fattorini. (1965). (vg) £8 - £10

▲ Bagpipes. Fattorini. (1970). £7 - £9

▲ Guitarist. Gomm. (1985). (vg) £5 - £7

▲ Skater. Miller. (1955). (g-vg) £16 - £20

▲ Tennis player. Miller. (1955). (g) £15 - £17

▲   Footballer. Fattorini. (1965). (vg) £8 - £10

▲ Golfer. Fattorini. (1970). (vg) £7 - £9

▲ Guitarist. Fattorini. (1965). (g-vg) £12 - £14

▲ Tennis player. Gomm. (1970). (g-vg) £8 - £10

▲ Standard. Gaunt. (1965). (vg) £12 - £14

ROBERTSON'S GOLLIES (Paper)

The paper gollies that were lodged behind the back label are also collectable. Some are harder to find than others. The paper golly (circa 1935) shown far right is hard to find.

▲ Standard. (1965). (vg) 50p - £1

▲ Cricketer. (1965). (vg) 80p - £1.20

▲ Timpanist. (1965). (vg) £1 - £1.50

▲ Golfer. (1965). (vg) £2 - £3

▲ Standard. (1935). (g) £8 - £10

▲ Accordionist. (1965). (vg) £1 - £1.50

▲ Bagpiper. (1965). (vg) £1 - £1.50

▲ Violinist. (1965). (vg) 70p - 90p

▲ Saxophonist. (1965). (vg) 80p - £1

▲ Cellist. (1965). (vg) £1 - £1.50

▲ Tennis Player. (1965). (vg) 70p - 90p

▲ Clarinettist. (1965). (vg) £1 - £1.50

▲ Footballer. (1965). (vg) £1 - £1.50

▲ Boxer. (1965). (vg) £2 - £3

▲ Skater. (1965). (vg) £1 - £1.50

▲ Lacrosse Player. (1965). (vg) £2 - £3

▲ Trombonist. (1965). (vg) £1.50 - £2

▲ Cymbalist. (1965). (vg) £1 - £1.50

▲ Guitarist. (1965). (vg) £1 - £1.50

▲ Hockey Player. (1965). (vg) £1 - £1.50

ROYALTY

Just about every large sized car boot sale will have some form of memorabilia relating to the Royal Family. This should tell its own story. There are heaps upon heaps of royal related collectables.

You are more likely to find pre-1950 ceramic bargains than later. The supply is still plentiful enough to be picky with your acquisitions.

Signed items are of particular interest.

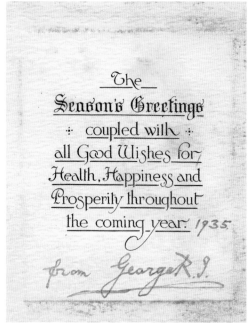

▲ King George V. Christmas card in fair condition. 1935. The signature is in clear blue ink. £300 - £350

▲ Coronation button badge. 1902. A rare example in very good condition. £15 - £20

◄ Thorne's Toffee Tin. A nice example in good condition for its age. (1925). HRH The Prince of Wales on lid. £15 - £20

▲ Queen Elizabeth II Coronation Souvenir Programme and ticket for procession viewing seat at Piccadilly (Stand 18, Block B). 2nd June 1953. £10 - £12

Monarchs of Great Britain

1702 - 1714	Anne
1714 - 1727	George I
1727 - 1760	George II
1760 - 1820	George III
1820 - 1830	George IV
1830 - 1837	William IV
1837 - 1901	Victoria
1901 - 1910	Edward VII
1910 - 1936	George V
1936 - 1936	Edward VIII
1936 - 1952	George VI
1952 -	Elizabeth II

ROYALTY

Official programmes for public events such as coronations and weddings are not sought after as much as private function publications. These are normally very small print runs and therefore the older they are, the less likely they are to have survived. This example here is a classic 'hard to find' piece of royal memorabilia. It is dated 20 June 1911 and was the programme and luncheon menu for the visit of King George V and Queen Mary to the Guildhall, London.

This was a seriously plush affair as the menu with its elegant silk ribbon menu will confirm. Lunch included Clear Turtle, Lobster Mayonnaise, Baron of Beef, Capons Stuffed With Ham, Hot Quails, Maltese Jelly and Ice Creams. The drinks list included Claret 1893, Cliquot Champagne 1900, Port 1896 and Courvoisier's Napoleon Brandy (80 years old).

Entertainment was provided by the Band of The Royal Regiment of Artillery.

Toasts: The King, The Queen (Mary), Queen Alexandra, The Prince of Wales and the other members of the Royal Family.

The programme/menu is in generally good condition. £30 - £40

Page 1

Pitkin Pictorials

Pitkin Pictorials was a publisher based in London, producing soft back books (approx 32 pages each) mainly 230 x 180mm size.

As well as publishing Royal Pictorial Souvenirs, they published the Pitkin "Pride of Britain" Series, which featured Cathedrals & Churches, Stately Homes, Famous Cities and Places.

Whilst fascinating and full of interesting photographs there's no great value to them.

▲ The Queen's Coronation Birthday Parade. 1953. 28 pages. (g-vg) £4 - £6

▲ Princess Margaret's Wedding Day. 1960. 36 pages. (g-vg) £3 - £4

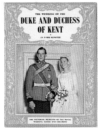

▲ Wedding of the Duke and Duchess of Kent. 1961. 36 pages. (g) £2 - £3

▲ Princess Anne First Souvenir book. 1950. 36 pages. (g) £3 - £4

▲ Princess Elizabeth's Wedding Day. 1947. 12 pages. (g-vg) £5 - £7

▲ Princess Alexandra's Wedding Day. 1963. 36 pages. (vg) £2 - £4

▲ Princess Margaret Wife and Mother. 1961. 36 pages. (f) £1 - £2

▲ Our Young Queen. 1953. 36 pages. (g) £3 - £4

ROYALTY - Postcards

Coronation of King George V

George V became King on 6 May 1910, upon the death of his father King Edward VII. George was crowned King on 22 June 1911 at Westminster Abbey, along with his beloved wife, who became Queen Mary.

George died on 20 January 1936 aged 70 and was buried at St. George's Chapel, Windsor Castle. He was succeeded by Edward VIII who then abdicated 11 months later.

▲ Souvenir (Faulkner) postcard. 1911. Coronation George V and Queen Mary. Postally unused. (vg) £6 - £8

▲ Coronation Procession Leaves Buckingham Palace. 1911. Beagles' postcard. Postally unused. (vg) £2 - £4

▲ Coronation Procession (Nearing Westminster). 1911. Rotary postcard. Postally unused. (vg) £1 - £2

▲ Coronation Procession Arriving At Westminster Abbey. 1911. Rotary postcard. Postally unused. (g-vg) £2 - £3

Coronation of King George VI

George ascended to the throne on 11 December 1936 and was crowned King on 12 May 1937 along with his wife, who became Queen Elizabeth.

▲ Crowning Ceremony in Westminster Abbey. 1937. Valentine's postcard. Postally unused. (vg) £2 - £3

▲ Coronation Procession at Victoria Memorial. 1937. Valentine's postcard. Postally unused. (vg) £2 - £3

Coronation of Queen Elizabeth II

Elizabeth became Queen upon the death of her father King George VI on 6 February 1952. As tradition dictated, her coronation was delayed whilst she and the rest of the country mourned the death of the King.

Her Coronation Day was 2 June 1953. It was the first coronation to be televised and became the first major international event to be broadcast live on television.

Outfits worn by the Royal Family were designed by Norman Hartnell. The ceremony was held at Westminster Abbey.

▲ Kneeling For Communion. 1953. Tuck's postcard. Postally unused. (vg) £2 - £3

► Coronation Scene. The Queen takes her seat in the Chair of State. 1953. Tuck's postcard. Postally unused. (vg) £2 - £3

ROYALTY - Charles & Diana

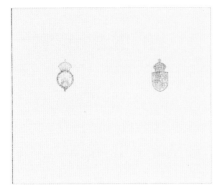

Front cover

Centre pages

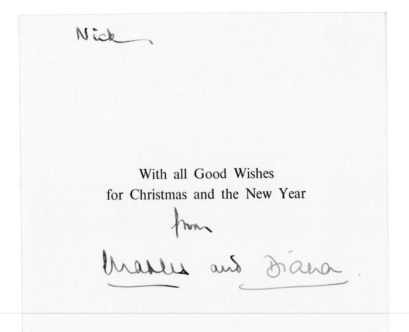

▲ Charles and Diana signed Christmas card. Clear, black and blue ink, 175 x 155mm. Dedicated. £500 - £550

ROYALTY - First day covers

▲ 25th Wedding Anniversary of Her Majesty The Queen. 20 Nov 1972. Stafford FDI postmark. Written address. (vg) 50p - £1

▲ The Royal Wedding. 22 Jul 1981. Gwynedd FDI postmark. Typed address. (ex) 50p - £1

▲ The Sixtieth Birthday of Her Majesty The Queen. 21 Apr 1986. Edinburgh FDI postmark. Typed address. (vg-ex) 50p - £1

▲ The Investiture of The Prince of Wales. 1 Jul 1969. Caernarvon FDI postmark. Typed address. (ex) 50p - £1

▲ The 40th Anniversary of The Accession. 6 Feb 1992. London FDI postmark. Typed address (Sunday Mirror Magazine). (ex) 50p - £1

▲ The Queen's Silver Jubilee Tour. 23 Jun 1977. West Glamorgan FDI postmark. Typed address. (vg) 50p - £1

▲ Royal Baby. 19 Jul 1982. Kingstown, St Vincent FDI postmark. No address. (vg-ex) £1 - £2

▲ 80th Birthday Her Majesty Queen Elizabeth The Queen Mother. 4 Aug 1980. Glamis Castle Forfar FDI postmark. Typed address. (vg-ex) 50p - £1

▲ Royal Baby. 12 Jul 1982. Charlestown, Nevis FDI postmark. No address. (ex) £1 - £2

▲ Commemorating the Wedding of HRH Princess Anne to Captain Mark Phillips. 14 Nov 1973. Horsham, Sussex FDI postmark. Typed address. (vg) 50p - £1

▲ Royal Baby. 14 Jul 1982. Funafuti, Tuvalu FDI postmark. No address. (ex) £1 - £2

▲ The Silver Jubilee of The Queen's Accession. 11 May 1977. Edinburgh FDI postmark. Written address. (vg) 50p - £1

▲ The Wedding of HRH The Prince of Wales. 22 Jul 1981. The Gambia, FDI postmark. No address. (g-vg) £1 - £3

▲ The Queen's Silver Jubilee Tour. 5 Aug 1977. Plymouth FDI postmark. Written address. (vg) 50p - £1

▲ Royal Wedding. 14 Nov 1973. Edinburgh FDI postmark. Typed address. (vg) £1 - £2

RUGBY

Rugby originally descended from a common form of football. Its origins are often disputed by historians but it is believed to have been developed by William Webb Ellis at Rugby School in 1823 (one of the oldest public schools in England, founded in 1567). The idea proved popular at Rugby School and the unnamed game spread to other areas of the country (albeit very slowly). In 1839, students at Cambridge University trialled the game, and they called it "Rugby's game". The game spread further round the country, including to most public schools in England. By the 1860s, there were two completely different types of football - handling and nonhandling.

The first Rugby Union was founded in 1871, and standard rules for the game were established. In 1895, there was a dispute between those who favoured strict amateurism of the game, and those who felt players should be paid as compensation for the time they had to take off work. This dispute resulted in the formation of the Northern Union (a breakaway body), which led to two separate sports - rugby league and rugby union (See Union or League?).

Rugby (both union and league) went on to become very popular sports throughout the world. Played in more than 100 countries, rugby has launched the careers of a number of incredibly successful sportsmen and has also been the subject of a number of fascinating collectables!

Over time, a wide range of collectables have been released to commemorate various rugby events and players. With such a wide amount of items available, it is probably best to focus your collecting to a specific theme - for example, focus all your attention on a particular club or country.

There have been many rugby collectables released that have a cross-category appeal (appealing to collectors of a separate area, as well as collectors of rugby memorabilia). For example, a range of First Day Covers have been released, which will appeal to First Day Cover collectors, as well as collectors of rugby memorabilia. A dual interest collectable such as this should be easier for you to sell as there will be a bigger market. The same principle applies to badges, beer mats, programmes, tickets, etc.

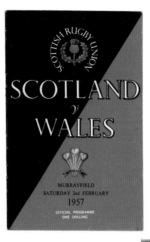

◄ Scotland v Wales programme. 2 February 1957. (vg) £3 - £5

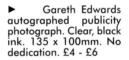

► Gareth Edwards autographed publicity photograph. Clear, black ink. 135 x 100mm. No dedication. £4 - £6

Union or League?

Rugby union and league initially had the same rules but they were soon changed. Although they both use the same prolate spheroid ball, they have become so different that they are now sometimes considered completely different sports. There are many differences with the rules and scoring systems, but the most noticeable difference is that rugby league sides include 13 players and rugby union sides include 15 players.

Rugby union is slightly more popular in the UK, with big names coming out of the sport including Will Carling and Jonny Wilkinson. Therefore, it could be argued that there is a bigger market for rugby union memorabilia, but both sports have a huge following so it shouldn't be too hard to find a buyer for memorabilia from either sport.

SAFE PLAQUES

When an old safe is broken up for scrap, the maker's name plaque is generally unscrewed from the door and saved. This is particularly the case when the plaque has an ornate design.

The majority of plaques over 100 years old, were made of brass.

Values today are influenced by condition, age and intricacy of the design.

It's an interesting collecting area with scope for investment potential. There's quite a thriving market on internet auction websites.

▲ Chipp Vine & Co. Safe plaque. (1900). 75 x 50mm. (vg) £7 - £9

▲ The Birmingham Safe Co. Safe plaque. (1900). 140 x 95mm. (vg) £16 - £18

SALT & PEPPER SHAKERS

Antique and upmarket fancy examples are generally referred to as 'condiment sets'.

Lower end collectors generally refer to them as 'salt and pepper shakers'. There are countless novelty variations.

▲ Playing card shakers. (1975). Ceramic. Unknown maker. (vg) £6 - £8

▲ Penguin salt and pepper shakers. (1965). Wood. Unknown maker. (f) £4 - £6

SCALEXTRIC

Fred Francis invented the track based slot car racing system in 1956. He had originally manufactured model racing cars, which he named Scalex. He added small electric motors to his cars and Scalextric became a massive success. Fred sold the business to Tri-ang in 1958.

▲ Scalextric third edition of the sales brochure. 1962. 275 x 210mm. 24 pages. (f) £5 - £7

◄ Scalextric model racing car. Police car with roof light. Model no. C.362. Not tested. Model (vg), box (f) £20 - £22

SCOUTS

In 1906, Robert Baden-Powell (a lieutenant in the British army) wrote a book for boys on the subject of scouting and reconnaissance. In 1907 he decided to test some of the theories he had written about in his book and he organised a camp at Brownsea Island (Dorset). The meeting was a success and Baden-Powell decided to progress the concept and he formed the Boy Scout Movement. It was originally restricted to boys aged between 11 and 18 years but in 1910 he extended the entry to younger boys via Cub Scouting. The popularity of scouting exploded worldwide and is, of course, still flourishing today. Baden-Powell died in 1941, aged 83.

▲ Robert Baden-Powell. Autographed postcard. Clear, black ink. No dedication. Postmarked South Kensington, 29 March 1905. (vg) £150 - £180

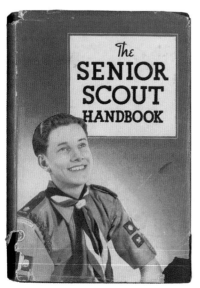

▲ The Senior Scout Handbook. Hardback book. 1949. 310 pages. (g) £4- £6

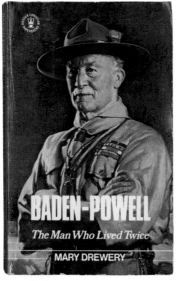

▲ Baden-Powell. The Man Who Lived Twice. Paperback book. 1975. (g-vg) £2 - £4

▲ Scout Movement Emblem. Car bar badge. (1985). 90mm diameter. (vg) £10 - £12

◄ Scout Camp real photograph. New Forest. 1948. (vg) £1 - £2

► Certificate of Merit. 1947. (vg) £1 - £3

SCOUTS - The Gang Show

The Gang Show was the brainchild of Ralph Reader.

Ralph was the son of a Salvation Army bandmaster. He joined the Boy Scouts at the age of 11 and when he later became a patrol leader he put on a show.

Having caught the entertainment bug, he moved to America and by the age of 21 had choreographed a Broadway show.

On his return to England, he maintained his link to the Scouts and in 1932 staged an all-Scout variety show at a London theatre. It was to become an institution.

In 1936 Ralph played the lead role in a feature film called 'The Gang Show'.

In 1937 Ralph and a group of The Gang Show Scouts became the first amateurs to appear in The Royal Variety Performance. On the show that night were a number of stars including George Formby, Gracie Fields and Max Miller.

In 1963 Ralph was the subject of the TV programme 'This Is Your Life' (hosted by Eamonn Andrews). Ralph died on 18 May 1982, aged 79.

▲ The Gang Show - 30th Year. EP record. 1962. Decca, DFE 8508. Vinyl (vg), cover (f-g) £6 - £8

This record was commissioned by Decca to mark the 30th anniversary of The Gang Show, a wonderful souvenir and tribute to Ralph Reader.

▲ Ralph Reader autograph (signed on a sheet music cover). Clear, blue ink, 160 x 120mm. No dedication. £40 - £50

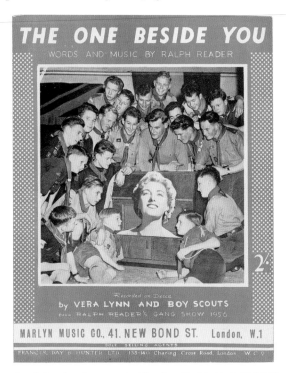

▲ Ralph Reader sheet music. 'The One Beside You'. 1957. The cover features Vera Lynn with Scouts from Ralph Reader's 1956 Gang Show. (vg) £3 - £5

▲ The Angel - The Gang Show. 45rpm single record. 1970. (Song written by Ralph Reader). Major Minor, MM764. Vinyl (vg), cover (vg) £3 - £4

SCOUTS - The Patrol Books

(153 x 122mm 36 pages)

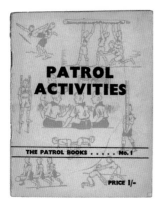

▲ Patrol Activities. No.1. 1951. (g) £4 - £6

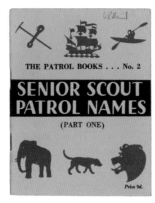

▲ Senior Scout Patrol Names. No.2. 1949. (vg) £3 - £5

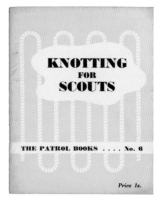

▲ Knotting For Scouts. No.6. 1956. (g-vg) £2 - £3

▲ More Knotting For Scouts. No.7. 1957. (vg) £2 - £4

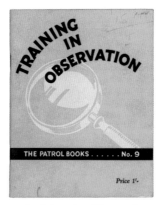

▲ Training In Observation. No.9. 1961. (g) £2 - £3

▲ Keeping Log Books. No.10. 1960. (g-vg) £2 - £3

▲ The Patrol Year. No.12. 1951. (g-vg) £6 - £8

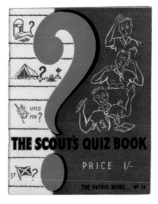

▲ The Scout's Quiz Book. No.14. 1962. (vg) £3 - £4

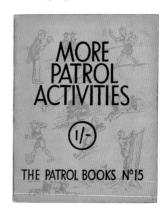

▲ More Patrol Activities. No.15. 1951. (g) £4 - £6

▲ Patrol Corners And Dens. No.16. 1954. (g-vg) £4 - £6

▲ Your Movement. No.20. 1956. (g-vg) £3 - £5

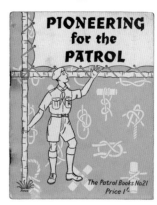

▲ Pioneering For The Patrol. No.21. 1959. (f-g) £1 - £2

SCRIPOPHILY

Scripophily is the collecting and research of old cancelled stock and bond certificates.

Historically (particularly at the end of the nineteenth century), companies issued attractively printed certificates in a bid to help maximise investment. These old certificates now offer a wealth of history and are often wonderful works of art. This is a fascinating collecting area and many examples can be purchased at reasonable prices.

Generally, the tip is to look out for certificates with interesting vignettes (pictorial designs that often fade gradually at the edges). Also look for specialist subject matter such as railroad construction, telegraphy, early aviation, mining, and electric power.

The hobby has international appeal, particularly in the USA, so the internet auction route is a useful marketing vehicle.

▲ Norfolk Estuary Company £50 share. 1847. 200 x 150mm. (g) £25 - £30

▲ San Antonio Land and Irrigation Company Ltd 10 shares. 1912. 285 x 190mm. (vg) £8 - £10

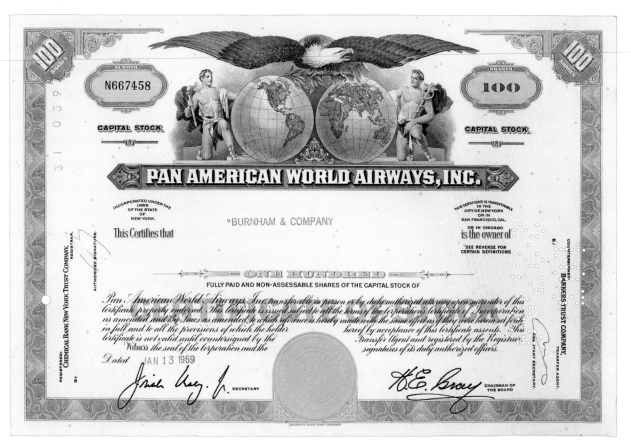

▲ Pan American World Airways 100 shares. 1969. 305 x 205mm. (vg) £16 - £18

SCRIPOPHILY

▲ $1000 certificate. The Philadelphia & Reading Railroad Company. 1882. 405 x 270mm. 4 pages. (g) £14 - £16

SHEET MUSIC

A big collection of old sheet music can build into a comprehensive work on popular entertainment spanning a 100 years period. Such a collection shouldn't cost a fortune.

Most sheet music features the artists who recorded the relevant songs, on the front covers. Often, it's a case of 'gone but not forgotten'.

▲ C'est Si Bon. (f) 50p - £1

▲ Put A Little Springtime. (f) £1 - £2

▲ Until You Fall In Love. (g) 50p - £1

▲ Say It Every Day. (f-g) £1 - £2

▲ To-Night You Belong To Me. (f-g) £1 - £2

▲ Don't Make A Memory Of Me. (f) £1 - £2

▲ You Belong To Me. (p-f) £1 - £2

▲ If You Love Me. (f-g) £1 - £2

▲ An Apple Blossom Wedding. (f) £1 - £2

▲ Friends And Neighbours. (g-vg) £1 - £2

▲ Confidentially. (g) £1 - £2

▲ Careless Hands. (g) £1 - £2

▲ Deep In The Heart Of Texas. (g-vg) £1 - £2

▲ I'll Remember April. (f) £1 - £2

▲ Light My Fire. (p) £2 - £3

▲ Forgotten. (g) £1 - £2

▲ Mona Lisa. (f-g) £1 - £2

▲ How About Me? (f-g) £1 - £2

▲ Bella Bella Marie. (p) £1 - £2

▲ I'm Sending My Blessings. (g) £1 - £2

▲ May The Good Lord Bless And Keep You. (f) 50p - £1

▲ Don't Let The Stars Get In Your Eyes. (f-g) £1 - £2

▲ Lazy River. (f) £2 - £4

▲ Life Is Nothing Without Music. (f) 50p - £1

▲ What More Can I Say. (f-g) £1 - £2

▲ Wake Up, Little Susie. (f) £1 - £3

SHEET MUSIC

▲ Dance Yourself Dizzy. (f) £2 - £3

▲ Just A Little Fond Affection. (f-g) £1 - £2

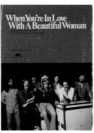

▲ When You're In Love With A Beautiful Woman. (p) £1 - £2

▲ The Theme From The Onedin Line. (f-g) £1 - £2

▲ Hi Ho Silver. (f-g) £1 - £2

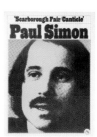

▲ Scarborough Fair (g) £2 - £3

▲ What Do We Care. (g) £1 - £2

▲ Meditation. (vg) 50p - £1

▲ More Than Ever. (g) 50p - £1

▲ You're In My Heart. (f-g) £2 - £3

▲ The Lamplighter's Serenade. (p) £1 - £2

▲ Love Theme From The Thorn Birds. (f) £2 - £3

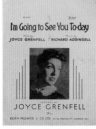

▲ I'm Going To See You To-day. (f) £1 - £2

▲ Love Is Blue. (f-g) £1 - £3

▲ Hors D'Oeuvre. (g) £1 - £2

▲ Poppa Piccolino. (f) £1 - £3

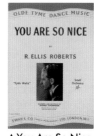

▲ You Are So Nice. (g) 50p - £1

▲ Breathless. (g) £1 - £2

▲ Pal Of My Cradle Days. (g) £1 - £2

▲ With These Hands. (g) £1 - £2

▲ How Deep Is Your Love. (g-vg) £2 - £3

▲ Yes, My Darling Daughter. (f-g) £1 - £2

▲ Lilli Marlene. (f) £1 - £2

▲ All My Love. (f) £1 - £2

▲ Hold My Hand. (f-g) £1 - £2

▲ Galway Bay. (p) £1 - £2

▲ On Top Of Old Smokey. (g) £2 - £3

▲ Down Forget-Me-Not Lane. (g) £1 - £2

▲ Oh! You Sweet One. (g) £1 - £2

▲ Burlington Bertie From Bow. (f) £1 - £2

SHEET MUSIC

▲ Howards' Way. (g) £1 - £2

▲ How Can You Buy Killarney? (g) £1 - £2

▲ When Bouzokis Played. (g-vg) £1 - £2

▲ Forgotten Dreams. (g-vg) £1 - £2

▲ The Northern Lights of Old Aberdeen. (g-vg) £1 - £2

▲ I've Got A Lovely Bunch Of Cocoanuts. (g) £2 - £4

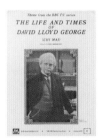

▲ The Life And Times Of David Lloyd George. (g-vg) £1 - £2

▲ Why Don't You Believe Me. (vg) £1 - £2

▲ Be Fair. (vg) £1 - £2

▲ Canadian Capers. (vg) £1 - £2

▲ Darling, Je Vous Aime Beaucoup. (vg) £1 - £2

▲ Happy To Be On An Island In The Sun. (vg) £1 - £2

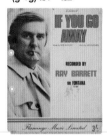

▲ If You Go Away. (p-f) £2 - £4

▲ Tennessee Waltz. (f) £1 - £2

▲ Matchstalk Men and Matchstalk Cats and Dogs. (g) £1 - £2

▲ My Son, My Son. (g) £1 - £2

▲ I Wish I Wuz. (vg) £1 - £2

▲ Oh, My Wonderful One Tell Me You're Mine. (g-vg) £1 - £2

▲ Zambezi. (f) £1 - £3

▲ The Petite Waltz. (f) £1 - £2

▲ The Little Shoemaker. (f-g) £1 - £2

▲ If I Ruled The World. (g) £1 - £2

▲ April In Portugal. (g-vg) £1 - £2

▲ Love's Old Sweet Melody. (f) £1 - £2

▲ The Gaucho Serenade. (f) £1 - £2

▲ Let The Rest Of The World Go By. (p-f) £1 - £2

▲ Beloved, Be Faithful. (f-g) £1 - £2

▲ Heart Of My Heart. (g) £1 - £2

▲ When You Hear Big Ben. (f) £1 - £3

▲ Velvet Moon. (g-vg) £1 - £2

SHOE POLISH

The obvious and easiest collectables to find are tins, which can often be sourced at car boots and on the internet. Advertising material such as enamel signs and boards are harder to find but a 'must' for anyone building a themed collection.

Original advertising postcards from 1904 - 1925 are of particular interest to people collecting shoe polish items.

Some of the most well known 'collectable' names are Cherry Blossom, Nugget, Wren and Kiwi.

▲ Berry's Boot Polish. Original advertising postcard. (1910). Postally unused. (vg) £10 - £12

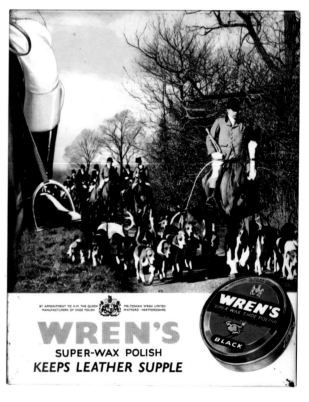

▲ Arpal boot polish tin. (1925). 70mm diameter. (g-vg) £7 - £9

▲ Wren's Puwite bottle. (1965). 95mm high. (g) £3 - £5

▲ Lane's boot polish tin. (1920). 60mm diameter. (vg) £7 - £9

▲ Lude boot polish tin. 70mm diameter. Made in China. (g-vg) 30p - 40p

▲ Wren's shoe polish. Tinplate advertising sign. (1960). 283 x 228mm. (g) £16 - £20

SNOOKER

The game of snooker was derived from billiards. The first World Snooker Championship was held in 1927. The game was dominated by Joe Davis until his retirement in 1946.

In 1969, the game was given a massive boost when BBC2 television used the sport to show off the potential of colour television. They called the programme 'Pot Black' and it became a big hit with the viewing public. The rest, as they say, "is history".

▲ Pot Black. BBC paperback. 1981. (vg) £1 - £2

Alex Higgins

The modern game of snooker owes much to Alex Higgins. His play was so fast; he acquired the nickname 'Hurricane'. His presence at the table was electric. He was an entertainer extraordinaire. He was World Champion in 1972 and 1982. Sadly, his new found fame and wealth was to lead to his demise. He became more famous for his addictions to alcohol and marijuana rather than his snooker skills. His inevitable death came in 2010.

◄ Alex Higgins autograph. Clear, blue ink, 125 x 75mm. No dedication. £30 - £40

► Alex Higgins. 1979. Card (160 x 120mm) from the Edito series. (vg) 40p - 60p

Dennis Taylor

On 29 April 1985 Dennis Taylor and Steve Davis had one of the most memorable snooker matches of all time. Over 18 million TV viewers witnessed Dennis winning the world championship with a dramatic last ball victory.

Dennis was born in Northern Ireland in 1949. He first became interested in the game when he was only eight years old. He turned professional in 1971. He beat the legendary Alex Higgins in 1982 to win his first major tournament.

Now retired from the professional circuit, Dennis concentrates on match commentating for BBC Television. He is also a seasoned after-dinner speaker and has appeared on numerous TV programmes including Strictly Come Dancing.

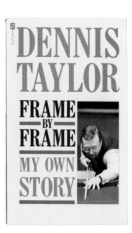

▲ Dennis Taylor. Frame By Frame My Own Story. Paperback book. 1986. (vg) £1 - £2

SNOOPY

Snoopy is a character from the long-running comic strip Peanuts. The comic was created by Charles M Schulz, and ran from 2 October 1950 until 13 February 2000 (the day after Schulz passed away following complications from colon cancer). While Snoopy started out as a rather ordinary beagle under the guardianship of Charlie Brown, he quickly developed some odd character traits and arguably became the strip's biggest star. He became something of a daydreamer, and he could often be found in dark sunglasses, hanging out at the Student Union under the alias "Joe Cool", or battling the Red Baron in desperate aerial combat (his own doghouse standing in for a plane). He also thought of himself as an author, and was always working on his great American novel, with the well-known opening line, "It was a dark and stormy night".

Those of us interested in collecting Peanuts (or specifically Snoopy) merchandise have a lot to keep us busy. As well as 17,897 comic strips, Charlie Brown and the gang appeared in television advertisements, books, several television shows, and more than 30 very memorable feature-length TV specials. The cute and comical nature of the characters also means they lend themselves well to general merchandising (much like Jim Davis's comic feline, Garfield), and there is a huge range of statues, stuffed toys, and games to be hunted down.

▲ Snoopy, Top Dog. Coronet paperback. 1982. (f-g) £1 - £2

▲ Snoopy china pencil holder. (1975). 70mm high. (g-vg) £2 - £3

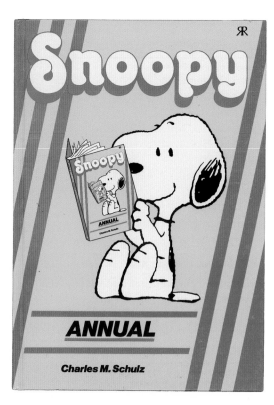

▲ Snoopy Annual. 1992. (vg) £2 - £3

▲ Snoopy McDonald's toy. 1999. 70mm high. (vg) 60p - 80p

SOAP

There's more to this subject than meets the eye. Products include soap bars for human body use, soap pads for washing-up, soap for washing clothes, etc....

Collecting areas include soap wrappers, advertising, soap powder boxes and bars of soap (including novelty shapes).

▲ Borax. Advertising Showcard. (1900). 220 x 195mm. (g-vg) £20 - £24

▲ Samphire Iodine Toilet Soap. Packet with the original (unused) soap bar. J.C. & J. Field, London. (1935). (vg) £8 - £10

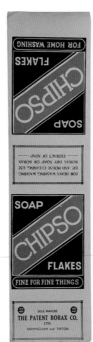

▲ Borax Extract of Soap. Label (for fine powder soap packet, for home laundries). (1900). 430 x 131mm. Unused. (vg) £3 - £4

◄ Chipso. Borax Co. Label for Chipso Soap Flakes packet. (1920). 440 x 112mm. Unused. (vg) £3 - £4

The Patent Borax Company was founded back in 1870 by Birmingham businessman Arthur Robottom.

▲ Morny soap dish. Plastic. Empty. 90 x 50mm. Commemorating the wedding of Charles and Diana. £2 - £4

▲ Hudson's Soap enamel advertising sign. (1910). 250 x 175mm. (f) £80 - £90

SOAP

Sunlight
Lever Brothers

Sunlight was the soap that began the phenomenal success of Lever Brothers.

The business was created by William Lever and his brother, James in 1884. Their formula for 'Honey Soap' was an instant hit and in 1885 the name was changed to 'Sunlight Soap'. It was the world's first branded and packaged laundry soap.

The soap was advertised widely, as a labour-saving device for housewives.

Marketing included a promise of a £1000 reward to any person who could prove that the soap contained "any harmful adulterant whatsoever". In addition to this, all shopkeepers were authorised to refund the purchase price to "anyone finding cause for complaint".

Instructions for use included the advice to shred the soap, which when mixed with water, created "rich, active suds". In 1899, Sunlight Soap boxes carried advertising for a new version of the soap, "You know the wonderful qualities of Sunlight Soap, NOW try Lever's NEW Sunlight Flakes". A year later, Lever's changed the name of Sunlight Flakes to 'Lux'.

With a rapidly expanding demand for the Lever Brothers products, the original factory at Warrington was quickly outgrown and manufacturing was switched to a new factory situated in 56 acres of land, located between New Ferry and Lower Bebington, on the Wirral Peninsula. Lever Brothers treated their employees with much respect and they built a village to house their employees. Facilities included a school, a church, a swimming pool and a concert hall.

The village was given the name 'Port Sunlight'. By 1920, the population had grown to 3,500.

Port Sunlight became widely famous. It was even celebrated by a West End musical (Gaiety Theatre) called 'The Sunshine Girl' starring the popular pin-up Phyllis Dare.

In August 1962, Ringo Starr made his first appearance as The Beatles new drummer, at a gig in Port Sunlight.

▲ Original pack of Sunlight Soap. 1899. With original unused soap (twin bars). (f-g) £10 - £14

(front)   (reverse)

▲ Advertising leaflet for Sunlight Soap. (1905). 155 x 104mm. (g-vg) £3 - £5

(front)   (reverse)

▲ Sunlight Soap leaflet. (1905). 155 x 111mm. (g) £3 - £4

◀ Book Mark. (1900) Advertising Sunlight Soap and other products. (g) £4 - £5

Interestingly, the advertisement text endorses the status of women at that time; "linen washed the Sunlight way will make a man look well and show the world that his laundress is up with the times".

SODA SYPHONS

The big names are Schweppes and Sparklets (BOC Ltd). However, there are plenty of makers to choose from (1910 - 1950) and the more obscure names (example: Barker & Son) are what collectors look for.

Soda syphons are also known as 'seltzer bottles'. Their purpose is to dispense carbonated or soda water.

▲ Sparklets Soda Tablets. Empty bottle. (1970). (g) £1 - £2

◄ ▲ Sparklets Soda Syphon. (1980). Plus various accessories, including 'charger'. Not tested but looks unused. (vg) with original box (f) £6 - £8

SOOTY

Sooty the bear first appeared in the stage routines of part-time magician Harry Corbett. The puppet was an instant hit, and in 1952 he appeared on television for the first time. At that time Sooty was completely yellow, but soot was put on his ears and nose to make him show up better on black and white television, hence his name. The closing words of each show, "bye bye everyone, bye, bye," became an institution.

Sooty never spoke, but he would "whisper" in Harry's ear in order to let him know what he was thinking. The cheeky bear would often experiment with magic, using the magic words "izzy wizzy let's get busy" as he waved his magic wand around, and he was also a keen xylophone player.

Sooty was later joined by a collection of other characters, including Sweep (a dog who communicated through squeaks), Soo (a panda), Kipper (a cat), Butch (another dog), Ramsbottom (a snake), Enry (a robot), Cousin Scamp (another bear), Miki (a Brazilian cat), and Maggie (a mouse).

Harry suffered a heart attack in 1975. He made a full recovery, but was unable to continue the show, so his son, Matthew, took over.

Sadly, Harry (who incidentally, was the nephew of fish and chip magnate Harry Ramsden), died in 1989. Matthew retired in the late '90s, but Sooty has continued to appear on television, and several shows are currently in production.

Over the years, the show has generated a huge amount of merchandise, much of which is now growing in collectability.

▲ Sooty ceramic egg cup. (1960). Sooty Concessions. (vg) £12 - £15

▲ Sooty Annual. 1964. (g) £4 - £6

SPARK PLUGS

Spark plugs have to go down as one of those obscure collecting areas that most people will have difficulty understanding. That is until you start delving into this vital component that has kept billions of vehicles on the road around the world.

There's a wonderful history to the spark plug. Early vehicle manufacturers were challenged to find a material for the core of the plug, one that would be capable of withstanding extreme vibration and heat. The answer rested with the mineral sillimanite which was added to porcelain. Albert Champion took advantage of this discovery, and the rest as they say, is history.

There are hundreds of varieties of spark plug and therefore lots of scope for the collector. Of particular interest are examples in their original (good condition) boxes and even better are those in tins.

▲ Champion Spark Plugs Enamel Sign. (1995). 200mm x 100mm. (vg) £6 - £8

▲ Champion Plugometer. Unused in original box. With original (colourful) instruction leaflet.(1960). (vg) £10 - £12

▲ Lodge. HNP. Unused spark plug. (1965). Box (f-g) £2 - £3

▲ Champion Spark Plug. (1960). Empty box (vg) £2 - £4

▲ AC Fire Ring Spark Plug. Unused. 45X1S. (1960). Box (f) £1 - £2

▲ CO-OP Spark Plug. Unused. C56H. USA. Box (vg-ex) £4 - £6

▲ Wipac Spark Plug. Unused. P10. (1955) Box (g) £2 - £4

▲ Dynamic Spark Plug. Unused. 10M. (1965). Australia. Box (g). £2 - £3

◄ NGK Spark Plugs. Cloth badge. (1980). 75mm diameter. (vg) £2 - £3

◄ KLG Spark Plugs. Unopened pack of four. FE 65P. (1965). Box (g-vg) £12 - £14

▲ NGK Spark Plug. Unused. BP6HS. (1995). Box (ex) £1 - £2

▲ Surefire Spark Plug. Unused. 8SP4376. (1975). Box (f) £1 - £2

▲ Autolite Spark Plug. Unused. AE62. (1980). Box (g-vg). £1 - £2

▲ KLG Spark Plug. Unused. PF50. (1965). Box (g) £2 - £3

▲ Lodge Spark Plug. Unused. C14. (1935). Box (g) £8 - £10

▲ Marchal Spark Plug. Unused. CR20C. (1960). France. Box (f) £3 - £5

SPEEDWAY

Introduced in the United Kingdom in 1928, the sport was an instant success. Early tracks included Belle Vue, Manchester and Perry Barr, Birmingham.

1947 was deemed a 'boom time' for the sport with more tracks licensed than ever before and many licence applications denied. Vic Duggan was the star rider. Jeff Lloyd set a new transfer fee record at £1000 (Newcastle to New Cross). A record crowd figure of 90,000 was set at Wembley's Empire Stadium.

Mass popularity of the sport declined with the advent of the television era in the mid-1950's. However, a core set of supporters have kept the sport well and truly alive.

Enamel badges, posters, autographs, old programmes and tickets are amongst the items sought after by collectors.

▲ Speedway News. Feb 1948. Staple rusting but otherwise in good condition. £4 - £6

▶ Wolves pennant. 1980. (vg) £3 - £5

▲ ▶ World Speedway Championship Final. Wembley Stadium, 13 Sep 1969. (g). Plus admission ticket. (ex) £5 - £7

▶ Wimbledon Supporters annual membership card. 1947. (g) £15 - £18

◀ Speedway Graphic. Vol 1. No.2. 1963. (g-vg) £3 - £4

Enamel badges

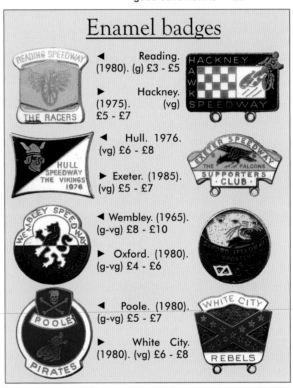

◀ Reading. (1980). (g) £3 - £5

▶ Hackney. (1975). (vg) £5 - £7

◀ Hull. 1976. (vg) £6 - £8

▶ Exeter. (1985). (vg) £5 - £7

◀ Wembley. (1965). (g-vg) £8 - £10

▶ Oxford. (1980). (g-vg) £4 - £6

◀ Poole. (1980). (g-vg) £5 - £7

▶ White City. (1980). (vg) £6 - £8

Speedway programmes

▲ Coventry v Southampton. 15 Jun 1963. (g) £2 - £3

▲ Long Eaton v Sheffield. 12 Apr 1966. (vg) £3 - £4

▲ Harringay. Wembley Coronation Cup. 22 Aug 1953. (g) £6 - £8

▲ Odsal v Wembley. 4 Oct 1947. (f) £10 - £12

▲ Poole v Oxford. 4 Aug 1958. (g) £3 - £4

▲ Belle Vue. 100 Guineas Trophy (final). 11 Oct 1952. (g) £7 - £9

▲ Halifax v Hackney. 21 May 1966. (vg) £3 - £4

▲ Newport v Swindon. 14 Jun 1968. (g) £1 - £3

▲ Southampton v Swedish Touring Team. 23 Jun 1959. (g) £2 - £3

▲ Hackney v Swindon. 26 May 1967. (g) £1 - £2

▲ Oxford v Edinburgh. 16 Jun 1966. (g) £1 - £3

▲ Wolves v Coventry. 18 Apr 1969. (f-g) £1 - £2

SPOONS

Apart from being an everyday utensil, the humble spoon is collected by the drawer full.

The British Museum houses a variety of ancient examples.

Antique collectors concentrate on old silver spoons and indeed some command decent sums. It really is a case of having to do your homework on this subject if you are thinking about investing in old and valuable spoons.

At the bottom end of the market, souvenir spoons are very popular. These feature events, people and places. They are generally purely decorative objects.

Wooden spoons are collected under the 'kitchenalia' banner.

Spoons are played as a musical instrument. They featured in several variety hall acts. Former Doctor Who actor Sylvester McCoy has mastered the art of playing the spoons.

▲ Commonwealth Games. Brisbane 1982. Souvenir spoon. (ex) £3 - £4

▲ Caravan Club. Souvenir spoon. (ex) £2 - £3

▲ SAAB. Promotional spoon. (vg) £2 - £3

Uri Geller

Uri Geller made his name by bending spoons using merely his mental prowess. Some sceptics passed the phenomenon off as 'sleight of hand magic'. Whatever the case, he made a fortune from this entertainment.

▲ Uri Geller. Autographed publicity photograph. Clear, black ink. 152 x 98mm. Dedicated. £4 - £6

Uri Geller was born on 20th December 1946 in Tel Aviv. He owns a 1976 Cadillac car which has hundreds of pieces of cutlery affixed to the outside bodywork. His good friend, the late Michael Jackson, was best man at Uri's renewal of wedding vows ceremony in 2001.

◄ Art & Humour (Souvenir Spoon) postcard. Postmarked Great Yarmouth Oct 1928. (g) £2 - £4

► Bulldog Souvenirs. Christchurch spoon. Unopened pack. £1 - £2

▲ Rare Breeds Survival Trust. Souvenir spoon. (vg) £1 - £2

▲ Harrods. Silver plated souvenir spoon. (g-vg) £1 - £3

▲ Arun Lifeboat. Silver plated souvenir spoon. (ex) £1 - £2

◄ Severn Valley Railway. Souvenir spoon. (g-vg) £1 - £2

► Thames Television. Promotional spoon. (g) £2 - £3

◄ Swanage Souvenir tea caddy spoon. (g) £1 - £2

► Worthington Shops. 1938 Commemorative tea caddy spoon. (g) £3 - £4

▲ Wilson's promotional spoon. (1935). Wilson's Café, North End, Croydon. One of these spoons would have been used by a customer at the table, to scoop tea leaves into a teapot before the addition of hot water. (vg) £6 - £8

STAR WARS

Young visionary George Lucas, bloody, beaten, but unbowed by intense levels of stress during production, finally released his "space opera" in the summer of 1977. Escalating production costs during the shoot had pushed the budget from an agreed $8million to $11million. Most of the crew didn't "get" the movie and hadn't taken it seriously. Mark Hamill was involved in a car accident, and the resulting facial injuries he received meant reshoots had not been possible. Harrison Ford thought the movie was weird, and claimed the dialogue was unspeakable. It looked like it was going to be a disaster.

It wasn't.

Fast-forward 40 years, and you would be hard-pressed to name a more influential movie, or one that has spawned such an epic franchise. Seven movies, one "Holiday Special", various spin-off movies about the Ewoks, and several cartoon series have generated a wealth of memorabilia, both old and new, and where to begin a collection is often daunting.

Name something – anything – and it is more than likely to have been made with Star Wars branding at some point. There are computer and video games, books, comics, graphic novels, pencil sharpeners, notebooks, chess sets, board games, bubble bath, pencils, watches, mugs, action figures, and more. It can be a baffling minefield, and there is plenty of fake memorabilia out there to trick the unwary collector, but the wealth of options available gives a perfect opportunity to create a fun, themed collection.

▲ Star Wars R2-D2 telephone. 2005. Unused in original box. (mnt) £40 - £50

The original series of action figures, produced by Kenner from 1977 until 1985, are generally considered to be the most interesting and most desirable Star Wars merchandise. Find a collector of Star Wars memorabilia and he or she is sure to have at least one Kenner figure somewhere.

Commonly referred to as the 3 3/4inch scale figures, this fantastic range of toys offered over 100 posable heroes and villains, plus lots of oddly out-of-scale vehicles and playsets, enabling a whole generation of children to recreate their favourite movie scenes.

Of course, as with many toys, it is becoming increasingly difficult to find good condition examples. The figures were often played with until they broke, and then they were discarded. Those that have survived are generally missing their accessories, have faded, or have limbs that have worked loose. For this reason, collecting the action figures can be quite a task, and you may need deep pockets to get a complete set.

▲ Star Wars Weekly. Marvel comic. No.8. 29 Mar 1978. (vg) £8 - £10

STOCKINGS

Yet another affordable collecting area (and one that has investment potential as well).

The era we are concentrating on is 1960 to 1980 (due to the packaging). The more attractive the package image and the better the condition of the pack (preferably with the original contents intact and unopened), the greater the value.

Some packages have no images but do have the manufacturers name or logo. These are still collectable but normally less desirable.

Even in the relatively short time span of thirty years, many of the illustrations and pictures portray changing fashion styles and form their own little piece of social history.

Places to find them include charity shops, web auctions, boot sales and collectors' fairs. You could try an offer on a large quantity (assuming the seller has a stock) and maybe walk away with a really good deal.

▲ Two-Way S.T.R.E.T.C.H. One Size. (1965). Unopened. (vg) £10 - £12

▲ Wolford. Plain. Austria. (1965). Unopened. (vg) £8 - £10

▲ Exquisite Nylons. (1960). Unopened. (vg) £8 - £10

▲ Kayser Extra Top. (1975). Unopened. (vg) £3 - £4

▲ Gay-Gal by Dorothy Vernon stockings. (1960). Unopened. (vg) £8 - £10

▲ Dora. Non-run tights. (1970). Unopened. (vg) £6 - £8

SWEET CIGARETTE PACKETS

They began around 1910 as sticks of chocolate and packaged as 'chocolate cigarettes'. Early manufacturers included Fry's. Around 1940 they evolved into white sugary sticks and then in the 1950's and 1960's they became hugely popular, with a proliferation of branded products, many of which related to TV shows of the era. Some examples being Primrose Confectionery's Popeye, Dad's Army, Joe 90 and Z Cars, all of which examples also included series of trade cards given away in the packs (another collecting subject).

Some of the 'cigarettes' had red tips to resemble the lit end and at one point Kane Products offered 10 Navy Cut Cigarettes in packs that resembled a pack of real cigarettes.

In the 1980's the 'politically correct brigade' persuaded the Government to ban the sale of sweet cigarettes because they encouraged children to take up smoking. Manufacturers were forced to re-name the product as 'Candy Sticks'.

The body of the packet is known as the 'hull' and the inside die-cut card holder for the cigarettes is known as the 'slide'. Collectors of sweet cigarette packets prefer examples with both hull and slide.

▲ Superman. Empty packet with slide. Primrose Confectionery. 1966. (vg) £35 - £40

▲ Popeye. Empty packet with slide. Primrose Confectionery. (1965). (vg) £8 - £10

▲ Wise Cracks. Empty packet, no slide. Barratt. (1965). (g-vg) £12 - £14

Sweet cigarette packet fronts

▲ Play Cricket. (g) £2 - £3

▲ Gold Flake (g-vg) £3 - £4

▲ William Tell. (vg) £3 - £4

▲ Cadet. (vg) £4 - £5

▲ Adventurer. (g) £3 - £4

▲ Space Patrol. (vg) £5 - £6

▲ Tom and Jerry. (vg) £2 - £3

▲ Treasure Island. (vg) £4 - £5

TAX DISCS
(Velology)

Collectors have been busily building collections since approximately 1960, however, the serious market in tax discs has only developed since 1995.

The collecting of, and study of tax discs and vehicle excise licensing is known as velology.

When the Government announced that tax discs would be abolished in October 2014, the interest in collecting old expired tax discs increased. The rarest examples have now acquired price tags of £1000+.

The requirement to display a tax disc on a motor vehicle became law in 1920 and the first tax disc expired in March 1921. The tax disc was effectively proof of purchase of the licence. This was not the beginning of motor vehicle licensing, it had been in place since the earliest days of the motor vehicle and before that, licences were required to keep and use horse drawn carriages on the public highway. Indeed, from October 2014 the requirement to keep motor vehicles licensed, remained unchanged.

Collectors are particularly interested in rare issues and also tax discs with intact selvedge (the paper surrounding the perforations of the disc) because the majority of motorists religiously tore around the perforations of the disc and discarded the selvedge. This means that the few discs that remain in existence with their selvedge intact can have significant added value.

The condition of tax discs is of crucial importance to collectors. Very good examples are in the minority, for the simple and obvious reason that tax discs were not always torn carefully from the selvedge and then they were exposed to the sun for the valid period of the licence.

The tax discs in this book are generally in very good condition and therefore the values are at the high end.

▲ September 1921. Quarterly. Paper residue reverse, one hole punch and two other small holes but otherwise very good. £1000 - £1200

▲ 1921 Annual. Paper residue reverse. (g) £750 - £850

▲ March 1922 Quarterly. (vg) £1000 - £1200

——————— ADVERTISEMENT ———————

TRADE AND COLLECT

TAX DISCS

A COLLECTICUS BOOK

TRADE AND COLLECT TAX DISCS

100 page book (limpback)

Full colour throughout

This is believed to be the most comprehensive book ever published on the subject of expired tax discs. A goldmine of information.

Price £4.95

Order from: Collecticus

Tel: 01380 811750

Internet: www.collecticus.co.uk

By post: Collecticus, P.O.Box 100, Devizes, Wiltshire, SN10 4TE

(Cheques/Postal Order's payable 'Hartley Publications Ltd')

TAX DISCS

▲ Sept 1922 Quarterly. Small hole. (g-vg) £1000 - £1200

▲ 1922 Annual. Paper residue reverse. (g-vg) £700 - £900

▲ Mar 1923 Quarterly. Staple holes. (vg) £1000 - £1200

▲ 1923 Annual. Staple holes. (vg) £700 - £900

▲ Sept 1924 Quarterly. Small hole, damage to reverse. (g) £600 - £800

▲ Sept 1925 Quarterly. Paper residue reverse. (vg) £900 - £1100

▲ Dec 1925 Quarterly. Affixed to paper. (g) £600 - £800

▲ 1925 Annual. (vg) £500 - £600

▲ Jun 1926 Quarterly. Staple holes, Paper residue reverse. (vg) £400 - £500

▲ Sept 1926 Quarterly. (vg) £400 - £500

▲ Dec 1926 Quarterly. (vg) £350 - £450

▲ Jun 1927 Quart. Paper residue reverse, small hole. (g-vg) £350 - £400

▲ 1928 Annual. (vg) £200 - £300

▲ Jun 1929 Quarterly. Affixed to paper. (g-vg) £250 - £350

▲ Sept 1929 Quarterly. (vg) £250 - £350

TAX DISCS

▲ Mar 1930 Quarterly. (g-vg) £150 - £200

▲ Jun 1930 Quarterly. (g-vg) £150 - £200

▲ Jun 1931 Quarterly. (g-vg) £150 -£200

▲ 1931 Annual. (vg) £80 - £100

▲ Sept 1932 Quarterly. (vg-ex) £80 - £100

▲ 1932 Annual. (g-vg) £60 - £80

▲ Mar 1933 Quarterly. (g-vg) £80 - £100

▲ Jun 1933 Quarterly. (vg) £100 - £120

▲ Jun 1934 Quarterly. (g) £60 - £70

▲ Dec 1934 Quarterly. (g) £60 - £70

▲ Sept 1935 Quarterly. (g-vg) £60 - £80

▲ 1935 Annual. (g) £50 - £60

▲ Mar 1936 Quarterly. (g-vg) £80 - £100

▲ 1936 Annual. (g-vg) £60 - £70

▲ Jun 1937 Quarterly. (vg-ex) £80 - £100

▲ Sept 1937 Quarterly. (g-vg) £60 - £80

▲ Jun 1938 Quarterly. (vg-ex) £80 - £100

▲ 1938 Annual. (vg-ex) £70 - £90

▲ Jun 1939 Quarterly. (vg-ex) £60 - £80

▲ 1939 Annual. (g-vg) £50 - £70

TAX DISCS

▲ Mar 1940 Quarterly. (vg-ex) £100 - £120

▲ 1940 Annual. (vg-ex). £80 - £100

▲ Mar 1941 Quarterly. (vg) £80 - £100

▲ 1941 Annual. (vg-ex) £80 - £100

▲ Mar 1942 Quarterly. (g-vg) £70 - £90

▲ Sept 1942 Quarterly. (g) £60 - £80

▲ Sept 1943 Quarterly. (g-vg) £80 - £100

▲ 1943 Annual. (vg) £70 - £90

▲ Dec 1944 Quarterly. (g-vg) £100 - £120

▲ 1944 Annual. (g-vg) £80 - £100

▲ Jun 1945 Quarterly. (g) £70 - £90

▲ 1945 Annual. (g-vg) £60 - £80

▲ Mar 1946 Quarterly. (g-vg) £80 - £100

▲ Sept 1946 Quarterly. (g-vg) £90 - £110

▲ Mar 1947 Quarterly. (vg-ex) £100 - £120

▲ Dec 1947 Quarterly. (vg-ex) £100 - £120

▲ Jun 1948 Quarterly. (vg-ex) £90 - £110

▲ 1948 Annual. (g-vg) £60 - £80

▲ Mar 1949 Quarterly. (g-vg) £80 - £100

▲ 1949 Annual. (g-vg) £60 - £80

TAX DISCS

▲ Jun 1950 Quarterly. (g-vg)
£50 - £70

▲ Sept 1950 Quarterly.
(g-vg) £50 - £70

▲ Mar 1951 Quarterly. (vg)
£70 - £90

▲ 1951 Annual. (vg-ex)
£60 - £80

▲ Mar 1952 Quarterly. (vg)
£60 - £80

▲ Dec 1952 Quarterly. (vg)
£60 - £80

▲ Sept 1953 Quarterly. (vg)
£60 - £80

▲ 1953 Annual. (vg-ex)
£50 - £60

▲ Jun 1954 Quarterly. (vg)
£60 - £80

▲ 1954 Annual. (g-vg)
£40 - £60

▲ Mar 1955 Quarterly.
(vg-ex) £50 - £70

▲ Jun 1955 Quarterly. (vg-ex)
£50 - £70

▲ Jun 1956 Quarterly. (vg)
£40 - £60

▲ Sept 1956 Quarterly.
(vg-ex) £50 - £70

▲ Sept 1957 Quarterly. (vg)
£40 - £50

▲ Dec 1957 Quarterly. (vg)
£40 - £50

▲ Sept 1958 Quarterly. (vg)
£40 - £50

▲ 1958 Annual. (vg-ex)
£40 - £50

▲ Sept 1959 Quarterly.
(vg-ex) £50 - £70

▲ 1959 Annual. (vg-ex)
£40 - £50

TAX DISCS

▲ Mar 1960 Quarterly. (vg) £10 - £12

▲ Jun 1960 Quarterly. (vg-ex) £14 - £16

▲ Sept 1960 Quarterly. (vg) £10 - £12

▲ 1960 Annual. (vg-ex) £8 - £10

▲ Jan 1961. (g) £14 - £16

FEB 61
▲ Feb 1961. (f-g) £1000 - £1200

▲ Apr 1961. (vg) £100 - £150

▲ May 1961. Staple holes. (g) £50 - £60

▲ Aug 1961. (g-vg) £200 - £300

▲ Sept 1961. (vg) £100 - £150

▲ Nov 1961. Paper residue reverse. (g-vg) £300 - £400

▲ Jan 1962. (vg-ex) £150 - £200

▲ Feb 1962. (vg) £40 - £50

▲ Mar 1962. (g) £20 - £30

▲ Apr 1962. (g) £30 - £40

▲ Jun 1962. (g) £40 - £50

▲ Aug 1962. (g-vg) £80 - £100

▲ Sept 1962. (vg) £40 - £60

▲ Oct 1962. (vg) £100 - £140

▲ Nov 1962. (g) £150 - £200

▲ Jan 1963. (vg) £60 - £80

▲ Feb 1963. (g) £100 - £140

▲ Mar 1963. (g) £70 - £90

▲ Apr 1963. Paper residue reverse. (g-vg) £80 - £100

▲ May 1963. (g-vg) £60 - £80

▲ Jun 1963. (g-vg) £80 - £100

▲ Aug 1963. Paper residue reverse (vg) £60 - £80

▲ Sept 1963. (g-vg) £40 - £50

▲ Oct 1963. (vg) £70 - £90

▲ Nov 1963. Writing on reverse. (g) £60 - £80

▲ Dec 1963. (vg-ex) £12 - £14

▲ Jan 1964. (vg-ex) £14 - £16

▲ Feb 1964. (g-vg) £30 - £40

▲ Mar 1964. (vg) £40 - £50

▲ Apr 1964. (vg) £40 - £50

▲ May 1964. (vg) £10 - £12

▲ Jun 1964. (g) £8 - £10

▲ Jul 1964. (g) £12 - £14

▲ Aug 1964. (g) £20 - £30

▲ Sept 1964. (vg) £10 - £12

▲ Oct 1964. (vg) £20 - £30

▲ Nov 1964. (g) £8 - £10

▲ Dec 1964. Paper residue reverse (vg) £8 - £10

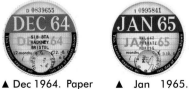
▲ Jan 1965. (vg) £8 - £10

▲ Feb 1965. (vg) £10 - £12

▲ Mar 1965. (vg) £10 - £14

▲ Apr 1965. (g-vg) £8 - £10

MAY 65
▲ May 1965. Paper residue reverse. (vg) £7 - £9

TAX DISCS

▲   Jun   1965.
(g-vg) £5 - £7

▲   Jul   1965.
(vg) £7 - £9

▲ Aug 1965. Paper
residue   reverse.
(g-vg) £6 - £8

▲   Sept 1965.
(vg) £5 - £7

▲   Oct   1965.
(vg-ex) £6 - £8

▲   Nov   1965.
Damage to reverse.
(g-vg) £4 - £6

▲ Dec 1965. (vg)
£4 - £6

▲ Jan 1966. Paper
residue   reverse.
(g-vg) £6 - £8

▲ Feb 1966. (vg)
£6 - £8

▲ Mar 1966.
(vg) £16 - £20

▲ Apr 1966. (vg)
£5 - £7

▲   May 1966.
(vg) £6 - £8

▲   Jun   1966.
(vg-ex) £8 - £12

▲ Jul 1966. (vg)
£6 - £8

▲   Aug 1966.
(vg) £5 - £7

▲ Sept 1966.
(vg) £5 - £7

▲ Oct 1966. (vg)
£12 - £14

▲   Nov   1966.
(vg-ex) £14 - £18

▲ Dec 1966. Paper
residue   reverse.
(vg-ex) £6 - £8

▲ Feb 1967. (vg)
£7 - £9

▲   Mar 1967.
(vg) £8 - £10

▲   May 1967.
(vg) £4 - £6

▲ Jun 1967. (vg)
£5 - £7

▲ Jul 1967. (vg)
£12 - £14

▲   Sept   1967.
(vg-ex) £12 - £16

▲ Oct 1967. (vg)
£10 - £12

▲   Nov   1967.
(g-vg) £8 - £10

▲ Dec 1967. (vg)
£4 - £6

▲   Jan 1968.
(vg) £8 - £10

▲ Feb 1968. (vg)
£8 - £10

▲   Mar 1968.
(vg-ex) £10 - £12

▲ Apr 1968. Paper
residue   reverse.
(vg-ex) £8 - £10

▲   May 1968.
(g-vg) £12 - £14

▲   Jun   1968.
(g-vg) £12 - £14

▲   Jul   1968.
(vg-ex) £12 - £16

▲ Oct 1968. (g)
£18 - £22

▲   Nov   1968.
(vg) £12 - £14

▲   Dec   1968.
(g-vg) £7 - £9

▲ Jan 1969. Paper
residue   reverse.
(vg) £10 - £12

▲ Feb 1969. (vg)
£12 - £14

▲ Apr 1969. Paper
residue   reverse.
(vg-ex) £14 - £16

▲   May   1969.
(g-vg) £6 - £8

▲ Jun 1969. (vg)
£14 - £16

▲   Jul   1969.
(vg-ex) £16 - £18

▲   Sept 1969.
(vg) £10 - £12

▲ Oct 1969. (vg)
£12 - £14

▲ Nov 1969. Paper
residue reverse. (vg)
£18 - £22

▲   Dec   1969.
(vg) £12 - £14

TAX DISCS

▲ Jan 1970. Paper residue reverse. (vg) £6 - £8

▲ Mar 1970. Paper residue reverse. (g) £8 - £10

▲ Apr 1970. Paper residue reverse. (vg) £7 - £9

▲ Jun 1970. (vg) £6 - £8

▲ Nov 1970. (vg-ex) £15 - £20

▲ Feb 1971. (vg-ex) £10 - £12

▲ May 1971. (vg - ex) £12 - £14

▲ Aug 1971. Paper residue reverse. (vg) £12 - £14

▲ Nov 1971. (vg-ex) £15 - £20

▲ Mar 1972. (ex) £12 - £14

▲ Aug 1972. (vg-ex) £20 - £22

▲ Sept 1972. Staple holes. (vg) £12 - £14

▲ Nov 1972. (vg-ex) £12 - £14

▲ Dec 1972. (g) £4 - £6

▲ Jan 1973. (vg-ex) £10 - £12

▲ May 1973. Staple holes. (vg-ex) £15 - £18

▲ Aug 1973. Paper residue reverse. (vg) £18 - £22

▲ Oct 1973. (vg) £12 - £14

▲ Nov 1973. (vg) £8 -£10

▲ Apr 1974. Staple holes. (g) £4 - £6

▲ Jun 1974. (vg) £16 - £18

▲ Aug 1974. (g-vg) £14 - £16

▲ Oct 1974. Staple holes. (g-vg) £16 - £18

▲ Jan 1975. (g) £22 - £24

▲ Feb 1975. (vg-ex) £22 - £24

▲ May 1975. (vg) £22 - £24

▲ Sept 1975. (vg-ex) £26 - £30

▲ Oct 1975. (vg-ex) £26 - £30

▲ Nov 1975. (vg-ex) £22 - £26

▲ Feb 1976. (vg-ex) £24 - £26

▲ May 1976. (vg-ex) £24 - £26

▲ Jun 1976. (vg-ex) £18 - £22

▲ Sept 1976. (vg) £18 - £22

▲ Oct 1976. (vg-ex) £14 - £18

▲ Feb 1977. (g-vg) £8 - £10

▲ Mar 1977. (vg) £8 - £10

▲ Apr 1977. (vg) £6 - £8

▲ May 1977. (vg-ex) £8 - £10

▲ Sept 1977. (vg) £10 - £12

▲ Oct 1977. (g-vg) £18 - £22

▲ Nov 1977. (g-vg) £18 - £22

▲ Jan 1978. (g) £60 - £70

▲ Feb 1978. (g) £80 - £100

▲ Mar 1978. (vg) £80 - £100

▲ Apr 1978. (vg) £80 - £100

▲ May 1978. (vg) £20 - £24

▲ Jun 1978. (vg-ex) £22 - £26

▲ Jan 1979. (vg) £4 - £6

TAX DISCS

▲ Jan 1980. (vg) £10 - £12	▲ Feb 1980. (vg-ex) £10 - £12	▲ Mar 1980. (vg-ex) £10 - £12
▲ Apr 1980. (vg-ex) £10 - £12	▲ May 1980. (vg) £8 - £10	▲ Jun 1980. (vg-ex) £10 - £12

▲ Jul 1980. (vg-ex) £14 - £16	▲ Aug 1980. (vg-ex) £12 - £14	▲ Sept 1980. (vg) £8 - £10
▲ Oct 1980. (vg-ex) £8 - £10	▲ Nov 1980. (vg-ex) £12 - £14	▲ Dec 1980. (g-vg) £6 - £8

▲ Jan 1981. (vg-ex) £12 - £14	▲ Feb 1981. (ex) £10 - £12	▲ Mar 1981. (ex) £14 - £16
▲ Apr 1981. (ex) £12 - £14	▲ May 1981. (vg-ex) £12 - £14	▲ Jun 1981. (g-vg) £6 - £8

▲ Jul 1981. (vg) £8 - £10	▲ Oct 1981. (vg) £10 - £12	▲ Nov 1981. (vg) £6 - £8
▲ Dec 1981. (vg) £6 - £8	▲ Jan 1982. (vg) £12 - £14	▲ Feb 1982. (vg) £12 - £14

▲ Mar 1982. (vg-ex) £16 - £18	▲ Apr 1982. (vg) £12 - £14	▲ May 1982. (vg-ex) £20 - £26
▲ Jun 1982. Paper residue reverse. (vg) £6 - £8	▲ Jul 1982. (vg) £14 - £18	▲ Aug 1982. (ex) £16 - £18

▲ Sept 1982. (vg) £10 - £12	▲ Oct 1982. (vg) £10- £12	▲ Nov 1982. (g-vg) £8 - £10
▲ Dec 1982. (g-vg) £8 - £10	▲ Jan 1983. (ex) £10 - £14	▲ Feb 1983. (ex) £10 - £14

▲ Mar 1983. (vg) £8 - £10	▲ Apr 1983. (vg-ex) £10 - £14	▲ May 1983. (vg) £10 - £12
▲ Jun 1983. (vg) £10 - £12	▲ Jul 1983. (vg) £4 - £6	▲ Nov 1983. (vg-ex) £6 - £8

▲ Jan 1984. (ex) £10 - £14	▲ Feb 1984. (ex) £10 - £14	▲ May 1984. (vg) £10 - £12
▲ Jul 1984. (vg-ex) £10 - £14	▲ Aug 1984. (ex) £12 - £16	▲ Dec 1984. (ex) £12 - £16

TAX DISCS

▲ Jan 1985. (g-vg) £4 - £6

▲ Feb 1985. (ex) £10 - £12

▲ Mar 1985. (g-vg) £7 - £9

▲ Apr 1985. (vg-ex) £10 - £12

▲ May 1985. (g) £16 - £18

▲ Jun 1985. (vg) £16 - £18

▲ Jul 1985. (vg) £4 - £6

▲ Oct 1985. (g-vg) £6 - £8

▲ Nov 1985. (g-vg) £8 - £12

▲ Dec 1985. (g-vg) £6 - £8

▲ Feb 1986. (vg) £6 - £8

▲ Mar 1986. (vg-ex) £7 - £9

▲ May 1986. (vg) £12 - £14

▲ Jun 1986. (vg) £12 - £14

▲ Jul 1986. (vg) £4 - £6

▲ Aug 1986. (vg) £6 - £8

▲ Sept 1986. (vg) £7 - £9

▲ Oct 1986. (vg) £12 - £14

▲ Nov 1986. (vg) £4 - £6

▲ Dec 1986. (vg) £4 - £6

▲ Jan 1987. (vg-ex) £7 - £9

▲ Feb 1987. (ex) £10 - £12

▲ Mar 1987. (vg-ex) £10 - £12

▲ Apr 1987. (vg) £8 - £10

▲ May 1987. (g-vg) £8 - £10

▲ Jun 1987. (vg) £8 - £10

▲ Jul 1987. (g-vg) £4 - £6

▲ Aug 1987. (vg) £6 - £8

▲ Sept 1987. (vg) £6 - £8

▲ Oct 1987. Staple hole. (vg) £8 - £10

▲ Nov 1987. (vg) £8 - £10

▲ Dec 1987. (vg) £7 - £9

▲ Mar 1988. (vg) £8 - £10

▲ May 1988. (g-vg) £12 - £14

▲ Jun 1988. (vg-ex) £10 -£12

▲ Jul 1988. (vg) £4 - £6

▲ Aug 1988. (vg) £6 - £8

▲ Sept 1988. (ex) £6 - £8

▲ Oct 1988. Staple hole. (vg) £4 - £6

▲ Nov 1988. (g-vg) £3 - £4

▲ Jan 1989. (vg) £6 - £8

▲ Feb 1989. (g-vg) £3 - £4

▲ Mar 1989. Staple hole. (vg-ex) £4 - £6

▲ May 1989. (vg) £3 - £5

▲ Jun 1989. Staple hole. (g-vg) £4 - £6

▲ Sept 1989. (ex) £5 - £7

▲ Nov 1989. (vg) £4 - £6

▲ Dec 1989. Staple hole. (vg-ex) £4 - £6

TEAPOTS

These have been made in Great Britain and around the world for several hundred years, so there's plenty of scope for serious antique collectors to search out truly valuable examples.

At the lower end of the market is the modern novelty teapot and there's a plentiful supply of ingenious creations. They can be quite difficult to date, particularly because there have been many imports from around the world.

Given the huge supply, the novelty teapot collector should be patient and only select unmarked and unchipped examples.

The problem with the building of a teapot collection is that they take up a lot of space and they require regular cleaning and to cap it all, they are fragile.

Many of the modern novelty examples are not suitable for making tea, they are merely ornaments. The weight of a full pot of tea would be too much for many.

There is another side to novelty teapots and that's the classic pots made by the Staffordshire potteries from the early 1800's to the mid - 1950's. Some of these, including Clarice Cliff creations, make decent money.

Away from the novelty pots there's some demand for standard British teapots. The Staffordshire pottery firm 'Gibsons' is an example of a classic manufacturer of 1950's pots that could be found in many homes.

▲Playing Cards. Novelty teapot. South-West Ceramics. 1990. (g-vg) £10 - £12

▲Cottage Restaurant. Novelty teapot. Unknown maker. (2005). (vg) £3 - £4

◄ Small teapot. Gibsons. (1955). 90mm high. (vg) £15 - £20

Some people equip and decorate their kitchens to a retro theme. An old teapot becomes essential and because they are not too difficult to find in good condition, they can be used and replaced if accidentally broken.

Even if you are not going to the extreme of a retro kitchen, just having a lovely 50 year old teapot that is used occasionally, can spark conversation and is a great way to enjoy a collectable.

Low value novelty teapots can be found at many car boot sales. More desirable and therefore, more expensive examples can be found at most large collectors' fairs.

▲Wise Owl. Novelty teapot. Unknown maker. (2005). (g) £1 - £2

TETLEY TEA FOLK

The animated Folk were a big hit with audiences, securing their place in the history books as one of the best-loved of advertising characters (along with characters such as the Cadbury's Smash alien robots), and they were put to good use not only on television, but as premiums issued free with the tea. It is these premiums that form the bulk of the merchandise collectors are now seeking.

One of the loveliest aspects of the Tetley merchandise is that there is something to suit the tastes of almost everyone. Tetley have released small plastic figurines for children, tiny collectable teapots and "houses" made from resin, drinks coasters, and even teapots and cookie jars. Whatever your interests, and whatever your budget, it is almost certain there will be some Tea Folk branded merchandise that fits the bill.

Of course, much of the merchandise will never be worth much money, but there is a good chance some of it will, particularly the beautiful ceramic products that are still manufactured by Wade. As always, the best advice is to keep an eye out for boxed items in good condition, as these will offer you the best chance of making a profit should you sell them later on.

GAFFER

The "Doc" of the Tetley crew. Was voiced in the television adverts by talented British actor Brian Glover until his death in 1997.

◄ Gaffer plastic figurine. (g) 50p - £1

SYDNEY

An unofficial "right hand man". A little dopey, and quite often making mistakes, but always first to get the kettle on.

► Sydney plastic figurine. (g-vg) 50p - £1

GORDON

Like all the Tea Folk, Gordon's first passion is a nice cuppa, but he is also a keen gardener.

◄ Gordon plastic figurine. (g) 50p - £1

MAURICE

The resident "fix-it" man with a pencil permanently stuck behind his ear. When he's puzzling over how to complete his latest invention, it's no surprise that a cup of tea is always on the cards.

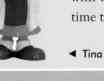

► Maurice plastic figurine. (g) 50p - £1

TINA (TEANA)

The only girl in the mix. Always ready with biscuits and cakes; the perfect tea time treats!

◄ Tina plastic figurine. (vg) 50p - £1

CLARENCE

The 'Waker-Upper' who ensured other tea folk got to work on time.

► Clarence plastic figurine. (g) 50p - £1

ARCHIE

Quite often referred to simply as "Nephew", Archie is the youngest member of the team. He doesn't actually work for Tetley, he's still at school, but he enjoys visiting and having a brew with everyone else.

◄ Archie plastic figurine. (g) 50p - £1

THEATRE

There's a wealth of history and plenty of collectables associated with the theatre. Programmes, posters, tickets, autographs, postcards, records, photographs etc....

Sybil Thorndike

Dame Sybil Thorndike was a celebrated Shakespearean actress. Born in 1882, she began her career as a pianist but suffered piano cramp and switched career to acting. She was the subject of 'This Is Your Life' in 1960. She died aged 93 in 1976.

▲ Sybil Thorndike hardback book. By T C Trewin. (1955). (f-g) £1 - £2

▲ Princes Theatre London programme. 1927. (f) £3 - £5

▲ Sybil Thorndike autograph. Clear, blue ink, 150 x 100mm. No dedication. £25 - £30

Piccadilly Hayride

Piccadilly Hayride was a revue that ran from 1946 - 1948 at the Prince of Wales Theatre, London. It featured Sid Field. The cast included popular comedian Terry Thomas and The Ross Sisters (a dancing and singing act from the USA). Veda Ross married top British entertainer Dickie Henderson.

◄ Piccadilly Hayride. Programme (1948). (f-g). Plus sheet music (g) of the Ross Sisters song from the show 'Five Minutes More'. £3 - £4

Glossary

BURLESQUE - A drama or musical with a comic undertone, often ribald and bordering the ridiculous. American roots.

MELODRAMA - an over-the-top drama whereby the action is deliberately exaggerated.

MUSIC HALL - A predominantly British form of entertainment, the forerunner of variety. Included speciality acts such as juggling, magic, dancing dogs etc... The term took its name from the establishments in which the shows were performed.

REPERTORY - Plays, ballets and operas performed by a theatrical company at short regular intervals.

REVUE - A show performed by multiple entertainers featuring music, dance and sketches.

VARIETY - A mix of various types of entertainment in one show.

VAUDEVILLE - A British version of burlesque.

Paul Eddington

Although better known as a TV actor, Paul Eddington (born 1927 in London) was an accomplished theatrical actor.

Prior to his successful roles in the TV shows The Good Life and Yes Minister, he spent 25 years treading the boards.

Paul died of skin cancer in 1995.

► Paul Eddington autograph. Clear, black ink, 150 x 100mm. No dedication. £10 - £12.

◄ Theatre Royal, Bristol, programme. Becket. 1962. Paul Eddington played the role of King Henry in this Bristol Old Vic production. (g) £2 - £3

(Front)   (Page 4)

THEATRE - Programmes

This is a great collecting theme as programmes are not too space consuming and they can be purchased inexpensively.

Thanks to so many people keeping the programmes from their visits to the theatre, the supply is plentiful. In fact, there are so many available that the collector can afford to be choosy.

As with all collectables, condition is important. However, what you really need to look out for are autographs on old programmes. The bigger the star, the more desirable, and of course, the more valuable.

You could consider collecting to a theme, such as pre-1950 pantomimes or maybe programmes from theatres that have since been closed down.

Pop groups appeared at grand theatres throughout the sixties era in variety shows. Find something like The Honeycombs on the Morecambe & Wise Show in Blackpool, you could be looking at £4 - £6 in good condition and, if signed by the group, it could be as much as £40 - £60.

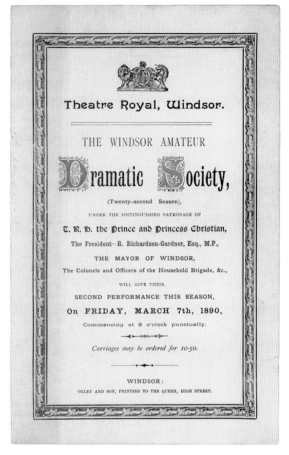

▲ Theatre Royal, Windsor. Friday 7 March 1890. (g) £20 - £25

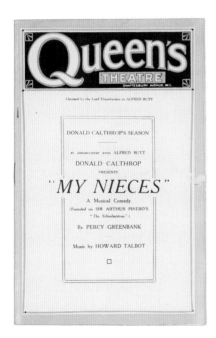

▲ Queen's Theatre, Shaftesbury Avenue, London. 1921. Cast included Binnie Hale. (f-g) £8 - £9

▲ Chiswick Empire, London. Variety Show. 1951. Featured Issy Bonn. (g) £3 - £4

▲ Palace Theatre, Shaftesbury Avenue, London. 1947. A Bernard Delfont Production. (g) £2 - £4

THEATRE - Programmes

The Theatre Royal, Haymarket. London is the third oldest London playhouse that is still in operation. It dates back to 1792.

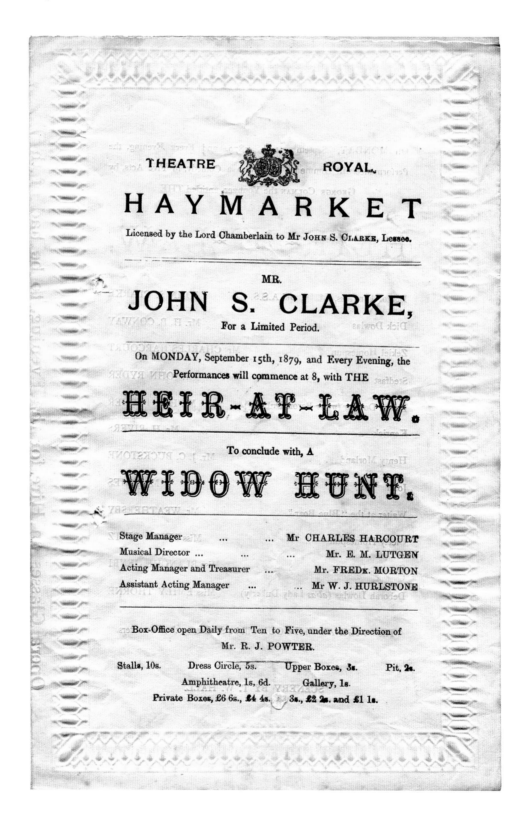

▲ Theatre Royal, Haymarket, London programme. September 1879. 240 x 153mm. The cast included John S. Clarke, Charles Harcourt and Blanche Henri. (g) £25 - £30

THEATRE - Postcards

▲ Comic postcard. The Empire Theatre. Postmarked Southampton 22 Apr 1913. Message in ink. (g-vg) £10 - £12

▲ Promotional postcard. Fox Theatre, Detroit, USA. (1920). Postally unused. (vg) £4 - £6

▲ The London Coliseum. Tuck's postcard. (1905). Postally unused. (g-vg) £6 - £8

▲ Promotional postcard. Touring theatrical act. (1910). Postally unused. (g) £5 - £7

▲ New Gaiety Theatre, The Strand, London. Postmarked Luton 6 Aug 1908. Message in ink. (f-g) £6 - £8

THIMBLES

The earliest known example is a Roman thimble, found in Pompeii, that dates back to the first century AD. Collecting thimbles is now a common hobby, and collectors are often referred to as digitabulists.

Thimbles have been popular collectables for decades and consequently have been used as marketing tools to promote seaside resorts and commerce. Some commemorate particular events such as royal coronations.

They are ideal to buy and sell as they take up little space, they are light to post (although good packaging is essential), and they don't break the bank.

Another plus factor is that thimbles often have dual collecting value.

Look out for them at car boot sales; you have a good chance of finding little gems in boxes of 'junk.'

▲ Niagara Falls souvenir. (1990). (vg) 20p - 30p

▲ Prince Andrew wedding souvenir. 1986. (vg) 60p - 80p

▲ The Sun Edwina Currie promotion. 1989. (vg) £1 - £2

▲ Dudley Museum souvenir. (1985). (vg) 20p - 30p

TIMPO

The Timpo Company was created in 1938 by Sally Gawrylovitz - The Toy Importers Company.

(Box)

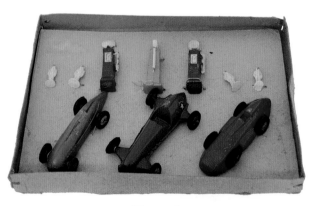

(Contents)

▲ Timpo Racing Set. (1948). Diecast, full set in very good condition. Complete with original box (g) £200 - £250

TINS

This is one of those collecting areas that not only has plenty of crossover subject matter but can also serve as ornaments to be displayed in the home. Perhaps a shelf full of old tins in the kitchen.

▲ National Dried Milk. (1945). (180 x 110mm). Empty. £10 - £12

▲ Lavendo. Silicone Lavender Wax. (1965). 90 x 25mm. Empty. (vg) £6 - £8

▲ Barker & Dobson. Regal Fruit Drops. (1965). 155 X 100 x 35mm. Empty. (g) £4 - £6

▲ Beech-Nut. Chewing gum. Hard to find retailer's tin. (1950). 135 x 115 x 90mm. Empty. (f) £25 - £30

▲ The Ivy Series. Drawing Pins. (1960). 80 x 55 x 20mm. Empty. (g-vg) £3 - £4

▲ Bibbings' I.D.L Tooth Powder. (1920). 70 x 25mm. Empty. (g) £8 - £12

TOAST RACKS

Rather an obscure collecting subject. A large collection would require a lot of valuable storage space. Ceramics are prone to damage. Early examples or novelty items are the highest on collectors' lists.

The average kitchen may already have at least one toast rack in its inventory and there would certainly be no harm in adding a nice collectable for the fun of it and for regular use.

▲ Marmite. Cleverly shaped ceramic to resemble a row of Marmite jars. (2010). (ex) £5 - £7

▲ Clover. Seven Dwarfs toast rack. (1995). (vg) £10 - £12

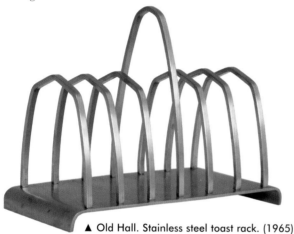

▲ Old Hall. Stainless steel toast rack. (1965) £6 - £8

▲   Hovis ceramic toast rack. Carlton Ware. (1985). 110 x 50 x 70mm. (vg) £8 - £10

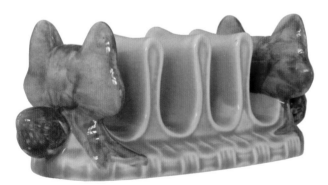

▲ Shorter & Son ceramic toast rack. (1950). (vg) £10 - £12

▲   Gemma crested china. (Ayr). Miniature toast rack. 70 x 40 x 50mm. (1960). (vg) £4 - £6

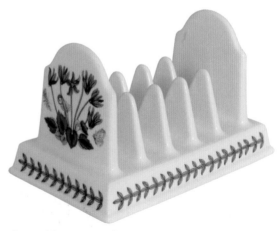

▲ Portmeirion toast rack. Botanic Garden series. Ceramic. (2010). (ex) £10 - £14

TOBACCIANA

▲ Wills' Woodbines button badge. (1960). 32mm diam. (vg) £6 - £8

As the name implies, 'tobacciana' relates to just about anything relating to the tobacco industry.

There's plenty of scope for collectors and social historians. Until the 1970's, smoking was portrayed by tobacco companies as a healthy pursuit.

In 1786 Henry Overton Wills and his partner, Mr Watkins, founded a new tobacco importing and cigarette manufacturing company. Mr Watkins retired in 1789, and William Day Wills and Henry Overton Wills took over from their father in 1826. The company first assumed the name of W.D. & H.O. Wills in 1830. The company was responsible for many well known brands, including Bristol, Three Castles, Woodbine, and Embassy. In 1901, it merged with seven other British tobacco companies to form the Imperial Tobacco Company.

▲ Ogdens Battle Axe. Boxed tobacco bar. (1965). Unopened (ex) £8 - £10

Thomas Ogden established his first tobacco shop in Park Lane, Liverpool, in 1860. By the time of his death, in 1890, the company had expanded to the point where it was operating from six different factories and warehouses. At that time it was one of the largest tobacco companies in Britain. Ogden's was a big name in the industry until ceasing production in 1962. Memorabilia relating to the company (including an extensive range of cigarette cards) is in demand.

▲ Woodbine matchbook. (1965). (g) £3 - £4

▲ Bristol matchbook. (1960). (g) £4 - £5

▲ Abdulla matchbook. (1965). (f-g) £2 - £3

▲ Marlboro matchbook. (1970). (g) £1 - £2

▲ Salem matchbook. (1975). (g) 60p - 80p

TOBACCIANA - Tobacco tins

Just like most collectables, the condition of a tobacco tin will help determine the value. The problem is that they easily scratch and once this happens, they are normally damaged forever. If you are lucky enough to find a good example at a car boot, the first thing you need to do is cover it with a protective wrapping.

To attribute a specific date to a tobacco tin can be quite tricky, therefore we have given just a rough guide by decade.

▲ The Greys. Major Drapkin & Co. (1920-1930). 50 tin. 140 x 75mm. (g) £8 - £10

▲ Ogden's Sliced. Walnut Plug. (1910-1920). 80 x 55mm. (f) £6 - £8

▲ Edgeworth. 1900-1910. 80 x 55mm. (g) £16 - £20

▲ Mitchell's Prize Crop. (1920-1930). 50 tin. 165 x 80mm. (f) £4 - £6

▲ Player's Whiffs. 1940-1950. 12 tin. 130 x 95mm. (g-vg) £8 - £10

▲ Marcovitch Red & White. 1960-1970. 90 x 75mm. (vg) £2 - £4

▲ Rhodian No.3. (1930-1940). 30 tin. 115 x 75mm. (f) £6 - £8

▲ Melachrino. (1900-1910). 100 tin. 150 x 75mm. (p-f) £14 - £16

▲ Salmon & Gluckstein's Dandy Fifth. (1890-1900). 50 tin. 170 x 80mm. (p-f) £24 - £28

TOBACCIANA - Ashtrays

▲ Bristol Cigarettes. Ceramic. (1965). 220 x 180mm. (vg) £16 - £20

▲ Craven A. Ceramic. (1960). 120mm. (g-vg) £6 - £10

▲ Players brass ashtray. (1960). 115mm. (vg) £6 - £8

▲ Wills's Star. Ceramic. (1955). 95mm. (vg) £14 - £18

▲ State Express King Size 555. Ceramic. (1965). 230mm. (vg) £7 - £9

▲ Wills's Golden Flake. Glass. (1950). 120mm. (f) £10 - £12

TOFFEE HAMMERS

Toffee hammers are relatively easy to find at car boot sales and collectors' fairs, and they have long term investment potential. Look out for hammers from companies that are no longer in business as these can be very desirable and are likely to fetch a good sale price.

▲ Williams's Toffee. Liverpool. (1930). 188mm long. (vg) £15 - £20

▲ Walters Palm Toffee. (1950). 158mm long. (g) £8 - £10

▲ Radiance Toffee. (1930). 95mm long. (g) £10 - £12

▲ McCowans Toffee. (1980). 105mm long. (vg) £2 - £4

▲ Blue Bird Toffee. (1970). 105mm long. (g-vg) £2 - £3

▲ Walkers Toffee. (1980). 105mm long. (vg) £2 - £3

▲ Sharps Toffee. (1965). 110mm long. (g) £3 - £5

Blue Bird Toffee

Blue Bird toffee was founded by Harry Vincent in 1898. The toffee was originally called Harvino, but Harry changed the name after watching a play entitled The Blue Bird of Happiness.

TOILET

A pursuit since the beginning of the human race. Not the most popular of collecting areas, as you may imagine. Nevertheless, there are some interesting collectables out there, if you look hard enough.

◄ Bronco toilet roll. (1960). Unopened packet. (f-g) £4 - £5

▲ Bamforth comic postcard. Postmarked Newcastle-On-Tyne, 13 Aug 1941. Message in ink. (f-g) £3 - £5

► Miniature matchbox. China (1970). Advertising Red Lantern toilet paper. 45 x 30mm. (g) 20p - 30p

TOKENS

In the 16th, 17th and 18th centuries, tokens were issued by banks, due to shortages of currency. Collectors grade them like coins.

There are of course, plenty more tokens to collect, promotional, gaming etc....

◄ Irish Bank Token. Thirty Pence. 1808. (f) £30 - £40

(Obverse) (Reverse)

Irish bank tokens

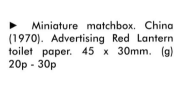

In 1804 the Irish Bank issued token coins of various denominations. A thirty pence token coin was issued in 1808. The reverse featured the portrait of George III and the obverse a seated figure of Hibernia, with the words 'BANK TOKEN' split either side.

TOUR PROGRAMMES

The market for old tour programmes is somewhat limited as collectors tend to mainly be the fans and enthusiasts who support particular artistes. Consequently, it's a case of finding the right buyer, willing to spend the right money. For example, the 1989 Aerosmith tour programme is a collectable gem and worth about £15 - £20 in good condition, but of virtually zero interest to a member of the Des O'Connor fan club.

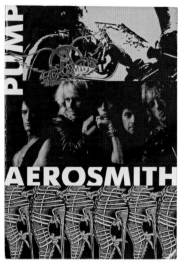

▲ Aerosmith UK Tour Programme. 1989. 415 x 295mm. (g) £4 - £8

▲ Magnum. European (Wings of Heaven) Tour. 1988. 305 x 305mm. (vg) £4 - £6

▲ Bruce Springsteen. Born in the USA Tour. 1984. 355 x 285mm. (g) £4 - £6

▲ Cliff Richard. 20th Anniversary Tour. 1978. 300 x 210mm. (vg) £3 - £5

▲ Meat Loaf. 20/20 World Tour. 1987. 335 x 240mm. (g) £3 - £4

▲ Grateful Dead. European Tour Programme. 1990. 300 x 300mm. (g-vg) £5- £8

▲ Foreigner. Agent Provocatour. 1985. 305 x 225mm. (vg) £3 - £4

▲ Prince. Nude Tour. 1990. 355 x 280mm. (g-vg) £5 - £7

▲ Siouxsie And The Banshees. 1981. 315 x 245mm. (g) £4 - £6

▲ Eric Clapton. European Tour Programme. 1995. 280 x 280mm. (g-vg) £4 - £8

▲ Foster & Allen. Souvenirs Tour. 1990/91. 295 x 210mm. (vg) £1 - £3

▲ Neil Young. Transworld Tour. 1982. 295 x 210mm. Back page cut out. (g) £3 - £5

▲ Cliff Richard. Gospel Concert Tour. 1984. Signed by Cliff Richard. 295 x 210mm. (g) £5 - £8

TRADE CARDS

Trade cards follow the same concept as cigarette cards. They were given away with the product. Trade cards generally refer to cards that were given away with any product or service, other than cigarettes.

(Front)

(Reverse)

▲ Weetabix trade card. No.10 of 25. 1959. (vg) 20p - 30p

(Reverse)

(Front)

Cardmaster is an interesting quirk for trade card collectors. Back in the 50's and 60's a buyer inserted a 3d coin into a vending machine to buy three cards, with a piece of chewing gum being given away free with them. Albums were also available (by postal application) and these are now quite hard to find.

◀ Jet Aircraft of The World. No.3 of 100. The Master Vending Machine Co. (g) 30p - 40p.

J Bibby & Sons (TRex)

In 1955, J Bibby & Sons, the manufacturers of Trex cooking fat, produced six sets of trade cards. These cards were released with accompanying albums and were issued to members of the Trex Club.

The albums were cleverly designed so that cards could be slotted into place without the need for glue. Consequently, it does not devalue a set of Trex cards if they have been placed into an album. Unfortunately, the albums are often well-thumbed and it can be difficult to find examples in very good condition. We currently value mint condition albums (without the cards) at £25, and the albums for the Good Dogs and They Gave It a Name series are worth even more.

As it was possible to store cards in the albums without glue, Trex cards were usually well protected and can now be found in good condition much more easily than the albums can. Full sets of cards in excellent condition or better can usually sell for £25 - £50.

(Front cover)

(Back cover)

▲ Good Dogs. 1955. J.Bibby & Sons. Full set of 25 cards in the album. (vg) £30 - £40

TRADE CARDS

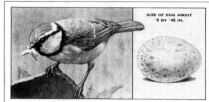

◀ ▲ The Swiss Family Robinson. Typhoo Tea. 1935. Full set of 25. (g-vg) £25 - £30

▲ ▶ British Birds and their Eggs. Typhoo Tea. 1936. Full set of 25. (g) £15 - £20

Ty-phoo Tea produced many series over the years, some of which were oddly shaped, as shown here. These cards measure 100 x 35mm and each had a special offer printed on the reverse. To purchase, the customer had to send the requisite price portions from the tea packets together with the relevant payment.

There's one particularly valuable set of Ty-phoo Tea cards. 'Our Empire's Defenders' published in 1916 and valued around £600 if in very good condition.

▲ ▶ Important Industries of the British Empire. Typhoo Tea. 1939. Incomplete set, number 11 missing. (g-vg) £3 - £5

◀ Wild Flowers in their Families. Typhoo Tea. 1936. Full set of 25. (g) £10 - £12

▲ Discover Australia with Shell. Shells, Fish and Coral (61-120). Shell (Oil). 1959. Full set of 60. (ex) £13 - £15

▲ Discover Australia with Shell. Birds (121-180). Shell (Oil). 1960. Full set of 60. (vg-ex) £12 - £14

▲ Discover Australia with Shell. Butterflies and Moths (181-240). Shell (Oil).1960. Full set of 60. (ex) £10 - £12

▲ Transportation Series (241 - 300). Shell (Oil). 1961. Full set of 60. (vg-ex) £12 - £14

TV SHOWS

Many of us can relate to particular television shows and that adds to the interest in collectable items relating to these shows. Television is part of our social history.

▲ Families. Granada promotional photograph of Jude Law. Facsimile autograph. (ex) £3 - £4

Deputy Dawg

This Terrytoons Cartoon was produced for CBS in the early sixties. Deputy Dawg was a deputy sheriff who spent much of his time protecting his produce from Vince and Muskie.

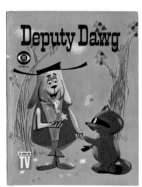

▲ Deputy Dawg. Hardback book. 1963. 22 pages. (vg) £2 - £3

Families

A daytime soap that ran from April 1990 to August 1993. Eighteen year old actor Jude Law landed the role of Nathan Thompson in 1990 and continued in the show for almost two years.

Follyfoot

Produced by Yorkshire Television, this children's TV series was based on a story by Monica Dickens and starred Gillian Blake as Dora and Steve Hodson as Steve. It originally ran from 1971 to 1973 and was repeated for a further two years after that. The theme song for the series was 'The Lightning Tree' sung by folk group 'The Settlers'. The song was released as a single 45rpm on the York Records label and reached no.36 in the charts.

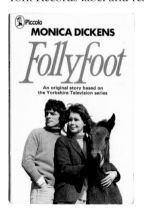

▲ Monica Dickens Autograph. Clear, blue ink, 125 x 65mm. No dedication. £8 - £12

◄ Paperback book. Follyfoot. 1971. (vg) £2 - £3

The Iron Horse

Produced in the USA, this Western television series ran from 1966 to 1968 and starred Dale Robertson as railroad mogul Ben Calhoun.

◄ TV Tornado magazine. Issue no.50 23rd December 1967. Dale Robertson featured on the cover. (g-vg) £6 - £8

Most of Dale Robertson's work was in the Western genre, and while he appeared in 63 films, he is likely to be best known for playing Jim Hardie in the television series Tales of Wells Fargo. The series ran from March 1957 until June 1962, for a total of 200 episodes over six seasons. Robertson also starred in The Iron Horse and the first season of Dynasty.

Dale Robertson died in 2013 aged 90.

No Hiding Place

This was a hugely popular TV series that ran from 1959 to 1967. It was a sequel to two other crime series 'Murder Bag' and 'Crime Sheet', both of which featured the 'No Hiding Place' star, Raymond Francis, as Superintendent Lockhart.

The show was produced by ATV. An amazing total of 236 episodes were made.

The role of Sergeant Russel was played by Johnny Briggs who later found stardom playing the role of Mike Baldwin in Coronation Street.

Although Raymond Francis will always be remembered for his role as Lockhart, he was also a noted stage actor. He was often typecast as an aristocrat, thanks to his distinguished appearance. He died in 1987 at the age of 76.

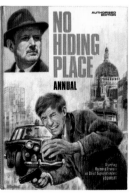

▲ No Hiding Place. TV annual. 1967. (vg) £10 - £12

▲ Raymond Francis. Autographed publicity photograph. Clear, black ink, 140 x 85mm. No dedication. £20 - £25

TYPEWRITER RIBBON TINS

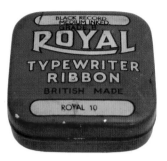

▲ Royal Tin. With ribbon. (1930). (g) £4 - £6

The very first typewriter (circa 1870) required the use of an inked ribbon through which type struck the paper. Approximately 20 years later, tins were used as containers for the ribbons. Tins were eventually replaced by plastic containers in the early 1970s.

Collectors look for colourful, artistic designs and they have thousands to choose from, from all parts of the world.

We are more interested in UK tins and the market for the older tins is strong.

Look out for some really good examples at Collectors' Fairs, quite often reasonably priced. However, some of the best sources are internet auctions.

▲ Imperitype. With ribbon. (1955). (g) £3 - £5

▲ Classic. Empty tin. (1930). (g) £5 - £7

▲ Swallow. Empty tin. (1950). (g) £4 - £6

▲ Pegasus. Empty Tin. (1960). (vg) £3 - £4

▲ Proco. Empty tin (1920). (f) £8 - £10

▲ Caribonum (purple). With ribbon. (1945). (g-vg) £4 - £6

▲ Caribonum (red). With ribbon. (1945). (g-vg) £3 - £4

U.N.C.L.E

The Man From U.N.C.L.E

American television series, The Man from U.N.C.L.E., ran from 22 September 1964 to 15 January 1968 (a total of 104 episodes over four seasons).

The show featured the adventures of Napoleon Solo and Illya Kuryakin (played by Robert Vaughn and David McCallum), operatives of the secret organisation United Network Command for Law and Enforcement (U.N.C.L.E.). Originally, Solo was supposed to be the only main protagonist, but fan support for a briefly seen Russian called Kuryakin led to the two being permanently paired for the rest of the shows. The head of the organisation, Mr Waverly, was played by Leo G Carroll, who is also well-known for his work on six Hitchcock movies, including Rebecca, Strangers on a Train, and North by Northwest.

The show was eventually cancelled during its fourth season, due to falling ratings, most likely due to a perceived move by the producers of the series away from serious action to a more humorous show.

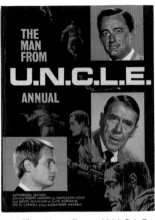

▲ The Man From U.N.C.L.E Annual. 1967. (vg) £8 - £10

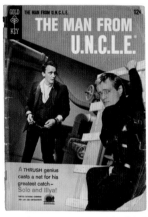

▲ The Man From U.N.C.L.E No.7 American comic. 1966. (p-f) £3 - £5

▲ The Man From U.N.C.L.E paperback. Souvenir Press, No.1. 1965. (g) £3 - £5

▲ The Man From U.N.C.L.E paperback. Souvenir Press, No.7. 1966. (f-g) £3 - £4

▲ The Man From U.N.C.L.E paperback. Souvenir Press, No.2. 1966. (f-g) £3 - £4

The Girl From U.N.C.L.E

A spin-off starring Stephanie Powers, Noel Harrison and Leo G.Carroll. The show was cancelled after just one series.

Noel Harrison (1934 - 2013). The late son of the late Rex Harrison (1908 - 1990)

▶ The Girl From U.N.C.L.E paperback. Souvenir Press, No.2. 1967. (g) £3 - £4

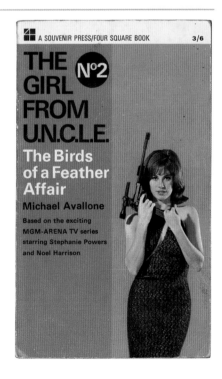

VIEW-MASTER

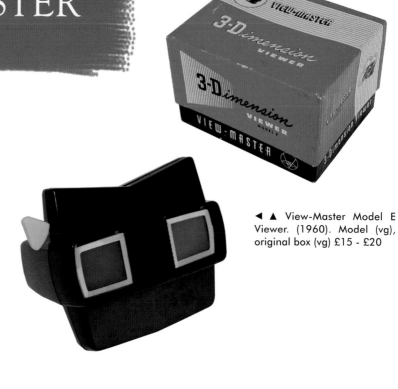

There's a lot to the subject of collecting View-Master. You can collect viewers, projectors, reels, books, containers, and more. The demand is out there and consequently there's normally a willing buyer for everything related to View-Master. Look out for items at car boot sales. You may accidentally pick up a rare variation that a seasoned collector will pay way over the odds for. Furthermore, many people are completely unaware of the existence of a buoyant market and just about anything can often be bought below its true value.

◀ ▲ View-Master Model E Viewer. (1960). Model (vg), original box (vg) £15 - £20

View-Master began in 1938 when Harold Graves (president of Sawyer's Photographic Services) saw the potential for a stereo photographic system devised by William Gruber. The two men joined forces and that was the start of View-Master. Although no longer owned by Sawyer's, View-Master continues today.

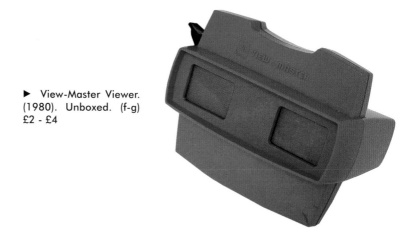

▶ View-Master Viewer. (1980). Unboxed. (f-g) £2 - £4

▲ Wonders Of The Deep. 1967. Three reels & booklet. (vg) £6 - £8

▲ Belgium. 1967. Two reels & booklet. (vg) £4 - £6

▲ History Of Flight. 1973. Three reels & booklet. (vg) £5 - £7

▲ Las Vegas. 1979. Three reels & booklet. (vg) £5 - £7

WADE WHIMSIES

The origins of George Wade Pottery began in 1810 in Burslem. In 1927, they first produced a range of figurines which proved very popular. During World War II, wartime restrictions meant domestic ceramic production was limited, meaning these miniature figures were no longer produced.

After the restriction was lifted, George Wade Pottery decided to reintroduce the animal figurines in 1953, calling them Whimsies. In the late 1950s, Wade produced a number of sets of Whimsies, before entering the premiums market in the 1960s (Whimsies were given away with tea bags and crackers).

Collectors seemed to love the miniature animal figurines and they were once again introduced for retail sale in 1971 (for the first time being sold in individual boxes, as well as the packaged sets).

Due to the high volume (several hundred different porcelain figurines in multiple different sets) and long manufacturing run of the Whimsies, there are a number of variations but they all have one common feature - the fine moulded parallel ridges on the bottom of the base (except for the 1st retail set which were smooth).

Whimsies were taken off the market in 1984 but have recently returned (and are still available today).

▲ Bear Cub. No.11. (vg), box (vg) £5 - £7

▲ Lamb. No.30. (vg), box (vg) £5 - £7

▶ Fox. No.10. (vg), box (g) £4 - £6

▲ Gorilla. No.33. (vg), box (f-g) £3 - £5

WEIGHING SCALES

Many of our homes contain a set of weighing scales of some description. Particularly, kitchen scales and/or bathroom scales. This indicates that there will be plenty of old examples for us collectors to beaver out.

Realistically, this is not likely to ever be a truly popular collecting subject, as quite often weighing scales can be bulky and heavy. Variations to the theme include postal weighing scales and even smaller and lighter, are handheld scales for measuring gold etc.

▲ Shop weighing scale. Mattocks. (1960). Heavy duty. 440 x 410mm. (g-vg) £30 - £40

▲ Exella weighing scales with pan. (1960). 250 x 200mm. (g-vg) £15 - £20

▲ Postal Scales. Unknown maker. (1920). Good working order with five weights from 4 ounces to ¼ ounce. 200 x 95mm. (g-vg) £15 - £20

◄ Stow-a-Weigh. Salter. Compact kitchen scale. 1982. 75mm high x 135mm diameter. Excellent unused condition. Original box (f-g) £4 - £6

The Salter business was started around 1760 when Richard Salter began making pocket spring scales. Some sixty years later the business was in the hands of Richard's nephew, George. At this time, the business began making bathroom scales.

WHISTLES

An interesting collecting area with plenty of history and variants.

The best known whistles are J. Hudson. The company name was created by Joseph Hudson (1848 - 1930). He and his brother formed J.Hudson & Co. (Birmingham). The company is still in business today.

The 'Acme' name was chosen because it's the Greek word for 'high point'. Interpreted by Hudson because of the high decibel produced by the whistle.

The Acme name was also reversed by Hudson & Co to read 'Emca'.

▲ The Emca City Whistle. (1955). (g-vg) £6 - £8

◄ The Acme. (1960). Girl Guide emblem on both sides. (f-g) £6 - £8

► The Acme Thunderer. (1950). (g) £6 - £8

WINNIE-THE-POOH

The lovable and rather famous teddy bear, Winnie-the-Pooh, was the creation of English author A.A.Milne (1882 - 1956).

A mountain of merchandise has been created over the years.

▲ Winnie-The-Pooh stuffed toy. 170mm high. (vg) 60p - 80p

◄ Winnie-The-Pooh tinplate pencil case. (2000). (vg) £1 - £2

WORLD WAR I

World War I began on 28 July 1914 and ended 11 November 1918. It was also known as the Great War.

▲ Greetings card, Christmas 1918. Message in pencil on reverse. (p-f) £3 - £4

The Salonika Army was a British field army.

▲ World War I submarine Bamforth postcard. Postmarked 1915. Message in pencil. (g) £3 - £4

▲ World War I troops postcard. (1915). Postally unused. (g) £2 - £3

▲ World War I troops at camp postcard. (1915). Postally unused. Creased (f) £1 - £2

▲ Victory March, The Mall, 1919. Beagles postcard. Postally unused. (g) £3 - £4

▲ Victory March, London, 1919. Beagles postcard. Postally unused. (f-g) £2 - £3

WORLD WAR II

World War II began in 1939 and ended in 1945. It was the most deadly war in human history.

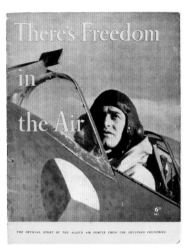

▲ There's Freedom In the Air. HMSO publication. 1944. (g) £4 - £6

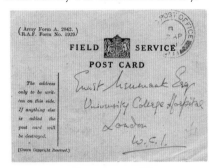

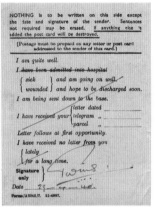

▲ Information booklet. (1945) For British troops in Durban, South Africa. Includes a street map and special entertainment offers for troops. 220 x 95mm. £3 - £5

◀ The Battle Of Britain, Aug - Oct 1940. A 38 page limpback published in 1941. Issued by The Ministry of Information on behalf of The Air Ministry. (vg) £1 - £2

▲ Field Service Post Card. These were designed to allow communications between active service personnel and their intended recipients, without disclosing any information that may benefit the enemy. This card was posted in April 1940 and has a Field Post Office postmark. (vg) £3 - £4

Neuengamme

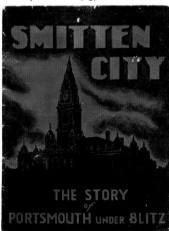

▲ Neuengamme copper ash tray. 116mm diam. (vg) £12 - £16

Neuengamme is a quarter of Hamburg in Germany, where a Nazi concentration camp was established during World War II. Tragically, more than half of the 106,000 prisoners held at the camp died. Neuengamme was liberated on 2 May 1945 by the Royal Northumberland Fusiliers and was subsequently used to house Nazi prisoners until 1948.

▲ Smitten City. A 64 page limpback published in 1944 by The Evening News Portsmouth. This is the story of 67 German air raids on Portsmouth between 1940 - 1944. Contains approx' 100 photographs. Such publications have considerably greater value to people living in the relevant area. (g) £6 - £8

▲ The Washing on the Siegfried Line. Sheet music. Written by Capt. Jimmy Kennedy whilst he was serving in the British Expeditionary Force in the early stages of the war. The Siegfried Line was a fortification chain running along the western border of Germany. 1939. (g-vg) £1 - £2

WRESTLING

The televising of wrestling matches in the 1960's created household names of the wrestlers, hosts and even the referees. The sport remains popular today.

Collectable items from the 1960's and 1970's are of particular interest to collectors.

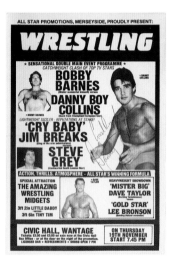

◄ Flyer. 1981. Bobby Barnes and others. Civic Hall Wantage. Signed by Danny Boy Collins. Clear, black ink, no dedication. (vg) £10 - £12

▲ Big Daddy poster. 2 October 1974. 610 x 425mm. Downham Market, Town Hall. Folded. (vg) £10 - £12

Big Daddy's real name was Shirley Crabtree (1930 - 1997).

◄ Mitzi Mueller. Autographed promotional photograph. Clear, red ink, 252 x 190mm. £15 - £20

Mitzi's legendary career in the ring began in 1963 and ended in 1987.

▲ Kendo Nagasaki. Autographed promotional photograph. Clear, blue ink, 245 x 140mm. No dedication. £10 - £12

(Vic Falkner - Card No.53)   (Billy Two Rivers - Card No.3)   (Steve Logan - Card No.43)

▲ Somportex. Bubble gum trade cards. Famous TV Wrestlers. 1966. Hard to find a full set in such good condition. Full set. (vg) £100 - £120

BUSINESS PLAN
TO TURN A £300 INVESTMENT INTO A STOCK
VALUED £50,000, BY TRADING COLLECTABLES

The great thing about collectables is that there's an endless supply. The secret is to establish the best places to buy and the best places to sell your stock. It's obvious really.

Like any business venture, getting established is the hardest part. You have to do your homework before you start buying. Learning about collectables is not exactly tedious work. This is one of the most fascinating, interesting and educating industries to get wrapped-up in. A computer and internet connection is almost essential. You can use 'search engines' to find information on the majority of collectables and also auction house sales results (and internet auction results) to help you establish values. Attending some of the largest collectors' fairs will also considerably help your learning curve.

Once you are confident that you know what an item should sell for, you are ready to start buying. You are working for yourself, so there's no rush. However, if you are hoping to achieve a £50,000 (or more) a year profit, understand from the very start that it is going to be hard work.

It will seriously help your cause if you are the type of person who is motivated by the prospect of long term success. You will need to maintain a dynamic and enthusiastic approach. You do not need to be brainy but you will need commonsense.

This business plan assumes that you have started doing your homework and also assumes that you do not have a great deal of money to get the venture off the ground.

If you do not already have a computer and do not have your own transport, then the costs of these could possibly be an issue for you and you are likely to take longer to reach a £50,000 stock target level. A suggestion to get over this little problem is to go along to a local car boot sale or collectors fair and try to find a stallholder who is obviously working his stall as a business. Offer to help him free of charge in exchange for sharing transport and if he's using an internet auction, offer to share costs. Very often, a trader will be only too pleased to have some free help from an honest individual but do make sure you are well presented and maybe it would help if you have done plenty of homework on at least one collectables subject, to stimulate initial discussion.

This book, with its wide variety of categories, should prove to be very helpful. The items that you see, are examples of the sort of stock you could be looking out for in your quest to build a quality base for your business. Your task is to acquire similar stock at the low end price range and sell for a decent profit. Again, all very obvious.

Other pages in this book will give you plenty of tips on buying and selling. It wouldn't hurt if you go back over these from time to time.

A good starting tip is to avoid the higher value items. You are looking to bulk-buy small items that don't weigh very much and then split the acquired stock into individual lots for sale. If you start with £300, you should be able to spend this sum at large car boot sales or at auction houses, very wisely. You may need to visit more than one over a 7 day period. Whatever you do, don't get impatient and buy rubbish. If the quality is not there to buy, your business plan will simply be delayed. Many people are likely to fail at this early point in the plan because they haven't bought correctly. If you can afford to start with more than £300 then so much the better. A £1000 starter bank would be an ideal figure. The Business Plan could also be adapted to cope with an initial investment as low as £30.

The following plan is based on an initial investment of £300:-

WEEK 1 Spend £150 on stock.

WEEK 2 List half of your stock (the lesser quality items) on trusted internet auction websites. Your task is to at least double your money with these lower value items, whilst also making a sufficient margin to cover the auction listing costs.

WEEK 3 Spend another £100 on stock.

WEEK 4 Assuming you have amassed a varied and decent quantity of stock. Take a stand at a car boot sale or a small collectors' fair (you can find them listed in local newspapers or via Google). Take all your stock that you have not listed on auction websites. Your cost for the stand at a car boot should not exceed £10 or £30 at a small collectors fair. These 'marketing' costs are unavoidable but essential. Your goods have to be placed where potential buyers can see them.

Don't make the classic mistake of holding on to stock that you want to collect yourself. You can do this at a later stage. Your task for now is to at least double your money on each (lower value) item that you sell. Keep remembering that the supply is endless. Your most important job for the minute is to get the money rolling in.

Now, at this very early stage of the business plan, it must be assumed that you are going to make mistakes on both the buying and selling sides. You will learn from these mistakes, they are an essential inevitability. Realistically, even if you have been selective in your buying, it is quite possible that you will only have sold £80 worth of items. The items cost you £40 and your marketing costs have been £40. Your profit so far is £0. However, you do have £40 of your 'capital' back. The car boot and the fair will have been a great learning exercise. There's no substitute for it.

Even if you made a small loss, it wouldn't be a great worry, these early days are learning days.

WEEK 5 Your internet auction sales are now coming through. You may perhaps, have only sold less than 50% of the items you put up for auction but your sales revenue amounted to £50, less £20 auction costs and the £25 you spent to acquire the stock. You have therefore made your first 'profit'. It may only be £5

but once again you have been through a vital learning curve. Could you have listed the items for sale in a different way? Were they the right items to put in an internet auction?

At this point, plenty of people would have given up. Five weeks work for a profit of £5. Wow, you have earned £1 a week!!!

Don't forget that all the time you should be getting your cost of stock back and this is ready to be used again to buy more stock.

Once your stock starts making you a profit, then plough the profit back into buying more stock. This is how you will begin to reach your £50,000 stock level target.

Don't be tempted to spend your profits on items for yourself or improving your lifestyle. Until your business is big enough to become a full time occupation, it is essential that your everyday needs are met by employment or some other venture or income stream.

Assuming you have kept the faith and are beginning to see the potential and if, particularly, you are beginning to enjoy the business of buying and selling collectables, then you are on course for success.

WEEK 6 You should have at least £200 to spend on stock. By now you should have started to establish some specialist knowledge on one or two particular collectable subjects.

This specialist knowledge is absolutely key to the success of your business.

Let's take just one particular collecting subject as an example. Brooke Bond tea card albums. Most members of the public will not have a clue how to value these, yet there weren't that many variations to the theme. They can genuinely be sold as collectables. They have their own little place in our social history. So many were issued by Brooke Bond, they are (generally) not rare at all. You can buy them in bulk at plenty of car boots. Suppose you pay 50p each, you should be able to sell your average condition stock at £1 each.

WEEK 7-22 You should be able to identify many different items that can double your money and you will also soon have the confidence to buy higher value stock (accepting that you are likely to have to settle for lower margins). Before long your turnover will be rising significantly and your stock value should, with plenty of hard work and enthusiasm, risen from the original £300 to £2500 or thereabouts.

You are not bound by any particular time schedule in your business venture, so don't worry if you are taking longer than hoped for.

WEEK 23-38 Your knowledge of collectables should now be widening significantly. Remember, to be successful, you MUST put the effort in. The more specialist subjects you add to your portfolio of expertise, the better.

You should now be at the point where you are becoming quite expert at buying low value stock which you know can be sold on for a decent margin. However, you will also recognise that your stock value is likely to increase by also buying higher value items but with much lower margins. For example, you may spot a boxed Dinky toy lorry dated 1965, that you know you can easily sell on for £120 and therefore you have no problem risking £100 on purchasing the item from someone else in the first place. You will make mistakes and lose on some but generally, with sufficient expert knowledge behind you, (approx) 20% margins should be achievable and desirable for your higher value stock.

Yes, you may occasionally find a real bargain on someone's car boot stall but generally, you will need to accept that much of your best stock will require some risk taking.

By now, your £2500 stock value should have reached approximately £5000.

WEEK 39-52 This will bring you neatly to the end of your first year of trading and your stock value should now be in the region of £10,000, assuming you have kept the energy levels up.

If you are nowhere near your target figure by now, take a step back and ask yourself why. The answer is almost certainly going to be that you haven't put sufficient time and energy into it. Alternatively, you may have tried to run before you can walk and lost on too many deals. The reason will be there, so establish it and take corrective measures.

WEEK 53-78 Now you should be flying and enjoying the experience immensely. By the end of this period, you should comfortably be looking at finishing with a stock level of £25,000.

You will think nothing of taking £1000 cash to a large car boot sale and spending the lot in a few hours. You could also be making your presence felt at auction houses specialising in collectables and ending up with bills of over £3000 for your day's purchases. Your buying opportunities will be increasing (assuming you have been working hard and establishing where they are in the first place).

WEEK 79-104 You are entering the final months of your target to reach a stock level valued at £50,000.

Very well done, if you achieve it. Your hard work and endurance will have paid off, now you are ready to get your business moving to even greater things.

The following pages feature some buying and selling tips to help your business along.

BUYING AND SELLING TIPS

Sourcing collectable items

The good old car boot sale is the best starting point for anyone wanting to make money from collectables.

Just about every town in the land hold such sales but some car boots are much larger than others. Seek out the bigger sales.

Internet auction sites offer endless opportunities to purchase but it's often a case of much patience being required.

Collectors' Fairs are an excellent source of collectables and a great guide to current values.

Thought provoking sales tips for fairs & car boots

If you take a stall at a car boot sale, it's probably a 'no-brainer' that the items you offer for sale should be low value. Likewise, if you are paying good money for a stand at a big Collectors' Fair, then it would make sense to fill your stall with your highest value stock.

However, there are arguments to have high and low value items at both. The reason being that at any decent size car boot sale, it's a virtual certainty that traders will be scouring the stalls in search of quality collectables. Of course, they are hoping not to pay too much, so the less professional your stand looks, the better. Whether or not you can strike a deal, trader to trader, is another matter.

At the big Collectors' Fair there will be plenty of potential customers looking for bargains.

By strategically positioning some of your better quality bargain items (including stock that had previously been overpriced), you will catch the eye of the majority of browsers.

Joining forces with other traders at a car boot or collectors' fair makes good sense. As long as all the items are clearly priced (but not with sticky labels that will damage the goods or packaging etc..., when peeled off), you will (a) share the cost of the stand, (b) improve security, (c) potentially offer a wider range of items, (d) get time off for breaks. You may also find that you can share transportation costs and maybe even share the driving, thereby opening up new long distance locations that you would previously have dismissed.

If you club together with three other collectables traders, you could take quite a large stand in a good position at a prestigious fair. Not only could this be a profitable venture for all of you, it's likely to also be a lot of fun. Many traders are in the collectables business because they love the thrill of the chase. A busy trading day can really get the adrenalin flowing.

Time is money

It pays to be well organised with your cash when buying at a car boot sale or collectors fair. The average trade buyer is likely to make a purchase from 20 or so traders at any large boot or fair, so having the correct cash can save valuable time.

If you had to wait an average of just 60 seconds for the trader to give you back your due change, it could cost you a total of 20 minutes or so .There's no way you should ever contemplate standing around for a total of 5 minutes, let alone 20 minutes, when you could be busily scurrying around the stalls, so serious thought should be given to the subject of cash before you set out.

Because it's not at all unusual for the seller not to have the correct change, a not uncommon scenario is that the seller has shot off telling you he is getting some change from his friend. Meanwhile his friend is busy serving a customer and you get trapped in a long wait, maybe three minutes or more.

A money belt/bag strapped to your waist, not only keeps your cash handy and where you can see it, most bags are usefully compartmentalised.

If you are carrying large sums of cash in your money belt, be mindful of who is observing you when you are handing over your cash. A criminal may be watching.

Get the maximum value from your sales stall

If you are selling items at a car boot, make it obvious that you specialise in particular subjects. Using beer mats as an **example**, you could have a folder full of individually priced high value stock (keeping a close eye on the folder of course) and also a box of lowest value beer mat stock. Next to the box, you could stand a sign stating "OLD BEER MATS WANTED". It only takes one or two people at the sale to tell you that they have loads of beer mats and that you are welcome to make an offer for them. Try to make an early appointment to view them at their homes (assuming local to the sale), after the sale has ended.

If you make regular appearances at car boots it could lead to some people agreeing to bring some of the items you are looking to buy, to your stall 'next week'.

Given that some people will not understand that some of your beer mats are being offered for sale at relatively high

sums because they are rarer, you could choose to adopt a policy of not offering higher value items at a sale where you are trying to **buy** higher value stock (at a trade price).

You will be surprised at how cheaply you can sometimes buy certain collectable items directly from the public. It's often the case that a collection has been inherited or interest in a particular subject has waned. Some people may consider that you are doing them a favour by taking away a large box of items.

Of course, there will always be members of the public who ask 'silly money' for a collection of items. It could pay to be very polite and say something like "well, these are nice items, but I am sorry to say the price you are looking for, would not give me a margin, however, here's my business card and please give me a ring or send me an email if you decide to drop your asking price at any time in the future".

Auction houses

Apart from being a thrilling experience, attending a live auction event can be a great source for acquiring collectable items.

Check out your local newspaper for auctions of collectables, or better still, use the internet and 'Google'.

Once you have sourced the best local collectables auctions, ask to be put on the mailing list. With any luck they will post you free catalogues of future auctions.

Choosing local auctions will cut the travelling time.

Some auctions run over two or more days. Then there's the pre-sale essential requisite of checking out the items before you contemplate bidding.

Quite often, the expert who compiled the auction catalogue will be there in person at the viewing times. He or she will normally be delighted to answer any questions you may have.

Nowadays, there's an alternative to viewing the items in person, although still not recommended (you can't beat seeing and holding the item). Auction houses often photograph all the items and post the images and descriptions of each lot on their websites. If you are unable to view in person, this is the next best thing.

Bidding in person at the auction will normally give you an edge over telephone, 'book' and internet bidders, because the auctioneer will normally take the bids in the room as a priority. It could be the difference between winning and losing the lot.

If you are new to live auction bidding then a good tip is to attend an auction as a 'dummy run' by bidding at an auction of cheap household items (which incidentally, can also be the source of collectable items). You need to be bold and decisive with your bidding.

A good tip for bidding, is to seat yourself in a prominent position in the front of the room near the auctioneer. Open the bidding and be swift and positive with your bids, this could help frighten off the opposition, who may get cold feet believing that you mean business.

Some auctioneers like to move the sale along quickly and may use you to get the bids moving, this could mean that you secure some of the lots with bids that others were treating as their limits.

Honest John or dishonest Joe?

Dealers have to make a profit from the items they buy and sell, otherwise they will quickly go out of business.

However, how the profit is achieved, could be another matter entirely. For example, pretending that a modern reproduction is a 50 year old original, is definitely a case of 'Dishonest Joe'.

When buying at a car boot or collectors' fair, or wherever, it could pay you to test the dealer by asking a question that you know the answer to. **For example**; you may know that a Dinky toy is an obvious 'repaint job'. Then if the dealer tries to tell you that it's not a repaint job, you can form an instant opinion of whether or not you wish to carry on looking at the goods on his stall.

Some unscrupulous dealers will often try to hide damage. For example, a ceramic jug may appear to be absolutely perfect but the dealer may be hiding a crack by deliberately showing you the jug at a particular angle and hoping that you don't notice the damage.

Careful examination of all items being purchased is always highly recommended. Even 'Honest John' may have genuinely missed some damage.

There are countless tricks of the trade. As a buyer, you need to be one step ahead. Constant vigilance is essential.

Putting a date on some collectable items can quite often be tricky. There is a reasonable expectation that a dealer will supply you with honest information. The dealer who tells you that he isn't sure of the date, is quite possibly, more likely to be an honest individual. However, if the dealer obviously specialises in the particular item you are interested in buying, then there's a greater expectation that he will have a good idea of the date.

There are some instances when you have to place your faith in the seller. For example, if you are buying a vintage 500 piece jigsaw puzzle, you can hardly spend the time checking that it's complete, before you agree to buy it.

If you are at a collectors fair and you believe that a dealer is selling counterfeit goods, discreetly and confidentially report him to the organiser of the fair.

Networking

Once you find one or more collectable areas that you decide to specialise in, you can begin to 'network' (spread the word that you are interested in buying). Before long you can establish a network of dealers, friends and relations who will look out for items they believe will interest you.

However, there are dangers. One dealer will tell another dealer and a little chain of deals can happen, which, if you are not careful, can work against you.

The classic 'backfire' is where one of your 'contacts' bids against you for the same item on an internet auction website or worse still, have visited a local auction house and left some 'bids in the book' and then you end up bidding against a person who is actually trying to win the item for you, thinking you will be delighted.

The tip is to make sure that your 'networkers' are aware that you are actively buying (particularly locally) and also to make it clear that you are not guaranteeing to buy everything that is offered. Then, your networkers are more likely to check with you first or simply alert you to where a particular item is being sold.

By attending a 'swap meet' you are 'networking'. You are going to a place where a group of like-minded enthusiasts/traders gather together to swap items (often to improve particular examples within a collection). These meetings are often organised by enthusiasts clubs and the best way to find out about them is to talk to others or 'Google'.

A great way to 'network' is to take a stand yourself at a collectors' fair. Offer your items for sale and make it clear that you are also buying. Traders, as well as members of the public, are likely to introduce themselves as fellow enthusiasts for whatever it may be that you are specialising in.

Building a client database

Because you never know what the future will bring, assume that you may become an expert trader in any one of many collecting subjects.

For example; next week you may receive a catalogue from an auction house that contains one particular lot - a collection of Wade Whimsies. You end up as the highest bidder and take the large quantity of Wade Whimsies away. Now the fun begins. You knew very little about this subject and have to start learning from scratch. You then become quite an expert, which then enables you to buy more from other sources at the right price.

Before this, you may have sold the odd one or two Wade Whimsies. Your buyers will have one thing in common, they are interested in this subject and they may be looking for particular models or may have duplicates to sell.

The message here is to ask each private buyer (or serious browser) if they would like to receive your list of Wade Whimsies for sale at some time in the future. You can offer to contact them by post or by email. Preferably both contacts are best as emails have a habit of being changed much more regularly than a home address.

You need to explain that at present you do not have such a list but this could change at any time, or better still, if you have just a few in stock that are not on display on your stall, you can say that your list only has a few at the moment but could increase at any time.

Obviously, the most cost effective method of communicating with your clients, is by email, as there are no postage and printing costs. It therefore follows that getting the email address absolutely correct is essential. If the client is present, check that you are interpreting the writing correctly and if you are seeking email addresses over the internet, use a double entry system to capture this vital data accurately.

Whenever you carry out an email or postal sales campaign, keep accurate figures of sales achieved. Such statistics will help you establish if your client list is responsive enough to warrant carrying out the exercise again. Although do beware that a poor sales response could be due to the quality of the stock you are offering for sale.

Taking friends to a car boot

Don't be tempted to take friends with you on your buying trips (car boots, fairs etc). There's often a temptation for you to 'show off' to them and this can backfire.

A problem arises when your friends get caught up in the excitement of it all and get an urge to join in, using their own cash.

You cannot hope to educate your inexperienced friends in the etiquette of buying and selling, in a few minutes. Furthermore, your exuberant outpourings may lead your friends to believe that they are obliged to join you in the buying spree. They may actually buy some of the very items that should have ended up in your swag bag.

Quite often your friends will have no idea (or desire) how to haggle a price down and therefore may be paying far more than they need to. The experience may rapidly become quite painful for you.

Friends may also slow your progress, they may start asking trivial questions, gobbling up your valuable buying time.

Another common problem is that their time is limited and then without much notice they inform you that they have to be at a certain place at a certain time and you have the only transport.

If you really must take your friends along, then it may be prudent to give them a thorough appraisal beforehand and politely advise them that you are there for a serious purpose and may have to leave them to their own devices.

Stock disposal

Quite a lot of collectors are also dealers in all sorts of collectables, even though their collecting interest revolves around just a single subject. For example, a collector of beer mats is likely to enjoy building a collection of rarities and would probably sell his duplicates on the open market. His own collection of beer mats (although not strictly speaking his stock) will therefore build and requires management.

All the other collectable items that he has acquired as part of his collectables trading stock also need to rotate. Unsold items that have been hanging around for a while with no buyer in sight, are not helping the bank balance and they are also likely to be taking up valuable storage space.

A good tip is to pass your unsold stock to another trader, on the understanding that he will pay you

50% of whatever he gets for it. Obviously, this is more applicable to lower value stock. Some of this stock will probably be in your accounts book at £0 anyway.

A classic reason for stock accruing at £0, is where a number of items have been acquired in a single purchase, the majority of which are not wanted but effectively came with the items that you really wanted to buy. For example the beer mat collector may have purchased a bulk lot of 200 beer mats but only because he rated 10 of them. He will try to sell the 190 but may eventually be stuck with 50 or so. It's this type of 'dead stock' that needs to be moved on.

If you get to the point where you have unsold stock that appears to have no hope of selling and is probably of very little value, it could be time to donate box loads to a local charity shop. They will often happily take anything and arrange disposal of anything they don't want. This helps a good cause and at the same time does you a favour by clearing your storage space.

Dealing with dealers

More and more antique dealers now stock collectables in their shops. Many items are there to 'catch the eye' as well as to be sold. For example, a 1965 framed original poster for a Beatles concert is hardly a traditional antique but it would look great on the wall of the shop and could attract more people in.

Whether you are interested in buying an antique or a collectable, a dealer has to make a living and needs to make a profit, therefore some may be quite offended if you make an offer that is way below the ticket price. Very few dealers overprice their stock to any great degree. The object of the game is to sell the goods in the shop.

There is an expectation that many potential buyers will make an offer, so it's fair to say that most dealers will have built in a bit of leeway. So make an offer by all means but don't insult the dealer with a ridiculous offer.

There have been a few television programmes on the subject of antiques, featuring experts who buy from antique shops and then sell the acquired items in an auction room, the winner being the person who makes the most profit. Whilst great entertainment, they are not always setting a good example. The dealers are letting the buyers get away with crazy low offers, presumably because it gets them some free publicity. The problem is that this can plant the idea in many peoples' minds that it's perfectly acceptable to make a stupid offer.

Dealers play a vital role in the antique and collectables world. Supporting them helps keep the market alive.

Add a trading arm to your collecting

There used to be a belief amongst some collectors that you should never buy collectable items unless you are going to love and cherish them for many years. The message was that items shouldn't be purchased with a view to making money.

The internet and postal auctions have changed all that. eBay has become the giant trading ground for a multitude of collectables.

For those who can't be bothered with the internet, *Collecticus* now boasts over ten years of national postal auctions, via a monthly magazine and website.

There's no excuse for any collector not to also buy and sell within (or outside) of his/her collecting area.

Becoming a part-time trader means that a collection can be improved by upgrading the quality/condition of the main collection.

Apart from the added obvious advantage of creating a revenue stream to help pay for your main collecting activity, 'trader' action will help increase your knowledge of specific collectable items, especially the values of the items in their relevant conditions.

Once you start trading there could be no stopping and the activity could become quite lucrative, so well worth investigating if at present, you are sitting on the fence.

A good tip to start a new collecting interest is to look for **collections** being sold at car boots or collectors fairs. Make an offer to buy the entire collection but not at the asking price.

Great gifts

If you have difficulty thinking of what present to buy for someone, why not consider a collectable item?

The scope is wide. Assuming you are a seasoned collectables hound, you are virtually certain to come across 'perfect presents' on your travels.

The selection process could take you outside of your normal search pattern. For example, if you buy and sell small items via internet auctions, you are unlikely to be interested in pieces of furniture. This happens to be a classic area full of possibilities and much of it at reasonable prices. Believe it or not, a good source for furniture is the car boot sale.

If you are looking at presents for the children, then maybe you can intuitively buy a low value collection of 'something or other' to spark a new hobby interest.

However, a word of warning, you do need to be careful that your presents are not in a dangerous condition. Most collectables are sold as 'not for the use for which they were designed'.

There are some classic presents that will often solve a problem for you and actually be something the recipient will be delighted with. You could consider; old coins and banknotes. If presented professionally they can really look great and give a feeling of being something special that can be treasured and kept for years, perhaps to increase in value.

Rather naughtily, you could buy a selection of potential presents but firstly try to sell them yourself as part of your trading activity, then if the item(s) don't sell, hey presto, you have instant presents.

A rather nice idea is to make a unique gift for someone. For example; you could get ten or so small collectable items such as old luggage labels and artistically affix them to a card, which you then get framed. The theme could be something you know the recipient has an interest in. For example; for someone interested in buses, it could be a framed montage of old bus tickets.

'Free' collectables

Unless a kindly relative gives you a quantity of old collectable items, there are not likely to be many opportunities for you to acquire collectables at no cost. However, there are plenty of opportunities to acquire 'free' collectables because you have already bought the items anyway. For example; if you go to a rock concert, you can keep the ticket, which in time could be worth more than you paid for it. A classic example of this was in 1966 when a ticket to see the pop group The Who, may have cost £1 or less. Now, if in good condition, could command £15 or more.

A good tip is to find an empty shoebox and store your 'free' collectables therein. You should aim to fill the box in five years. Such a long duration will help you focus on collecting small items. For example; commemorative

edition magazines are not ideal because they are so bulky and are not likely to become overly desirable in 20 years time. Today's collectors can often be heard saying "I had loads of those, if only I kept them".

Your shoebox treasure items should be stored in protective holders, otherwise if you are constantly rummaging through, the items may become damaged. The box should be kept in a draw or cupboard away from the threat of vermin attack. One dear little mouse could ruin your collection.

A flyer for a circus is the sort of thing you could add to your shoebox and another is a leaflet advertising a new model of motor vehicle. Chocolate bar wrappers (particularly from brands that you know are ending), the list is endless. Once you start your shoebox collection you are likely to constantly think before throwing anything away.

As well as your shoebox items, you could consider using some of the collectables you have bought. For example, if you bought a job lot of 100 old postcards, once you have removed the desirable ones, there may be plenty of unwanted 'postally unused' cards that can be used to send greetings or sales messages or whatever.

Succession planning

One thing is guaranteed, none of us collectors will live forever. In addition to this certainty, there's a risk that whilst we are still alive, we may become so incapacitated we are no longer able to function as normal.

The above scenario means that all the money, effort and energy you invested in your collection of collectables will be vulnerable to squandering.

Now is the time to prepare members of your family or close friends to protect the value of your collectables.

The danger is that it could be the case that only you know the true value of specialist collectable items. For example, a collection of old chocolate bar wrappers, could be dismissed as one of your whims. Whereas the collection could actually be worth hundreds of pounds.

Imagine the horror of the collection going to a car boot sale or being sold at auction, for peanuts.

Whilst other members of your family may not have the slightest interest in your collectables and may even consider them an irritation, their tune may soon change when you take the time and trouble to draw their attention to how much they are worth.

A good tip is to document the items, and if possible, list the sums you paid for each item.

As hard as it may be to accept this, many families have no interest in collectables and anything inherited is likely to be sold.

Very often, collectables will realise a much higher revenue if the items in the collection are sold individually. It may involve more effort but could be a decision that will pay huge dividends for the beneficiaries. It's this sort of discussion that makes for efficient succession planning.

It could be that once the beneficiaries understand the value of items, they may choose to keep the collection in the hope that the value will increase in years to come, or indeed, there may be a desire to add to the collection. The very people who pulled your leg about the extraordinary amount of time and devotion you spent caring for and building your set of old chocolate bar wrappers, may become expert collectors themselves.

BUYING AT CAR BOOT SALES

- Arrive early to catch the real treasures.

- Take a rucksack to carry what you buy.

- Make sure you have plenty of small change.

- Take a supply of plastic bags and some A4 plastic or card wallets for protecting your purchases.

- Watch out for pickpockets.

- The first stall you visit should be the latest one to set up.

- Dress like a pauper, so it's easier to haggle.

- Be careful when buying electrical items, they may not be safe to use. They may not work at all.

- ALWAYS HAGGLE.

- Be prepared to get down on your hands and knees to sift through boxes of oddments. Some great little treasures can be found at the bottom of a box of 'junk'.

- Never show excitement. A deadpan expression is required with every offer.

- Don't take your dog. Many boot sales now ban them.

- If it is a hot day, remember to take some sun cream. Conversely, if it is a cold day, wrap up warm.

- Take your own food and a flask of coffee, so you don't have to waste time queuing at the refreshment stands.

- Don't push and shove when looking at a stall. Boot sales are supposed to be friendly affairs.

- Tender the exact sum negotiated.

- Don't try to outbid someone else on an item he or she has already picked up. It's commonly accepted that once you hold an item in your hand, it's your first option.

- Don't be aggressive when you haggle.

- Don't tell a seller that his or her items are rubbish.

- Don't interfere with someone else's sale. Let the buyer and seller negotiate the arrangement themselves.

SELLING AT CAR BOOT SALES

- Don't take items that can be easily damaged.

- Be positive. If asked for a "best price," don't respond in a quizzical tone of voice, as if to say "Is that all right?"

- Do not put items aside for potential purchasers for any reason, unless you take a non-refundable deposit first.

- Take plenty of empty plastic bags and newspaper to wrap items.

- Don't keep your money anywhere that requires you to turn your back on your stall.

- Placing an item in a clear plastic wallet can give it a feeling of being valuable, and allows you to

attach a price sticker without causing damage.

- Try placing price tags underneath items, forcing potential buyers to pick up the items and turn them over. This gives you a clear indication of their interest. (Please note: this suggestion is not recommended for breakable items.)

- If the weather looks like it will be unpredictable, take a gazebo with you. These can be purchased quite cheaply from household stores, and can be a real lifesaver if you get caught in a downpour.

- When using a fold-up table, cover it with a white or cream sheet. This will help bring out the colour in your sale items, and will generally make the stall look more attractive. Your items may look even more valuable.

GLOSSARY & TERMINOLOGY

ACETATE - A record pressing made of aluminium with a coating of vinyl-like material, used for checking the quality of work in progress being recorded by a producer and artist. They are only designed for a few plays as the coating quickly wears out.

ADDORSED - Back to back.

AERONAUTICA - Collectable items relating to aircraft.

AEROPHILATELY - The collecting of air mail stamps and covers.

ALLOY - A mixture of metals.

AMERICANA - Items that are distinctive of America.

ANTHOLOGY - Collection of literary passages and works.

ARABESQUE - Symmetrical decoration in the form of flowing lines of branches, leaves and scrolling.

ARCTOPHILY - The collecting of teddy bears.

ARGYROTHECOLOGY - The collection and study of money boxes.

ART DÉCO - A style of interior decoration and manufactured objects, of the period (approximately) 1925 – 1940. Symmetrical designs adapted to mass production.

ART NOUVEAU - A style of decoration of the early 20th century. Based on soft curves and influenced by the example of Japanese art (particularly leaves and flowers).

ARTEFACT - An object shaped by human craft (such as a tool), usually with archaeological significance.

ASTROPHILATELY - Space related postage stamps.

AUDIOPHILY - The collecting of recorded sound.

AURICULAR - Shaped like the ear.

AUTOMATA - models of people, animals and things that move via clockwork. Fine working examples from approximately 1820 - 1920 are often of much interest.

AUTOMOBILIA - Items relating to motor vehicles.

BACK STAMP - A maker's marking on the underside of a ceramic piece. (Back Stamps scored through, indicate 'seconds').

BANDOPHILY - The collecting of cigar bands.

BEZEL - The metal frame around the glass of a watch or clock.

BIBELOT - A curious or attractive trinket. Alternative meaning; a miniature book.

BIBLIOPHILIA - The collecting of and love of, books and reading.

BIBLIOTICS - The study of documents to determine their authenticity.

BOOTERS - Buyers at a car boot sale.

BOXWOOD - Close grained light yellow wood of the box. A mustard spoon could typically be made of boxwood.

BRASSARD - An armlet. A piece of cloth (usually with insignia) worn around the upper arm.

BREWERIANA - Collectable items related to brewing.

BUFFED - Condition description for a vinyl record, where the surface looks as though it has been buffed with wire wool. In other words, the surface is multi scratched in poor condition.

CAGOPHILY - The collecting of keys.

CAMEO - A shell or stone carved in relief, in such a way that brings out the different colours of the material used.

CARD CASE - A case (usually with an ornate design) to carry calling/business cards. Originated in 18th century France.

CARTOGRAPHY - *The study, making, and collecting of maps.*

CARTOPHILY - *The collecting of cigarette cards.*

CAST IRON - *Ironwork produced by pouring molten iron into a pre-shaped mould.*

CERAMICS - *The generic term for pottery, porcelain, terracotta, etc.*

CHINOISERIE - *Decorative artwork with Chinese characteristics.*

CHIROGRAPHY - *The study of handwriting.*

CHRYSOLOGY - *The study of precious metals.*

CHURCHILLIANA - *Collectable items relating to Winston Churchill.*

CLYVESOPHILY - *Collecting of mugs.*

CODICOLOGY - *The study of early manuscripts.*

CONCHOLOGY - *The study of shells.*

COPOCLEPHILY - *The collecting of key rings.*

COTTAPENSOPHILY - *Collecting of coat hangers.*

CRAZING - *A fine network of cracks in the glaze of pottery and porcelain.*

CRIMINOLOGY - *The study of criminals and crime.*

CRYPTOLOGY - *The study of codes.*

DACTYLIOLOGY - *The study of rings.*

DECAL - *Short for decalcomania. The art or process of transferring a design from prepared paper onto another surface.*

DECOUPAGE - *The art of decorating objects with paper cut-outs, then painting and adding layers of varnish.*

DELFTWARE - *Earthenware named after the Dutch town of Delft.*

DELTIOLOGY - *The collecting of postcards.*

DIECAST - *Zinc alloy used to manufacture toys, enabling the production of strong, shiny, bright, permanently decorated items.*

DIE CUTTING - *A manufacturing process that enables specific shapes to be cut from materials such as; metal, fabric, plastic, wood, card, etc...*

DIGITABULIST - *A collector of thimbles.*

DISCOPHILY - *The collecting of recorded music.*

DISNEYANA - *Collectable items relating to Disney.*

EARTHENWARE - *Glazed pottery fired to a temperature of approximately 1000 degrees C. Normally red or brown with a low chipping resistance.*

ECCLESIOLOGY - *The study and collection of items relating to church.*

EDWARDIAN - *Relating to the period of the reign of King Edward VII (1901 – 1910).*

EGYPTOLOGY - *The study of Ancient Egypt.*

ENAMEL - *A semi-opaque form of glass fused on to metal surfaces to decorate them.*

ENCRUST - *To ornament by overlaying with a crust of something precious.*

ENIGMATOLOGY - *The study and collecting of puzzles.*

EPHEMERA - *Anything designed to be used and then thrown away, usually made of paper. For example, old bus tickets and cigarette packets.*

EPNS - *Electro Plated Nickel silver - silver plate.*

EROTICA - *Glamour related items.*

ESCAPEMENT - *Mechanical device that regulates the movement in a watch or clock.*

ESCUTCHEON - *Protective plate around a key hole, etc.*

A shield or an emblem bearing a coat of arms.

ETYMOLOGY - *The study of the origin of particular words and the changes to their meaning, as time has evolved.*

EXONUMIA - *Coin like objects (not money) such as Railway Pay Checks, medals, tokens, pit checks, dog tags etc....*

FLATWARE - *Tableware that is relatively flat and fashioned as a single unit (e.g. the meal-tray supplied by airlines). Also flat cutlery.*

FLIPBACK - *Vinyl record (picture) sleeve, laminated on the front only, with short fold-overs on the reverse. Most common in the sixties.*

FOXING - *The tarnishing (browning) on old documents, newspapers etc...*

FRESCO - *The art of painting in water-colour on plaster or mortar when not quite dry.*

FROMOLOGY - *Cheese label collecting.*

FUSILATELY - *The collecting of phone cards.*

GEMOLOGY - *The study of jewels and gems.*

GEORGIAN - *Relating to the period of the four King Georges, 1714 – 1830.*

GILDED - *Covered with a thin layer of gold.*

GLYPTOGRAPHY - *The art of engraving on gemstones.*

GLYPTOLOGY - *The study of gem engravings.*

GNOMONICS - *Items relating to the measuring of time with sundials.*

GUTTER - *The selvedge (borders) of a sheet of postage stamps, either unprinted or with plate numbers or other markings.*

HALLMARK - *A mark punched on to articles to guarantee a statutory degree of purity. Four stamps are; maker's mark, mark of quality, mark of the hall of Assay, and the year mark.*

HISTORIOGRAPHY - *The study of and writing history.*

HISTORIOLOGY - *Study of history.*

HOPLOLOGY - *The study of weaponry.*

HOROGRAPHY - *The art of constructing sundials or clocks.*

HOROLOGY - *The science of time measurement.*

HOSTELAPHILY - *The collecting of outdoor signs from inns.*

HYMNOGRAPHY - *The study of writing hymns.*

HYMNOLOGY - *The study of hymns.*

ICONOLOGY - *The study of icons and symbols.*

INFUNABULIST - *See 'Bandophily'.*

JUVENALIA - *Children's play items.*

KITCHENALIA - *Items relating to a kitchen.*

KITSCH - *Arguably, a tacky version of 'retro'. Popular because of its garishness and links to a particular era (largely 50s/60s/70s).*

LABEORPHILY - *The collecting of beer bottle labels.*

LACLABPHILY - *See 'Fromology'.*

LACQUER - *The application of several layers of paint and special varnish to produce a decorative surface.*

LAPIDARY - *Cutting and engraving precious stones.*

LEPIDOPTEROLOGY - *The study of butterflies and moths.*

LITHOGRAPHY - *A process of printing dating back to the end of the eighteenth century (discovered in Germany). The principle being that oil and water do not mix. The image is drawn with a special applicator on a flat surface over which water is then passed. When covered with ink, only the applied area will accept it.*

LORINERY - *The making, selling/buying, general interest in, horse bridles, stirrups, saddles and parts of the harness.*

LOTOLOGY - *The collecting of scratch cards and lottery related items.*

LUCITE - *Transparent thermoplastic acrylic resin.*

LUSTRE - *A glaze - surface coating for ceramics creating shine.*

MAGIRICS - *The art of cookery.*

MARQUETRY - *The artistic application of pieces of veneer to (mainly) wooden structures thereby creating decorative patterns.*

MATT GLAZE - *A dull-surfaced glaze, non-reflecting.*

MEMORABILIA - *Items to commemorate memorable events.*

MILITARIA - *Collecting of materials or objects relating to the military.*

MISCELLANY - *A whole variety of objects. Miscellaneous items.*

MODERNIST - *A style characteristic of modern times.*

MYTHOLOGY - *The study of myths and fables.*

NETSUKE - *Traditional Japanese clothing, such as the kimono, had no pockets, so it was necessary for people to carry items like pipes and tobacco in containers called sagemono. These sagemono were hung from the sash of the kimono (the obi), and were secured in place using specially carved toggles known as netsuke.*

NOTAPHILY - *The collecting of bank notes.*

NUMISMATICS - *The collecting of and study of coins.*

OBJECTS DE VIRTU - *Fine art objects and antiques.*

OBJETS D'ART - *As 'objects of virtu'.*

OBVERSE - *The side of a coin, or medal, on which the head or principal design is shown. The other side of the coin is called the 'reverse'.*

OENOLOGY - *The study of wine.*

OLEOGRAPH - *A lithographic reproduction of an oil painting.*

OOLOGY - *The collecting of and study of bird's eggs.*

OPERCULISM - *Collecting of milk tops.*

PALAEOBIOLOGY - *The study of fossil plants and animals.*

PALEONTOLOGY - *The study of ancient life and fossils.*

PAPIER-MACHE - *Layers of paper shredded into a pulp and then pressed into shapes.*

PAPYROLOGY - *The study of paper.*

PARANUMISTMATICA - *The UK word for coin-like objects (and the collecting of them). A sub-category of 'Numismatics'.*

PARAPHERNALIA - *Miscellany associated with particular interests and items.*

PARURE - *A full matching jewellery set comprising necklace, brooch, bracelet, and earrings.*

PETROLIANA - *Gas and oil related items.*

PHILATELY - *Stamp collecting and the study of postal history.*

PHILLUMENY - *The collecting of matchboxes and matchbox labels.*

PHILOGRAPHY - *The collecting of autographs.*

PHILOMETRY - *Collecting of First Day Covers.*

PHONOPHILY - *See 'Discophily'.*

PICTURE DISC - *A record pressed on clear vinyl, the*

middle of which is sandwiched with a picture. These are sometimes in shapes other than circular.

PLUMASSIER - Restorers of, and collectors of ornamental plumes or feathers.

POCILLOVY - Collecting of egg cups.

PORCELAIN - White form of stoneware usually translucent. Hard and non-porous. The most highly refined of all clay bodies and requiring the highest firing.

PRODUCTION STILLS - Photographs taken during the production of a motion picture. They are usually shot during principal photography, and show the interaction between the actors and director, camera crew, makeup and wardrobe department, or stunt team.

PROOF - Early impression of a stamp, coin or medal, struck as a specimen.

PROVENANCE - Proof of past ownership or of authenticity.

RAILWAYANA - Collectable items relating to the railway.

REGENCY - The style of furniture, buildings, literature etc., popular in Great Britain 1811 – 1820.

RECTO - Front (verso = reverse)

RETRO - A fashion design, décor or style reminiscent of things past.

RETRO CHIC - Stylish and elegant retro.

RETROPHILIA - A love for things of the past.

REVERSE - Of a coin or medal (see 'Obverse').

RHYKENOLOGY - The collection and study of woodworking tools.

ROCOCO - Typically European architectural and decorative asymmetrical designs of the first half of the eighteenth century.

RPM - (Revolutions per minute), the speed at which a record

is designed to play.

SCRIPOPHILY - The collecting of old financial documents, such as stocks and bonds certificates.

SEPIA - A brown ink or pigment. A photograph in a brown tint.

SHAGREEN - The rough hide of a shark or ray. Untanned leather with a granular surface that is often dyed green.

SIDEROGRAPHY - The art of engraving on steel.

SOCIOLOGY - The study of society.

SOLANDER BOX - A box designed to hold manuscripts, maps, books, etc. Named after Dr. Daniel Solander (1736 – 1782).

SPELTER - Zinc based metal, often called 'poor man's bronze'. Normally thinner and tinnier than bronze but of similar appearance.

STANHOPE - Novelty item with a tiny lens that reveals a photograph when held to light.

STIPPLE - Decoration consisting of tiny dots in an overall pattern.

STONEWARE - Glazed pottery in which both body and glaze are fused together.

SUCROLOGY - The collecting of sugar packets.

TAT - Tasteless, not worthy of serious collecting (by most people), tatty and generally of little value.

TAXIDERMY - The art of stuffing and mounting the skins of animals to give life-like appearances.

TEEKIN - American term for 'antiquing' (buying, browsing, selling).

TEGESTOLOGY - The collecting of beer mats.

TEST PRESSING - The first factory pressings of the record. For circulation to reviewers. Often plain white labels.

TOBACCIANA - *Smoking related collectable items.*

TREEN - *Small wooden objects. Not of joined construction, therefore furniture items not included.*

TUNBRIDGEWARE - *Decoratively inlaid woodwork, characteristic of Tunbridge, Kent 18th and 19th century. Often fashioned as a mosaic of varying coloured woods.*

TURNERY - *The art of turning in a lathe.*

TYPOGRAPHY - *The art of printing or using type.*

UK QUADS - *Film posters. Generally unique to the UK because they are landscape instead of portrait.*

VECTURIST - *Transport token collector.*

VELOLOGY - *The collecting of Vehicle Excise Licences (tax discs).*

VENEER - *A thin layer of wood used to surface or decorate a piece of furniture.*

VERSO - *Reverse (recto = front)*

VEXILLOLOGY - *The study of world national flags (and other flags).*

VICTORIANA - *Objects of the period of Queen Victoria's reign (1837 – 1901).*

VITREOUS - *Glass-like. Usually refers to a porcelain or stoneware fired body.*

VITRICS - *Glassware and the study of.*

XYLOGRAPHY - *The art of engraving on wood.*

XYLOLOGY - *The study of wood.*

ROMAN NUMERALS

The Romans were active in trade and commerce so developed a non-positional decimal system that does not include a zero. The system persisted until the 14th century, when they were abandoned in favour of Arabic numerals; however, Roman numerals are still used in certain circumstances, such as to indicate the order of ruling monarchs. Anybody collecting old books or ephemera will find it useful to have a good knowledge of Roman numerals, because they are often used to represent published copyright dates.

Roman numerals make use of seven different symbols that are combined to form additions and subtractions that create all the numbers required. The symbols are:

I	=	1
V	=	5
X	=	10
L	=	50
C	=	100
D	=	500
M	=	1000

When forming numbers, the symbols are generally placed in order value, and then added together. For example:

MMD = 2500.

However, sometimes smaller numbers are placed in front of larger numbers, and in these situations the smaller values are subtracted from the larger value immediately following. For example:

XL	=	40	(50 – 10)
XLIV	=	44	((50 – 10) + (5-1))
CXLIX	=	149	(100 + (50-10) + (10 -1))

1	I	60	LX
2	II	70	LXX
3	III	80	LXXX
4	IV	90	XC
5	V	100	C
6	VI	200	CC
7	VII	300	CCC
8	VIII	400	CD
9	IX	500	D
10	X	600	DC
11	XI	700	DCC
12	XII	800	DCCC
15	XV	900	CM
20	XX	1000	M
30	XXX	1500	MD
40	XL	2000	MM
50	L		

OLD MONEY

d	=	pence. One penny = 1d.
s	=	shilling (bob). One shilling = 1/-.
£ (or L)	=	pound (quid). 20/- = £1.
6d	=	Sixpence (tanner).
12d	=	Twelve pence (1/-).
Half Crown	=	2/6d.
Florin	=	2/-.
Crown	=	5/-.

Decimal equivalent

240d	=	£1 (100 new pence).
Ten shillings	=	50p.
2/-	=	10p.
1/-	=	5p.

	OLD VALUE	CEASED CIRCULATION
Farthing	¼ d	1956
Half penny	½ d	1967
One penny	1d	1967
Three pence (silver)	3d	1944
Three pence (bronze)	3d	1967
Groat	4d	1887
Six pence	6d	1967
One shilling	1/-	1967
Two shillings (Florin)	2/-	1967
Half Crown	2/6d	1967
Crown	5/-	Still minted today with £5 face value.
Ten shilling note	10/-	Last printed 1969
One pound note	£1	1983

ACRONYMS

AA	American Airlines.
AA	Automobile Association.
ACF	Automobile Club de France.
AD	Anno Domini.
AFS	Auxiliary Fire Service.
AMC	Army Medical Corps.
ARP	Air Raid Precautions.
ASA	Advertising Standards Authority.
ASC	Army Service Corps.
AT&T	American Telephone and Telegraph.
BA	British Airways.
BBC	British Broadcasting Corporation.
BBFC	British Board of Film Classification.
BC	Before Christ.
BC	British Columbia.
BEA	British European Airways.
BEF	British Expeditionary Forces.
BM	British Midland (airline).
BMA	British Medical Association.
BMC	British Motor Corporation.
BMW	Bayerische Motoren Werke.
BO	British Officer.
BOAC	British Overseas Airway Corporation.
BP	Blue Peter.
BP	British Petroleum.
BR	British Rail.
BSA	Birmingham Small Arms.
BSI	British Standards Institution.
BT	British Telecommunications.
DC	Detective Comics.
DJ	Dust Jacket (of a book).
DVD	Digital Versatile Disc.
EP	Extended Play (record).
EU	European Union.
GMC	General Medical Council.
GMC	General Motors Corporation.
HA	Health Authority.
HM	Her (or His) Majesty.
HMS	Her (or His) Majesty's Ship.
HRH	Her (or His) Royal Highness.
ISBN	International Standard Book Number.
ISO	International Standards Organisation.
ITV	Independent Television.
KLM	Royal Dutch Airline.
LP	Long Playing (record).
MBE	Member of the Order of the British Empire.
MC	Military Cross.
MGM	Metro Goldwyn Mayer.
MP	Member of Parliament
MP	Military Police.
MS	Manuscript.
MS	Microsoft.
MS	Motor Ship.
NATO	North Atlantic Treaty Organisation.
NCO	Non-Commissioned Officer.
NHS	National Health Service.
NSC	National Screening Committee.
NTWF	National Transport Workers' Federation.
OBE	Officer of the Order of the British Empire.
PO	Petty Officer.
PO	Post Office.
P&O	Pacific and Orient.
RA	Royal Academy.
RA	Royal Artillery.
RAC	Royal Armoured Corps.
RAC	Royal Automobile Club.
RAF	Royal Air Force.
RAOC	Royal Army Ordnance Corps.
RASC	Royal Army Service Corps (ASC prior 1918).
RCT	Royal Corps of Transport.
RE	Royal Engineers.
REME	Royal Electrical and Mechanical Engineers.
RM	Royal Mail.
RMS	Royal Mail Ship.
RMS	Royal Merchant Ship.
RoSPA	Royal Society for the Prevention of Accidents.
RPM	Revolutions Per Minute.
RR	Rolls-Royce.
RSPB	Royal Society for the Protection of Birds.
RSPCA	Royal Society for the Prevention of Cruelty to Animals.
RSPCC	Royal Society for the Prevention of Cruelty to Children.
SNCF	Societe Nationale des Chemins de fer Francais.
SS	Steam Ship.
TA	Territorial Army.
TGWU	Transport and General Workers Union.
TRH	Their Royal Highnesses.
TWA	Trans World Airlines.
UN	United Nations.
USAF	United States Air Force.
USS	United States Ship.
VAT	Value Added Tax.
VHS	Video Home System.
WCW	World Championship Wrestling.
WO	Warrant Officer.
WWE	World Wrestling Entertainment.
WWF	World Wildlife Fund.
WWW	World Wide Web.